AUTOMOTIVE EMISSION CONTROL

**Books and Instructional Materials
by William H. Crouse and * Donald L. Anglin**

Automotive Air Conditioning*
  Workbook for Automotive Air Conditioning*
Automotive Chassis and Body*
  Workbook for Automotive Chassis and Body*
Automotive Electrical Equipment
  Workbook for Automotive Electrical Equipment*
Automotive Emission Control*
  Workbook for Automotive Emission Control*
Automotive Engines*
  Workbook for Automotive Engines*
Automotive Fuel, Lubricating, and Cooling Systems*
  Workbook for Automotive Fuel, Lubricating, and
  Cooling Systems*
Automotive Tools, Fasteners, and Measurements—A
  Text-Workbook*
Automotive Transmissions and Power Trains*
  Workbook for Automotive Transmissions and Power
    Trains*
  Transparencies for Automatic-Transmissions
    Hydraulic Circuits*
Automotive Tuneup*
  Workbook for Automotive Tuneup*
Automotive Service Business: Operation and
  Management
Automotive Engine Design
Workbook for Automotive Service and Trouble
  Diagnosis
Automotive Mechanics
  Study Guide for Automotive Mechanics
  Testbook for Automotive Mechanics*
  Workbook for Automotive Mechanics*
  Automotive Engines—Sound Filmstrip Program
    Set 1 and Set 2
      Preview-Review Exercises

Automotive Room Chart Series
  Automotive Electrical Equipment Charts
  Automotive Engines Charts
  Automotive Fuel Systems Charts
  Automotive Emissions Controls Charts
  Automotive Engines Cooling Systems, Heating, and
    Air Conditioning Charts
  Automotive Suspension, Steering, and Tires Charts
  Automotive Transmissions and Power Trains Charts
  Automotive Brakes Charts
  Automotive Troubleshooting Cards
The Auto Book
  Auto Shop Workbook*
  Auto Study Guide
  Auto Test Book*
  Auto Cassette Series
Pocket Automotive Dictionary*
General Power Mechanics (with Robert Worthington
  and Morton Margules*)
Small Engines: Operation and Maintenance
  Workbook for Small Engines: Operation and
    Maintenance

**Automotive Transparencies by
William H. Crouse and Jay D. Helsel**

Automotive Air Conditioning†
Automotive Brakes
Automotive Electrical Systems
Automotive Emission Control†
Automotive Engine Systems
Automotive Transmissions and Power Trains
Automotive Steering Systems
Automotive Suspension Systems
Engines and Fuel Systems

†*In production.*

AUTOMOTIVE EMISSION CONTROL

William H. Crouse
Donald L. Anglin

McGRAW-HILL BOOK COMPANY
GREGG DIVISION

NEW YORK
ST. LOUIS
DALLAS
SAN FRANCISCO
AUCKLAND
BOGOTÁ
DÜSSELDORF
JOHANNESBURG
LONDON
MADRID
MEXICO
MONTREAL
NEW DELHI
PANAMA
PARIS
SÃO PAULO
SINGAPORE
SYDNEY
TOKYO
TORONTO

ABOUT THE AUTHORS

William H. Crouse

Behind William H. Crouse's clear technical writing is a background of sound mechanical engineering training as well as a variety of practical industrial experience. After finishing high school, he spent a year working in a tinplate mill. Summers, while still in school, he worked in General Motors plants, and for three years he worked in the Delco-Remy Division shops. Later he became Director of Field Education in the Delco-Remy Division of General Motors Corporation for which he prepared service bulletins and educational literature.

During the war years, he wrote a number of technical manuals for the Armed Forces. After the war, he became Editor of Technical Education Books for the McGraw-Hill Book Company. He has contributed numerous articles to automotive and engineering magazines and has written many outstanding books about science and technology. He was the first Editor-in-Chief of the 15-volume McGraw-Hill Encyclopedia of Science and Technology. In addition, he has authored more than fifty technical books including *Automotive Mechanics,* which has sold over a million copies. His books have been widely translated and used in automotive mechanics training throughout the world.

William H. Crouse's outstanding work in the automotive field has earned for him membership in the Society of Automotive Engineers and in the American Society of Engineering Education.

Donald L. Anglin

Trained in the automotive and diesel service field, Donald L. Anglin has worked both as a mechanic and as a service manager. He has taught automotive courses in high school, trade schools, community colleges, and universities. He has also worked as curriculum supervisior and school administrator for an automotive trade school. Interested in all types of vehicle performance, he has served as a racing-car mechanic and as a consultant to truck fleets on maintenance problems.

Currently he serves as editorial assistant to William H. Crouse, visiting automotive instructors and service shops. Together they have coauthored magazine articles on automotive education and several books in the McGraw-Hill Automotive Technology Series.

Donald L. Anglin is a Certified General Automotive Mechanic and holds many other licenses and certificates in heavy duty truck mechanics, automotive education, service, and related areas. His work in the automotive service field has earned for him membership in the American Society of Mechanical Engineers and the Society of Automotive Engineers. In addition, he is an automotive instructor at Piedmont Virginia Community College, Charlottesville, Virginia.

Library of Congress Cataloging in Publication Data

Crouse, William Harry, (date)
   Automotive emission control.

   Includes index.
   1. Motor vehicles—Pollution control devices.
I. Anglin, Donald L., joint author.   II. Title.
TL214.P6C76 1977   629.2'52   76-50084
ISBN 0-07-014640-3

AUTOMOTIVE EMISSION CONTROL, Second Edition

  2 3 4 5 6 7 8 9 0 WCWC 7 8 3 2 1 0 9 8 7

The editors for this book were Ardelle Cleverdon and Myrna W. Breskin, the designer was Dennis Purdy, the art supervisor was George T. Resch, and the production supervisor was Rena Shindelman. It was set in Melior by York Graphic Services, Inc.
Printed and bound by Webcrafters, Incorporated.

CONTENTS

The internal-combustion engine has been put on probation as a major contributor to atmospheric pollution. In 1967, automotive vehicles contributed more than 138 million tons of pollutants to our air, as reported by the Environmental Protection Agency (EPA) in 1974. But the automobile is not the only polluter. Power plants and industrial sources contribute approximately another 90 million tons of pollutants to the atmosphere each year. But automobiles are getting the major headlines, and some stories would lead you to believe that the internal combustion engine is about to be phased out of the American scene, replaced by some other power source such as storage batteries, steam engines, or spinning flywheels.

Some headlines would also lead you to believe that the automotive industry has been slow to react to the problem, and that even now it is not doing all it can to eliminate air pollution from automobiles. Some critics go so far as to say that the automotive industry has failed to look into other possible power sources such as the steam engine or the electric motor powered by rechargeable batteries. People are choosing up sides in the debate, and more heat than light is being generated in their arguments.

It is time to set the record straight. This is one purpose of this second edition of *Automotive Emission Control*—to present the facts regarding atmospheric pollution from automobiles and to look at what the industry has done and is doing about it.

But this text goes beyond these considerations. It also describes in detail the sources of pollution from the automobile—the engine crankcase, the carburetor, the fuel tank, and the exhaust system. It explains how the industry is minimizing or eliminating the pollution from these sources by developing emission control devices. The book further explains how to keep these automotive emission controls in good condition. There are chapters describing the servicing of these controls, and how to tune-up engines to minimize pollution. Proper engine tuning is vitally important. There are tens of millions of cars on the highways that emit excessive pollutants because they are in need of an engine tune-up. Installation of a used car smog device, plus a proper engine tune-up, would reduce the pollutants from these cars as much as 50 percent, according to studies.

Thus, *Automotive Emission Control* is designed to be a source of information for everyone interested in atmospheric pollution and its control—from the lawmaker who formulates the pollution-control laws to the automotive technician who must reduce the emission from the cars being serviced. This is a practical book. The automotive technician will find in it detailed, step-by-step instructions on how to service the new emission controls and how to tune-up older cars to minimize their contribution to atmospheric pollution. The interested consumer will find the answers to questions on automotive pollution and what can be done with a personal car to alleviate the problem. The decision makers in industry as well as in government will find in the book a summing up of what has been done, is being done, and will be done to reduce pollutants from the automotive vehicle.

This edition of *Automotive Emission Control* has been completely rewritten. Much new material and many new illustrations have been added. The new developments covered include electronic and high-energy ignition systems, the most modern engine-testing instruments, stratified charge, the Honda system, new automotive emission control devices, overhead camshafts, catalytic converters, and so on. There are chapters on the alternative engines, a new chapter on engine tune-up, an updated trouble-diagnosis chapter, three chapters on new techniques and procedures for servicing automotive emission controls, and much more. A feature of the new edition is the introduction of the metric system of measurements. When a United States Customary measurement is used, it is usually followed by its metric equivalent in brackets, for example, 0.002 inch [0.0508 mm].

A new *Workbook for Automotive Emission Control* has been prepared. It includes the basic emission control-service jobs as proposed in the latest recommendations of the Motor Vehicle Manufacturers Association-American Vocational Association Industry Planning Council. Taken together, *Automotive Emission Control* and the *Workbook for Automotive Emission Control* supply the student with the background information and "hands-on" experience needed to become a qualified and certified automotive tune-up and emission control technician.

To assist the automotive instructor, the *Instructor's Planning Guide for Automotive Emission Control* is available from McGraw-Hill. The instructor's guide was prepared to help the automotive instructor do the best possible job of teaching by most effectively utilizing the textbook, workbook, and other related instructional materials. The instructor's guide contains suggestions on student motivation, classroom instruction and related shop activities, the automotive curriculum, and much more. It also includes the answer key for the tests at the end of each jobsheet in the *Workbook for Automotive Emission Control*.

Also in the instructor's guide is a list of various related textbooks and ancillary instructional materials available from McGraw-Hill. Used singly or together, these items form a comprehensive student learning and activity package. They provide the student with meaningful learning experiences and help the student develop job competencies in automotive mechanics and related fields. The instructor's guide explains how the various available materials can be used, either singly or in combination, to satisfy any teaching requirement.

The authors are deeply grateful to the many people, both in the industry and others, whose contributions and comments helped to shape this book. They share, with the authors, a grave concern over environmental pollution, and hope, with the authors, that this book will play a part in saving our air for the generations to come.

WILLIAM H. CROUSE
DONALD L. ANGLIN

ACKNOWLEDGMENTS

During the preparation of this second edition of *Automotive Emission Control,* the authors were given invaluable aid and inspiration by many people in the automotive industry and in the field of education. The authors gratefully acknowledge their indebtedness and offer their sincere thanks to these people. All cooperated with the aim of providing accurate and complete information that would be useful in training automotive mechanics.

Special thanks are owed to the following organizations for information and illustrations that they supplied: AC-Delco Division of General Motors Corporation; AC Spark Plug Division of General Motors Corporation; Air Quality Products, Inc.; American Motors Corporation; Buick Motor Division of General Motors Corporation; Cadillac Motor Car Division of General Motors Corporation; California Motor Vehicle Pollution Control Board; Carter Carburetor Division of AFC Industries; Champion Spark Plug Company; Chevrolet Motor Division of General Motors Corporation; Chrysler Corporation; Cummins Engine Company, Inc.; Delco-Remy Division of General Motors Corporation; Detroit Diesel Allison Division of General Motors Corporation; Eaton Corporation; Echlin Manufacturing Company; Ford Motor Company; Ford Motor Company of England, Ltd.; GMC Truck and Coach Division of General Motors Corporation; General Motors Corporation; Harrison Radiator Division of General Motors Corporation; Hercules Motor Corporation; Honda; Inter-Industry Emission Control Program; Lockheed Missiles and Space Company, Inc.; Los Angeles County Air Pollution Control District; Mercedes-Benz; Motor Vehicle Manufacturers Association; Oldsmobile Division of General Motors Corporation; Pontiac Motor Division of General Motors Corporation; Robert Bosch GmbH; STP Corporation; Smithsonian Institution; Snap-on Tools; Society of Automotive Engineers, Inc.; Standard Motor Products, Inc.; Sun Electric Corporation; Thermo Electron Corporation; Toyo Kogyo Company, Ltd.; Toyota Motor Sales, Limited; Waukesha Motor Company. To all these organizations and the people who represent them, sincere thanks.

WILLIAM H. CROUSE
DONALD L. ANGLIN

Automotive Emission Control is one of eight books in the McGraw-Hill Automotive Technology Series. These books cover in detail the construction, operation, and maintenance of automotive vehicles. They are designed to give you the complete background of information you need to become successful in the automotive service business. The books satisfy the recommendations of the Motor Vehicle Manufacturers Association-American Vocational Association Industry Planning Council. The books also meet the requirements for automotive mechanics certification and state vocational educational programs, and recommendations for automotive trade apprenticeship training. Furthermore the comprehensive coverage of the subject matter makes the books valuable additions to the library of anyone interested in automotive engineering, manufacturing, sales, service, and operation.

Meeting the Standards

The eight books in the McGraw-Hill Automotive Technology Series meet the standards of the Motor Vehicle Manufacturers Association (MVMA) for associate degrees in automotive servicing and automotive service management. These standards are described in the MVMA booklet "Community College Guide for Associate Degree Programs in Auto and Truck Service and Management." The books also cover the subjects recommended by the American National Standards Institute in their detailed standard D18.1-1972, "American National Standard for Training of Automotive Mechanics for Passenger Cars and Light Trucks."

In addition, the books cover the subject matter tested by the National Institute for Automotive Service Excellence (NIASE). The tests given by NIASE are used for certifying general automotive mechanics and automotive technicians working in specific areas of specialization under the NIASE voluntary mechanic testing and certification program.

Getting Practical Experience

At the same time that you study the books in the McGraw-Hill Automotive Technology Series, you should be getting practical experience in the shop. You should handle automotive parts, automotive tools, and automotive servicing equipment, and you should perform actual servicing jobs. This is what is meant by getting practical experience. To assist you in your shop work, there are workbooks for each book in the series. For example, the *Workbook for Automotive Emission Control* includes jobs that cover basic servicing procedures on automotive emission controls. If you do every job covered in the workbook, you will have had "hands-on" experience with various types of emission control-servicing work.

If you are taking an automotive mechanics course in school, you will have an instructor to guide you in your classroom and shop activities. But even if you are not taking a course, the workbook can act as an instructor. It tells you, step by step, how to do the various servicing jobs. Perhaps you can meet others who are taking a school course in automotive mechanics. You can talk over any problems you have with them. A local garage or service station is a good source of information. If you can get acquainted with the automotive mechanics there, you will find they have a great deal of practical information. Watch them at their work if you can. Make notes of important points for filing in your notebook.

Service Publications

While you are in the service shop, study the various publications received at the shop. Automobile manufacturers, as well as suppliers of parts, accessories, and tools, publish shop manuals, service bulletins, and parts catalogs. All these help service personnel do better jobs. In addition, numerous automotive magazines are published which deal with problems and methods of automotive service. All these publications will be of great value to you; study them carefully.

These activities will help you obtain practical experience in automotive mechanics. Sooner or later this experience, plus the knowledge that you have gained in studying the books in the McGraw-Hill Automotive Technology Series, will permit you to step into the automotive shop on a full-time basis. Or, if you are already in the shop, you will be equipped to step up to a better and a more responsible job.

Checking Up on Yourself

You can check up on your progress in your studies by answering the questions given every few pages in the book. There are two types of tests, progress quizzes and chapter checkups, the answers to which are given at the back of the book. Each progress quiz should be taken just after you have completed the pages preceding it. These quizzes allow you to check yourself as you finish a lesson. On the other hand, the chapter checkup may cover several lessons, since it is a review test of the entire chapter. Because it is a review test, you should review the entire chapter by rereading it or at least glancing through it to check important points before trying the test. If any of the questions stump you, reread the pages in the book that will give you the answer. This sort of review is valuable; it will help you to remember the information you need when you work in an automotive shop.

Keeping a Notebook

Keeping a notebook is a valuable part of your training. Start it now, at the beginning of your studies of automotive emission controls. Your notebook will help you in many ways: It will be a record of your progress; it will become a storehouse of valuable information you will refer to time after time; it will help you learn; and it will help you organize your training program so that it will do you the most good.

When you study a lesson in the book, have your notebook open in front of you. Start with a fresh notebook page at the beginning of each lesson. Write the lesson or textbook page number and date at the top of the page. As you read your lesson, jot down the important points.

In the shop, use a small scratch pad or cards to jot down important points. You can transfer your notes to your notebook later.

You can also make sketches in your notebook showing wiring or hose diagrams, fuel circuits, and so on. Save articles and illustrations from technical and hot-rod magazines. File them in your notebook.

Also, save instruction sheets that come with service parts. Piston-ring sets, for example, have instruction sheets explaining how to install the rings. Glue or tape these to sheets of paper and file them in your notebook.

As you can see, your notebook will become a valued possession—a permanent record of all you have learned about automotive emission controls.

Glossary and Index

A glossary (a definition list) of automotive terms is given in the back of the book. Whenever you have any doubt about the meaning of a term or what purpose some automotive part has, you should refer to this list. Also, there is an index at the back of the book. This index will steer you to the page in the book where you will find the information you are seeking.

And now, good luck to you. You are studying a fascinating, complex, and admirable machine—the automobile. Your studies can lead you to success in the automotive field, a field where opportunities are nearly unlimited.

PART ONE

AUTOMOTIVE AIR POLLUTION

Part One of *Automotive Emission Control* explains what automotive emissions are, how and why they occur, and the troubles they cause. It also discusses automotive engines—their construction and operation. This will allow us, in later chapters, to discuss emission-control systems and how they work on engines. Part One also includes a chapter on alternative power sources for automobiles. There are four chapters in Part One.

chapter 1

AIR POLLUTION, SMOG, AND THE AUTOMOBILE

Are we choking to death on air pollution that we, ourselves, have created? Is our atmosphere doomed? Are we destroying ourselves by excessively polluting our air, our water, and our land? Some pessimists think so. And many people who have gone through a smog visitation are sure that the end is near. Once you experience a bad smog, you will never forget it. You can't see very far, even at midday with the street lights turned on. It is difficult to breathe, and the air doesn't feel right. Your eyes smart, your throat gets sore, and you cough. Food and flower crops are seriously damaged. The paint on houses is affected.

Those are short-term effects. Long-term effects are more serious. Air pollution has been linked to such human ills as eczema, asthma, emphysema, heart troubles, and cancer of the lungs and stomach. The psychological effects may vary from mild to serious, but there is no doubt that it is depressing to live through a period of smog.

⊘ **1-1 Smog** Let us define smog and see what causes it. The word "smog" was coined many years ago from "smoke" and "fog." Actually, smog as we know it today is much more than just a mixture of fog and smoke. Many different chemicals and substances are involved.

Smog is not new. Neither is air pollution. Billions of years ago, when the planet earth was young, there were many volcanoes. The volcanoes threw millions of tons of ash and smoke into the air. At the same time, winds whipped up clouds of dust. Animal and vegetable matter decayed and sent gaseous matter into the air. This was natural air pollution.

When human beings came along, they began to produce their own kind of air pollution. They discovered fire. In the Middle Ages, people in cities such as London used soft coal to heat their homes. The smoke from their fires, combined with moisture in the air, created dense layers of smog. This smog would blanket the cities for days, particularly in the winter months. The heat generated in large cities tends to produce air circulation within a domelike shape, as shown in Fig. 1-1. This traps the smog and prevents its escape.

With the coming of great industries, big electric-power plants, modern cities with their heating plants and incinerators, and the internal-combustion engine, air pollution gradually became worse. However, the atmosphere which blankets the earth took in the pollution. For a long time the situation did not seem to be bad, except in the larger cities. But, in

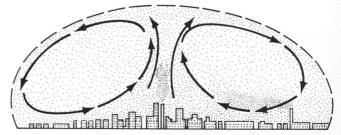

Fig. 1-1. The heat generated within a large city tends to produce a circulatory air pattern which traps smog within a dome.

recent years, people in many areas have begun to complain about air pollution. Engineers and scientists are also becoming alarmed.

⊘ **1-2 The Los Angeles Smog Problem** An example of the problem, and what has been done to help relieve it, can be found in the city of Los Angeles, California. Los Angeles is set in a basin. It is located in a valley, with the Pacific Ocean to the west and mountains to the east. When the wind comes from the mountains, it blows the smog out over the ocean, and the air in Los Angeles is reasonably clear. But when there is no wind, the air is still. The smoke from industry and the pollutants from automobiles do not blow away (Figs. 1-2 and 1-3). They are trapped over the city by the mountains. The dirty, still air covers Los Angeles like a blanket, gradually building up into a thick, smelly, foggy layer of smog.

Fig. 1-2. View of Los Angeles on a clear day. (*Los Angeles County Air Pollution Control District*)

Fig. 1-3. Same view of Los Angeles on a typical smoggy day. Note that many buildings are hidden. (*Los Angeles County Air Pollution Control District*)

Normally, the warm air near the ground would rise to the cooler layers of the atmosphere. It would carry the smog up and away from the city. However, Los Angeles is subject to a weather condition called an *inversion*. A relatively warmer layer of air hovers above the basin in which Los Angeles lies. It shuts off the upward movement of ground-level air and keeps the smog near the ground.

As the condition worsens, people begin to cough and sneeze; headaches develop, tires crack, and tempers shorten. People with respiratory diseases such as emphysema or with heart conditions become seriously ill, and some die. The paint on cars and buildings is damaged, as are food and flower crops. The long-term effects can be much more serious, not only as far as our health and well-being are concerned, but also as regards our total environment.

⊘ **1-3 Possible Weather Changes** Scientists point out that the increasing pollution of our atmosphere may be changing our weather patterns drastically. Pollutants in the air may shield the earth from the sun's radiant energy so that the earth will cool off, bringing on a new ice age. Or it may work in the opposite direction: Some of the pollutants may trap more of the sun's energy so that the earth will heat up. This could melt the polar ice caps and raise the level of the oceans as much as 200 ft (feet) [60.96 m (meters)]. Then, all low-lying port cities, such as New York, Philadelphia, and London, would be covered with 100 feet [30.48 m] or more of water (Fig. 1-4). Unfortunately, once this action starts, we may not be able to stop it. The weather change could act like an avalanche—once launched, it would continue, and we could do nothing to change the trend.

The city of Los Angeles, where the problem of smog has been very serious, has done much to help the condition locally. Early studies showed that the automobile was only one producer of air pollution. Some pollution came from incinerators and open fires. Some came from the smoking chimneys of industry and power plants. One early correctional measure was to ban unrestricted burning. Incinerators without pollution controls were outlawed. Industry was forced to change combustion processes and add pollution controls, so that the output from their chimneys would be cleaner.

Studies of the automobile indicated that it gave off pollutants from four sources, as shown in Fig. 1-5. These are the crankcase, the carburetor, the fuel tank, and the exhaust system. In a later chapter, we shall look more closely at all of these, to see what has been done to eliminate automobile pollution. First, however, we want to identify the pollutants.

⊘ **1-4 Chemistry of Combustion** Let us review a little chemistry. As you know, air and gasoline are mixed in the engine carburetor to form a combustible mixture. This mixture is burned in the engine to produce power. Gasoline is made up largely of hydrogen and carbon and is called a *hydrocarbon* (HC). In the combustion process, the carbon and hydrogen in the gasoline unite with oxygen in the air. They form carbon dioxide, which has the chemical formula CO_2, and hydrogen oxide, or water, which has the chemical formula H_2O. If combustion were perfect, only carbon dioxide, water, and unused air would come out the tail pipe (Fig. 1-6).

Unfortunately, the combustion process is not perfect (Fig. 1-7). First, some of the carbon and oxygen end up as carbon monoxide (CO), a dangerously poisonous gas. Carbon monoxide (CO) is formed as a result of burning gasoline with insufficient oxygen. A ratio of only 15 parts of carbon monoxide to 10,000 parts of air is dangerous to breathe. Higher concentrations can be fatal. This is why you should never run an engine in a closed garage. Enough carbon monoxide can be produced in 3 min (minutes) by a running engine in a closed one-car garage to cause paralysis and death!

Since not all of the gasoline burns, some of it exits from the tail pipe as gasoline vapor (or HC). In addition to the CO_2, CO, H_2O, and HC coming out of the tailpipe (Fig. 1-7), there are also oxides of nitrogen. These are sometimes called *nitrogen oxides,* and abbreviated NO_x. (Nitrogen is another gas in the air around us, which is about 80 percent nitrogen and 20 percent oxygen. The air also contains small amounts of other gases.) At low temperatures, nitrogen is *inert*. That is, it will not unite chemically with anything, except under very special circumstances. High temperatures are required to form oxides of nitrogen. During the combustion process in the engine, temperatures of several thousand degrees Fahrenheit (°F) are reached. At these high temperatures, some of the nitrogen in the air-fuel mixture

Fig. 1-4. Melting of the polar ice caps would flood all coastal cities.

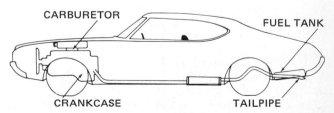

Fig. 1-5. Four possible sources of atmospheric pollution from the automobile.

Fig. 1-6. Complete combustion.

Fig. 1-7. Incomplete combustion.

unites with oxygen to form oxides of nitrogen (Fig. 1-8).

Several different oxides of nitrogen may form during the combustion process in the engine. They vary in the amount of oxygen that unites with the nitrogen. Some forms are highly *toxic*, meaning they can be poisonous to breathe in excessive amounts. One form is used in hospitals to anesthetize patients before operations. Another oxide of nitrogen forms an acid in the presence of sunshine and hydrocarbons (Fig. 1-9). This acid contributes to the eye-smarting, cough-producing effects of the smog. All these different oxides of nitrogen can be referred to by the symbol NO_x; the x stands for the varying amounts of oxygen.

⊘ **1-5 Other Pollutants in the Exhaust Gas** In addition to unburned gasoline (HC), partly burned gasoline (CO), and nitrogen oxides (NO_x), the exhaust gases contain other pollutants. One of these is lead; another is sulfur oxide, or SO_x. Lead is present because it is added to the gasoline in the form of tetra-

ethyl lead. This substance improves the antiknock, or octane, rating of gasoline. Tetraethyl lead has been considered a necessary additive for gasoline for many years. Now, however, because lead is toxic to human beings, some authorities are trying to ban the use of tetraethyl lead in gasoline.

The other pollutant mentioned above is sulfur oxide. This is produced by a device that has been added to the automobile to reduce the HC and CO in the exhaust gas. This device is the catalytic converter, which is described in detail in Chap. 9. If there is sulfur in the gasoline (and most gasolines have some sulfur), the catalytic converter changes the sulfur to sulfur oxide. After the sulfur oxide leaves the car and mixes with air, it is converted into sulfuric acid by the action of the sun.

OXYGEN (O) + NITROGEN (N) + HIGH TEMPERATURE =

NITROGEN OXIDES (NO_x)

Fig. 1-8. Formation of oxides of nitrogen.

$$\text{SUNSHINE} + \left\{ \begin{array}{c} \text{HYDROCARBONS} \\ \text{AND} \\ \text{OXIDES OF NITROGEN} \end{array} \right\} = \text{SMOG}$$

Fig. 1-9. One source of smog.

Another reason for banning lead in gasoline is that the lead can ruin the catalytic converter. There is more on catalytic converters, lead in gasoline, and sulfur-oxide pollution in Chap. 9.

⊘ **1-6 Three Basic Regulated Pollutants** Legal limits have been set for three basic pollutants from engines (Fig. 1-10): unburned gasoline (HC), carbon monoxide (CO), and nitrogen oxide (NO_x). Some HC vapor also escapes from the carburetor and the fuel tank in a car without emission control (Fig. 1-10). Gasoline (HC) is highly volatile; that is, it evaporates very easily. It must be made to evaporate easily, to produce the air-fuel mixture needed to run the engine. Gasoline stored in the fuel tank evaporates, and some of it passes out through the vent in the tank or cap. A small reservoir of gasoline is stored in the carburetor, and some of this evaporates after the engine has been turned off. So the carburetor and fuel tank are other sources of the pollutant gasoline vapor.

Of course the pollutants from one car really don't [...] uch. A typical car without emis-[...] good condition, will give off [...]s) [0.567 kg (kilogram)] of pollut-[...]ving. If the car is in poor shape, [...]neup, with fouled spark plugs [...]stently, an out-of-adjustment [...] it can be a real smogmaker. It [...]ee times as much pollutant as [...]. Even that doesn't seem like [...]e more than a hundred mil-[...]he United States. Each pro-[...]n, to add to the problem. It [...]the millions of cars operat-[...]in area give off about 2,000 [...]tants every day. The na-[...]e astonishing (Fig. 1-11). [...]ome estimates, internal-[...]about 64 million tons of

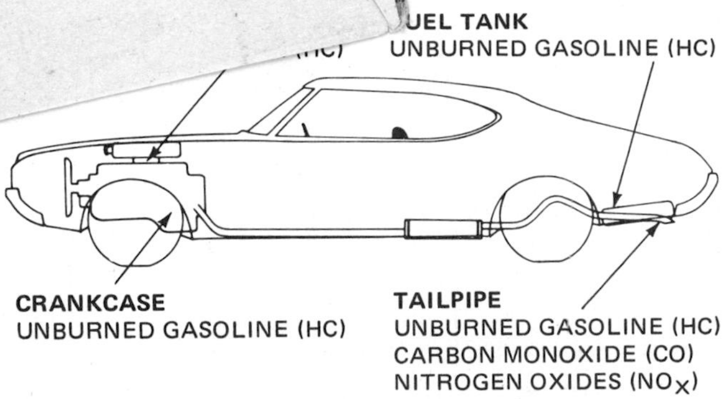

[...]UEL TANK
UNBURNED GASOLINE (HC)

CRANKCASE
UNBURNED GASOLINE (HC)

TAILPIPE
UNBURNED GASOLINE (HC)
CARBON MONOXIDE (CO)
NITROGEN OXIDES (NO_x)

Fig. 1-10. The sources and types of atmospheric pollutants from the automobile.

carbon monoxide every year—an average of about ⅔ ton [605.1 kg] of CO per car. And there are great amounts of the other pollutants: hydrocarbons and nitrogen oxides.

As you can see by studying Fig. 1-11, the problem is serious; everyone is, or should be, concerned about it. But Fig. 1-11 also shows that automotive engineers have done much to relieve the problem. Local, state, and national governing bodies are studying the problem and are passing laws. Automotive technicians, the men and women who service automobiles, are learning about the problem. Then, they can do what is necessary to reduce pollution from the cars they service. But this is not enough. Everyone who owns or drives cars is involved in the pollution problem. Everyone must do his or her part if the problem is to be solved. It does little good for new cars to be built almost pollution-free, if older cars are allowed to continue to pour out pollution because owners fail to have their cars maintained properly. Pollution from older cars can be substantially reduced by regular service, and by installation of available emission control device kits.

That is the subject of this book: To discover what we, as service technicians and as owners and drivers of cars, can do to reduce pollution from motor vehicles. In following chapters we shall explore the problem further. We shall examine in detail the changes in engine design, and the emission-control devices, that substantially reduce emissions from the newer cars. We shall then take a careful look at the engine tuneup procedures that help minimize the emissions from all cars, new and old, and the emission-control devices that can be installed on used cars.

Check Your Progress[1]

Progress Quiz 1-1 The following questions and exercises will help you find out how well you understand what you are studying. If you have trouble answering any question, study the chapter again. Most successful students make a practice of reading and studying their assignments several times, to make sure they understand them. Do not be discouraged if you cannot answer all the questions at once. The material you have been studying is not quite so easy to remember as the plot of a story or a movie. So, if you run into trouble as you do the exercises, just restudy the chapter and try the questions again. As you practice this technique of read and restudy, you will learn how to pick out the important facts that you should remember. After you have done this a number of times, you will find that the book is much easier to read and understand. You will be better able to sort out and retain the essential facts. This will mean that you are becoming an expert student. And the expert student, the person who can

<hr>

[1] Answers to questions in the quizzes and chapter check-ups are given at the end of the book.

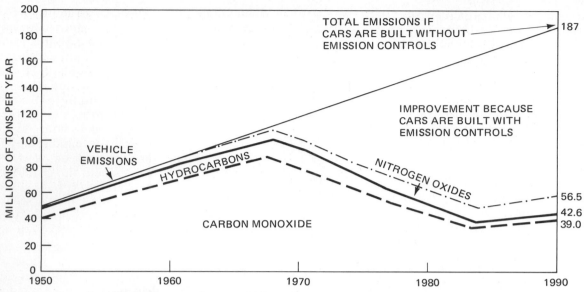

Fig. 1-11. The pollutants that would be released to the atmosphere from cars if there were no emission controls, compared with the pollutants released from cars with emission controls.

recall the facts, is headed for success in any chosen line of work. So being an expert student is a big step toward being an expert—and successful—automotive emission control technician.

Completing the Sentences The sentences below are incomplete. After each sentence there are several words or phrases, but only one of them correctly completes the sentence. Write each sentence in your notebook, ending it with the word or phrase that makes it correct.

1. Smog is a word made up from the words (a) sea and hog, (b) smoke and fog, (c) sun and moon, (d) sand and gravel.

2. People-made smog is the result of: (a) cutting grass, (b) farming, (c) drying clothes, (d) combustion.

3. Four sources of pollution in the automobile are the: (a) carburetor, fuel pump, fuel tank, and exhaust system, (b) crankcase, carburetor, ignition system, and exhaust system, (c) crankcase, carburetor, fuel tank, and exhaust system, (d) fuel tank, fuel filter, oil filter, and air cleaner.

4. Gasoline is made up largely of: (a) hydrogen and carbon, (b) hydrogen oxide and carbon monoxide, (c) water and oil, (d) carbon monoxide and carbon dioxide.

5. If combustion were perfect, all that would come out the tail pipe would be: (a) carbon dioxide, water, and excess air, (b) carbon monoxide and carbon dioxide, (c) water, oil, and smoke, (d) hydrocarbons, smog, and water.

6. Carbon monoxide is: (a) a product of complete combustion, (b) another name for water, (c) a dangerously poisonous gas, (d) a combustible mixture.

7. The air around us contains about 80 percent: (a) oxygen, (b) carbon monoxide, (c) carbon dioxide, (d) nitrogen.

8. Tetraethyl lead is added to gasoline to improve its: (a) cost per gallon, (b) octane rating, (c) color, (d) odor.

9. The three basic regulated pollutants from engines are: (a) HO, CO, and CO_2, (b) HC, CO, and NO_x, (c) H_2O, CO_2, and NO_x, (d) SO_x, NO_x, and FO_x.

10. A typical car without emission control gives off, in one driving day, pollutants that weigh about: (a) 1.25 lb [0.567 kg], (b) 10 lb [4.536 kg], (c) 2,000 tons [1,916,000 kg], (d) 1,333 lb [605.1 kg].

Chapter 1 Checkup

NOTE: Since the following is a chapter review test, you should review the chapter before taking the test.

You have completed one chapter of the book and have taken an important step toward better understanding of automotive emission control. The chapter you have just finished may not be as interesting as the later chapters, which deal directly with emission control device service. The chemistry of smog is often harder to understand and remember than specific details about the devices that control it. But this background on the smog problem is important to you. Once you do understand it, you will find that you can answer many puzzling questions about how automotive emissions are controlled. The following questions will give you a chance to see how well you understand and remember this material. It also will help you to remember the information better. The act of writing the answers to the questions will fix the facts more firmly in your mind.

Write your answers in your notebook. Then, later, your notebook will be filled with valuable and useful information which you can refer to quickly.

Problems Write each of the following problems and its answer in your notebook. Turn back into the chapter and do some rereading if you are not sure of the answer to any problem.

1. What are the short-term effects of smog? The long-term effects?
2. How is smog formed in nature?
3. Discuss the Los Angeles smog problem, and the land characteristics that make the problem worse.
4. If 1,000 cars in good condition and without any emission-control devices are on the road on the same day, how many pounds of pollutants are added to the air from these cars that day?
5. How many cars and trucks are there in the United States? In the area in which you live and work?

Matching In the left column below are 10 words or phrases from the chapter you just studied. In the right column are 10 more words or phrases; each of them means the same, or nearly the same, as a word or phrase in the left column. Write the left-hand column in your notebook. Then, next to each item, write the word or phrase from the right-hand column that is closest to it in meaning. When you have finished, check your answers at the end of the book. If you missed any, restudy the pages in the chapter that give you the correct answer.

1. Smog	source of people-made smog
2. Inversion	carbon dioxide and water
3. Combustion	carbon monoxide
4. Exhaust system	dangerously poisonous gas
5. Perfect combustion	80 percent nitrogen, 20 percent oxygen
6. Incomplete combustion	smog producer
7. Gasoline	improves gasoline octane ratings
8. Carbon monoxide	hydrocarbon
9. Air	smoke and fog
10. Tetraethyl lead	source of automobile pollution

Definitions In the following, you are asked to define certain terms. Write the definitions in your notebook. Writing the definitions will help you remember them. It will also provide you with a quick way to locate the meanings when you need them. If you cannot remember the meanings of the terms, look them up in the text or in the glossary at the back of the book.

1. What is smog?
2. Define "inversion."
3. What is combustion?
4. Define "HC."
5. Define "CO."
6. Define "CO_2,"
7. Define "H_2O."
8. What are oxides of nitrogen?
9. What is sulfur oxide?
10. What is a catalytic converter?

Suggestions for Further Study

The subject of automotive emission control receives a great deal of publicity in newspapers and magazines, and on radio and television. When you see an article dealing with the subject in a newspaper or magazine, cut it out and add it to your notebook. Also, if you have a question about smog formation, try to talk it over with your local school science or physics teacher.

chapter 2

HOW THE ENGINE OPERATES

Everyone knows, in a general way, how the engine operates. Gasoline is mixed with air by the carburetor. This mixture enters the cylinder when the intake valve opens and the piston moves down on the intake stroke. Then the intake valve closes, and the mixture is compressed by the piston on the compression stroke. A spark at the spark plug ignites the mixture. The resulting combustion forces the piston down in the cylinder on the power stroke. This produces the power to turn the crankshaft and move the car. When the piston reaches the bottom of the cylinder, the exhaust valve opens. It lets the exhaust gas escape from the cylinder when the piston moves up on the exhaust stroke. Then, the four strokes—intake, compression, power, and exhaust—are repeated again and again. And, of course, the exhaust gas contains the atmospheric pollutants we are studying.

How completely the gasoline burns in an engine determines the power that the gasoline produces. The completeness of combustion also determines the amount of exhaust pollutants coming from the engine. To understand how and where these pollutants are formed, we must first look at engine construction and operation.

⊘ **2-1 The Engine Cylinder** An engine cylinder is like a round tin can that is open on one end because the bottom has been left out (Fig. 2-1). A movable piston fits into the open end of the cylinder. The piston is usually made of aluminum. It weighs about 1 lb [0.454 kg] and is about 4 in (inches) [101.6 mm (millimeters)] in diameter. The piston fits snugly, but is loose enough to slide easily up and down inside the cylinder (Fig. 2-2). There are grooves cut around the side of the piston. Piston rings are fitted into these grooves. We shall explain the purpose of the piston rings later.

Fig. 2-2. When the piston is pushed up into the engine cylinder, air is trapped and compressed. The cylinder is drawn as though it were transparent, so that the action can be seen.

In Fig. 2-2, the piston has been pushed up into the cylinder. This upward movement of the piston traps air above it. The air has no place to go, so it is compressed, or squeezed, into a smaller volume. Now, suppose that the air has some gasoline vapor in it. If we could ignite this compressed air-and-gasoline-vapor mixture, we would have an explosion. As shown in Fig. 2-3, the explosion would blow the piston out of the cylinder.

In the actual engine, other parts keep the piston from blowing out of the cylinder. These other parts also push the piston back up into the cylinder after the explosion. That is, the piston is kept moving up and down, or *reciprocating*, in the cylinder.

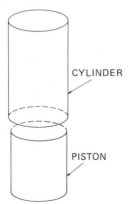

Fig. 2-1. The piston is a metal plug that fits snugly into the hollow cylinder.

CYLINDER

PISTON

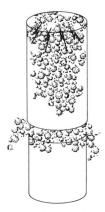

Fig. 2-3. As the mixture of air and gasoline vapor ignites, the increased pressure pushes the piston out of the cylinder.

⊘ **2-2 Reciprocating to Rotary Motion** As the crankshaft rotates, the piston moves up and down in the cylinder (Fig. 2-4). This straight-line motion is called *reciprocating* motion. The up-and-down reciprocating motion must be changed to *rotary* motion to make the car wheels rotate. A connecting rod

and a crankpin on the engine crankshaft change the reciprocating motion to rotary motion. The crankpin is an offset section of the crankshaft, as shown in Fig. 2-5. It swings around in a circle as the shaft rotates. The connecting rod connects the piston to the crankshaft. The crank end, or big end, of the connecting rod is attached to the crankpin by a rod cap. The rod cap is fastened to the connecting rod with rod bolts. Bearings in the rod and cap permit the crankpin to rotate freely within the rod.

Figure 2-5 also shows how the piston end, or small end, of the connecting rod is attached to the piston by the piston pin, or wrist pin. Bearings in the piston or in the rod permit the rod to tilt back and forth freely.

Now let us see what happens as the piston moves up and down in the cylinder. Follow the action of the connecting rod in Fig. 2-4. As the piston starts down, the connecting rod tilts to one side. This allows the lower end of the rod to follow the circular path of the crankpin. Then it tilts to the other side as the piston moves back up. The rod tilts first to one side and then to the other as the crank end moves in a circle with the crankpin.

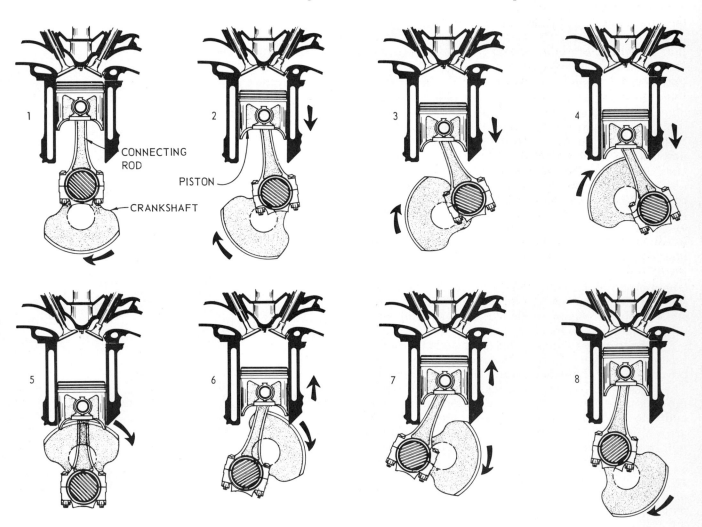

Fig. 2-4. Sequence of actions as the crankshaft completes one revolution and the piston moves from top to bottom to top again.

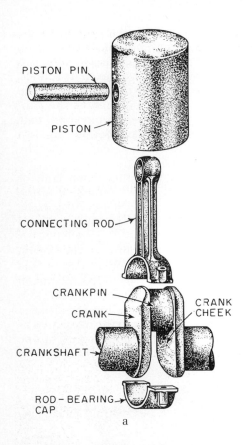

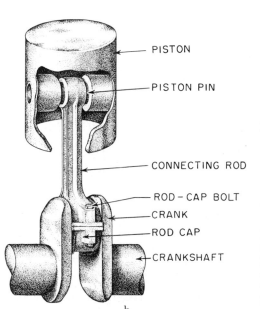

Fig. 2-5. (a) Piston, connecting rod, crank, and crankpin of a crankshaft in disassembled view. (b) Piston and connecting-rod assembly attached to the crankpin on the crankshaft. The piston rings are not shown. The piston is partly cut away to show how it is attached to the connecting rod with the piston pin.

⊘ **2-3 Piston Rings** On the typical engine piston (Fig. 2-6), there are three piston rings, one below the other. Piston rings have two purposes. One is to provide a gastight seal between the piston and the cylinder wall. The other is to scrape oil off the cylinder wall so it does not work its way up into the combustion chamber and burn. These two jobs require two different types of rings—compression rings and oil-control rings.

Compression rings provide a gastight seal between the cylinder wall and the piston. If the piston were made tight enough in the cylinder to provide this seal, it would not be able to move. Instead, two piston rings are installed in piston grooves to seal the compression and combustion gases in the combustion chamber. One or two oil-control rings are installed below the compression rings to keep oil out of the combustion chamber.

Here is how a compression ring seals the combustion chamber. During the compression and power strokes, there is pressure above the piston. The pressure forces the high-pressure gases through the clearance between the piston and cylinder wall and into the piston-ring groove, as shown by the arrows in Fig. 2-7. These gases press the ring down tightly against the bottom of the ring groove. They

Fig. 2-6. Piston and connecting-rod assembly, disassembled so that the various parts can be seen. When the parts are assembled and installed in the engine, the rings are installed in grooves in the piston. The connecting rod is attached to the piston by the piston pin. (*Ford Motor Company*)

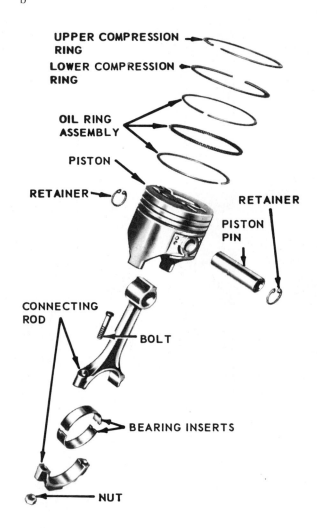

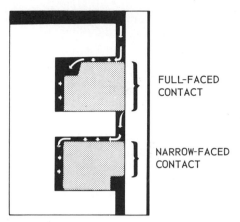

FULL-FACED CONTACT

NARROW-FACED CONTACT

Fig. 2-7. The pressure from the burning air-fuel mixture presses down and out on the ring. The pressure causes the ring to seal against the lower side of the ring groove in the piston.

also get in back of the compression ring and force the ring out tightly against the cylinder wall. Thus the two places where combustion gases could leak past the piston ring are sealed by the action of the ring itself. With this type of ring, the maximum ring pressure against the cylinder wall occurs when maximum combustion pressure occurs. This is what causes the deep ring ridge found at the very top of a worn engine cylinder.

⊘ **2-4 Blow-by** The gas that the top compression ring does not hold in the combustion chamber is mostly stopped by the lower (second) compression ring. But a small amount of high-pressure gas always escapes past the piston and rings. No piston ring seals perfectly. This leakage, shown in Fig. 2-8, is called *blowby*. The gases "blow by" the piston rings and into the lower part of the engine. This lower part

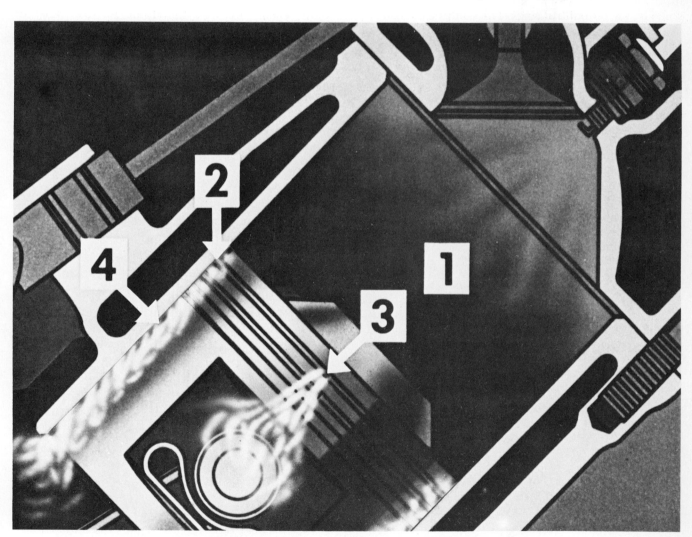

Fig. 2-8. The combustion-chamber gas that leaks past the piston and rings into the crankcase during the compression and power strokes is called *blow-by*. Blow-by is the result of (1) high combustion-chamber pressures; (2) necessary working clearances of piston rings in their grooves; (3) normal ring shifting that sometimes lines up the clearance gaps of two or more rings; (4) reduction in ring sealing-contact area with changes in the direction of piston travel. (*Chevrolet Motor Division of General Motors Corporation*)

is called the *crankcase* because it "encases" the crankshaft. The bottom of the cylinder block forms the upper part of the crankcase. The oil pan forms the lower part of the crankcase.

The amount of blow-by entering the crankcase generally increases with engine speed. The amount of blow-by also depends on other conditions, including piston, ring, and cylinder wear. The actual amount of wear may be small, perhaps only a few thousandths of an inch. But almost any amount is enough to weaken the sealing effect of the rings and permit blow-by to increase.

Piston, ring, and cylinder wear also allow oil to work up the cylinder walls into the combustion chamber and be burned. This burning of oil leaves a carbon residue which coats the spark plug, the piston, and the piston rings. The carbon residue reduces engine performance. Normally, in an engine with little wear, the excess oil is scraped off the cylinder walls by the oil-control rings. The compression rings also scrape some oil off cylinder walls. However, at high engine speeds, and with cylinder, piston, and ring wear, the piston rings are less effective in preventing oil from entering the combustion chamber.

⊘ **2-5 The Valve Train** There are two openings or ports at the top end of each cylinder (shown in Fig. 2-4). They are called the *intake port* and the *exhaust port*. The intake port allows the mixture of air and gasoline to enter the cylinder. Once in the cylinder, this mixture is compressed and burned to produce power. The exhaust port allows the burned gases to escape, or exhaust, from the cylinder.

Each port is opened and closed by a poppet valve. The head of the valve is also part of the combustion-chamber surface. The valve stem is assembled inside the port (Fig. 2-9). It is supported in a

valve guide which permits the valve to move up and down in a straight line. With the valve closed, the rim or face of the valve is tight against the valve seat. This seals the port so that no gas can enter or escape from the combustion chamber during a piston stroke.

A series of parts called the *valve train* is required to make the valves move. The valve train for the commonly used overhead-valve engine (Fig. 2-10), includes a camshaft, a means of rotating the camshaft (such as timing gears or timing chain), valve lifters or tappets, pushrods, and rocker arms. The camshaft (Fig. 2-11) is a steel shaft with a series of cams ground on it. The camshaft has one cam for each valve. That is, it has two cams for each cylinder, since each cylinder has two valves that open and close at different times.

A cam has an eccentric lobe, or bump, of almost any shape. On the engine camshaft, each cam is round except for one high lobe. As the camshaft rotates, this lobe moves around in a circle. When the lobe is under the valve lifter, it causes the lifter to move upward. This upward movement pushes the pushrod upward. The pushrod then pushes up on one end of the rocker arm. The arm is attached to a shaft or a ball joint at its center. When one end of the rocker arm is pushed up, the other end is pushed down. This pushes down on the end of the valve stem, and causes the valve to move down off the

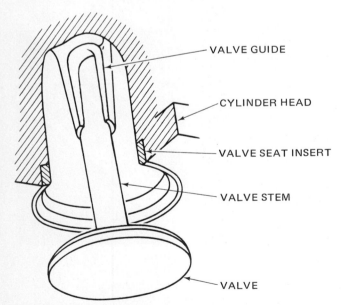

Fig. 2-9. A valve and valve seat in a cylinder head. The cylinder head, valve-seat insert, and valve guide have been partly cut away so that the valve stem can be seen.

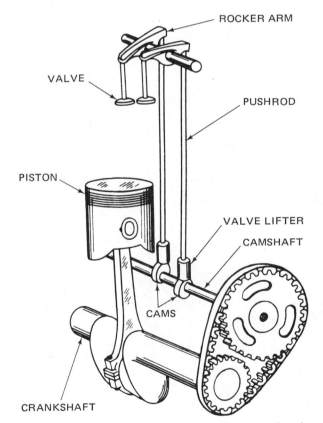

Fig. 2-10. Valve operating mechanism for an I-head, or overhead-valve, engine. Only the essential moving parts for one cylinder are shown here in simplified form.

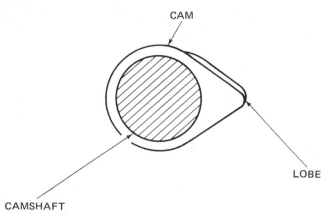

Fig. 2-11. The cams on the engine camshaft are round except for one high spot, or lobe.

valve seat and open the port. With the port open, gas can pass between the valve face and the valve seat.

Figure 2-12 shows a typical valve-operating mechanism in cutaway view. Actual valve trains are a little more complicated than what we just described. Valves have springs attached to the ends of their stems. These springs rest on the cylinder head and exert a strong force on the valve stems to keep the valves closed. The cam lobe must overcome this spring force, through valve-train operation, to open the valve. Thus, the valves are opened by the cam lobes.

The valves are closed by valve-spring tension. The spring force causes the valve to return to its seat after the cam lobe revolves past the valve lifter. A chain and sprockets drive the camshaft in most engines. Figure 2-13 shows a typical camshaft driven by a timing chain. Figure 2-14 shows two other methods of driving camshafts. On the left, a pair of gears drives the camshaft. On the right is a drive

Fig. 2-12. Partial cutaway view of a four-cylinder in-line engine with overhead valves. (*Chevrolet Motor Division of General Motors Corporation*)

Fig. 2-13. Crankshaft and camshaft sprockets with chain drive for a V-8 engine. (*Ford Motor Company*)

arrangement using sprockets and a toothed neoprene timing belt. The timing belt often is used on overhead-camshaft engines. All camshaft drive arrangements have this in common: They drive the camshaft so it turns at exactly one-half the speed of the crankshaft. There is a good reason for this, as you will see.

⊘ **2-6 The Four-Stroke Cycle** The four-stroke cycle, or Otto cycle, is a continuous repetition, in the engine, of four piston strokes—intake, compression, power, and exhaust. These key words represent the intake of a combustible air-fuel mixture, the "squeezing" of the mixture, the combustion or burning of the mixture for the power stroke, and the exhaust of the burned gases.

The *intake stroke* begins as the piston leaves top

dead center (TDC) (Fig. 2-15). At that time, the intake valve is open to admit the air-fuel mixture into the cylinder. When the piston reaches bottom dead center (BDC), the intake valve closes.

Now, the piston starts up as the rotating crankshaft begins to push upward on its connecting rod (Fig. 2-16). This upward movement is called the *compression stroke*. The mixture is trapped in the closed combustion chamber and is compressed by the piston. In many engines, the air-fuel mixture is compressed to one-eighth or one-ninth of its original volume. As shown in Fig. 2-17, an engine that compresses the air-fuel mixture to one-ninth of its original volume, for example, is said to have a *compression ratio* of 9 to 1 (written 9:1).

Near the end of the compression stroke, the ignition system produces an electric spark at the spark plug. The heat from the spark ignites the compressed mixture (see Fig. 2-18). As the mixture burns, a very high pressure is produced in the combustion chamber. The total force pushing down on a piston may be as much as 2 tons [1,814.4 kg]. This downward push is carried through the connecting rod to the crank on the crankshaft; it forces the crankshaft to rotate. The rotary motion is carried by gears and shafts to the car wheels so the car moves. This piston stroke is called the *power stroke* or *combustion stroke*.

At the end of the power stroke, the cylinder is filled with burned gases which must be removed from the cylinder. As the piston nears BDC, the exhaust valve opens. Camshaft rotation has carried the exhaust cam lobe under its valve lifter. The lifter moves up, forcing the pushrod to move up and the rocker arm to rock. This pushes the exhaust valve down to open the exhaust port. As the piston passes BDC and moves up in the cylinder, it pushes burned gases ahead of it and out of the cylinder (Fig. 2-19). This is called the *exhaust stroke*.

Fig. 2-14. Left, crankshaft and camshaft gears for a six-cylinder engine; note the timing marks on the gears. (*Buick Motor Division of General Motors Corporation*). Right, simplified drawing of the drive arrangement for an overhead-camshaft engine.

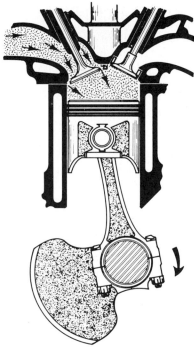

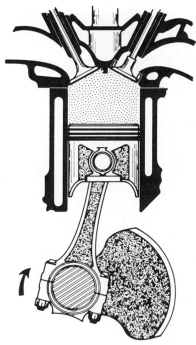

Fig. 2-15. Intake stroke. The intake valve (at left) has opened, and the piston is moving downward, drawing a mixture of air and gasoline vapor into the cylinder.

Fig. 2-16. Compression stroke. The intake valve has closed, and the piston is moving upward, compressing the mixture.

⊘ **2-7 Valve Overlap** There is a period, called *valve overlap,* during which the intake and exhaust valves are both open. The intake valve opens as the piston approaches TDC at the end of the exhaust stroke. The exhaust valve is already open. With both valves open, the incoming air-fuel mixture helps to clear the exhaust gases from the cylinder. The exhaust valve is held open for a number of crankshaft degrees after the piston leaves TDC to start the intake stroke. (Remember, there are 360 degrees in one complete rotation.) The total time, in crankshaft degrees, that both valves are open together is the valve

overlap. This valve overlap aids cylinder charging and improves volumetric efficiency. Volumetric efficiency is the ratio between the amount of air-fuel mixture that actually enters the cylinders and the amount that could enter under ideal conditions.

The exhaust stroke ends as the piston reaches TDC. When the piston starts down again on the intake stroke, a fresh charge of air-fuel mixture enters the cylinder. This entire four-stroke cycle continues to repeat itself in each cylinder as long as the engine is running.

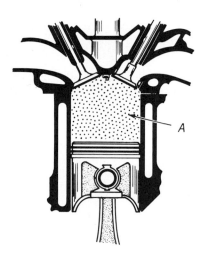

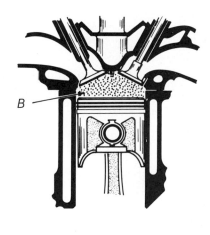

PISTON AT BDC   PISTON AT TDC

Fig. 2-17. The compression ratio is the volume in the cylinder with the piston at BDC divided by its volume with the piston at TDC, or *A* divided by *B*.

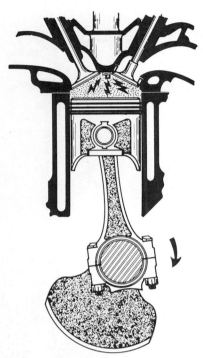

Fig. 2-18. Power stroke. The ignition system has delivered a spark to the spark plug to ignite the compressed mixture. As the mixture burns, high pressure is created, pushing the piston down.

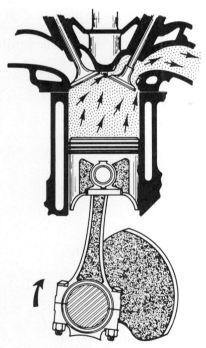

Fig. 2-19. Exhaust stroke. The exhaust valve has opened (right), and the piston is moving upward, forcing the burned gases from the cylinder.

Check Your Progress

Progress Quiz 2-1 When charging a battery, a good automotive technician checks it periodically to see how it is taking the charge. Likewise, in this book, we shall stop periodically to allow you to check your progress—to see how well you are "taking the charge" of new information. The following questions will help you find out whether you understand what you have just studied. Don't be discouraged if you have difficulty answering some of the questions. Just restudy the previous few pages, and then try to answer the questions again. Most good students know that new material must be studied several times. Rereading the pages and rechecking the questions helps you learn how to pick out the important facts. Before you finish this book, your ability to retain essential information will improve greatly. This ability will be of much help to you in your future work.

Correcting Lists The purpose of this exercise is to enable you to spot an unrelated item in a list. For example, suppose you were given the list "shoes, pants, shirt, milk, tie, coat." You would see that "milk" does not belong, because it is the only item that you cannot wear. There is one unrelated item in each of the following lists. Write each list in your notebook, but do not write the item that does not belong. Check your work with the answers at the end of the book.

1. The parts that change reciprocating motion to rotary motion are the camshaft, crankshaft, crankpin, and connecting rod.
2. The piston rings on a typical engine piston are the upper compression ring, lower compression ring, oil-control ring, and O ring.
3. The causes of increased blow-by are slower engine speed, piston and ring wear, cylinder wear, and faster engine speed.
4. The parts in a valve train include the camshaft, timing gears or chain, valve lifters, valve-cover gasket, and rocker arms.
5. The strokes in the four-stroke cycle are intake, compression, power, exhaust, and overlap.

Completing the Sentences The sentences below are incomplete. After each sentence there are several words or phrases, but only one of them correctly completes the sentence. Write each sentence in your notebook, ending it with the word or phrase that makes it correct.

1. Incomplete burning of gasoline in an engine produces: (*a*) fresh air, (*b*) exhaust pollutants, (*c*) water, (*d*) polar ice.
2. Pistons are usually made of: (*a*) cast iron, (*b*) steel, (*c*) magnesium, (*d*) aluminum.
3. The motion of the piston as it moves up and down in the cylinder is called: (*a*) reciprocating motion, (*b*) rotary motion, (*c*) circular motion, (*d*) displacement.

4. The motion of the crankshaft as it revolves in a circle is called: (a) revolving motion, (b) reciprocating motion, (c) rotary motion, (d) displacement.

5. The two types of piston rings used in an engine are: (a) compression rings and oil-control rings, (b) compression rings and sealing rings, (c) oil-control rings and scraping rings (d) sealing rings and scraping rings.

6. The purpose of the compression ring is to: (a) scrape oil off the cylinder wall, (b) provide a gastight seal between the piston and the cylinder wall, (c) control the compression ratio, (d) prevent piston wear.

7. Leakage past the piston rings during the compression and power strokes is called: (a) leakdown, (b) combustion, (c) blow-by, (d) compression.

8. Blow-by increases with engine wear and: (a) speed, (b) size, (c) bore, (d) stroke.

9. The intake and exhaust of gases from the combustion chamber are controlled by: (a) the piston, (b) piston rings, (c) the combustion chamber, (d) poppet valves.

10. Valves are opened by the action of the: (a) valve springs, (b) valve guides, (c) crankshaft, (d) cam lobes.

⊘ **2-8 The Ignition System** When the piston is near TDC at the end of the compression stroke, the compressed air-fuel mixture is set on fire, or ignited. This is done by a spark from the ignition system (Fig. 2-20).

The older type of ignition system consists of the ignition coil, ignition distributor, contact points and capacitor (condenser), ignition switch, low- and high-voltage wiring, spark plugs, and a source of electric energy (either the battery or an alternator). The electronic ignition system, now used on most cars and discussed in ⊘ 2-15, does not use contact points or a condenser. Instead, it uses a magnetic device in the distributor and an electronic amplifier. We discuss the contact-point system first.

The ignition system produces high-voltage surges and sends these surges, at the proper time, to the spark plugs in the engine cylinders. The surges cause sparks to jump the gaps in the spark plugs. Each spark must be timed to jump the gap just as the piston nears the end of the compression stroke. As the spark jumps from the center electrode of the spark plug, the heat of the current flow ignites the compressed mixture. This starts the power stroke.

⊘ **2-9 Primary and Secondary Circuits (Contact-Point System)** The ignition system consists of two separate circuits—the *primary* circuit and the *secondary* circuit. The primary circuit includes the battery, ammeter, ignition switch, resistor or calibrated resistance wire, primary winding of the ignition coil, distributor contact points and condenser, vehicle frame, and primary wiring (Fig. 2-21). The secondary circuit includes the coil secondary wiring, distribu-

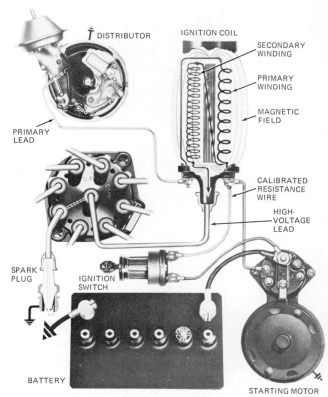

Fig. 2-20. Typical ignition system. It consists of the battery (source of power), ignition switch, ignition coil (shown schematically), distributor (shown in top view with its cap removed and placed below it), spark plugs (one shown in sectional view), and wiring. Magnetic lines of force are indicated by the curved lines around the ignition coil. (*Delco-Remy Division of General Motors Corporation*)

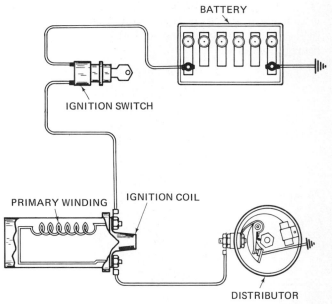

Fig. 2-21. Simplified diagram of the primary circuit in the contact-point-type ignition system.

tor cap and rotor, spark-plug cables, spark plugs, and vehicle frame (Fig. 2-22).

With the ignition switch closed (in the ON position), primary-circuit current flows from the battery. The current flows through the primary winding of the coil and the closed distributor contact points to ground (which is the return path), and then back to the battery. A cam mounted on the rotating distributor shaft causes the points to open and close at mechanically timed intervals. Figure 2-23 shows a typical distributor.

⊘ **2-10 The Ignition Coil** When the contact points are closed, current flows in the coil primary winding. The current flow through this winding causes a magnetic field to build up in the coil (Fig. 2-20). When the contact points open and break the circuit, the current flow stops and the magnetic field collapses. The collapsing field induces a very high voltage in the secondary winding. The secondary circuit sends the high voltage to the spark plug, to cause a spark to jump the spark-plug gap. The high voltage is produced at the proper time to begin the power stroke.

⊘ **2-11 Contact Points and Condenser** The ignition spark occurs at the spark plug at almost the instant the contact points open. When the contact points begin to open, a voltage of up to 250 V (volts) is induced in the primary circuit. This voltage is sometimes called the ignition-system *intermediate* voltage. It causes a small, momentary arc to form across the contact points. The arc forms when the current tries to flow across the points as they open and break the primary circuit. This arc could damage the points and shorten their useful life. To reduce the arc, a capacitor (or condenser) is connected across the contact points. The condenser has two purposes: (1) to bring the primary current to a quick stop, which helps collapse the magnetic field; and (2) to prevent or greatly reduce arcing across the points, thereby ensuring longer contact-point life.

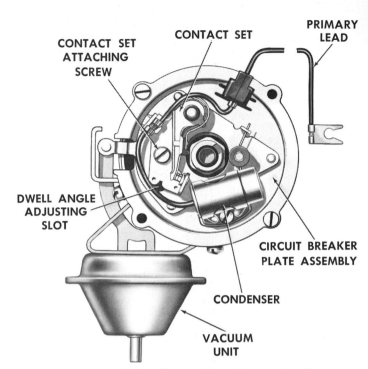

Fig. 2-23. Typical distributor. Note the cam in the center, which opens the points; the condenser, which controls arcing of the points; and the contact set or "points." (*Delco-Remy Division of General Motors Corporation*)

⊘ **2-12 High-Voltage Surge** The high-voltage surge flows from the coil secondary winding, across the distributor-rotor gap and spark-plug gap, to the spark-plug ground electrode (Fig. 2-24). As the high-voltage surge jumps the spark-plug gap, it ignites the compressed air-fuel mixture in the cylinder to start the power stroke. The contact points then close, and the ignition cycle repeats itself. This time it fires the next cylinder in the firing order. That is, when the points again open, the distributor rotor is aligned with the distributor-cap insert that is connected to the next spark plug to be fired.

⊘ **2-13 The Primary Resistor** In many contact-point ignition systems, there is a resistor in the circuit between the ignition switch and the coil primary terminal. This resistor may be a calibrated resistance wire, an externally mounted resistor, or an internal resistance in the coil. The primary-circuit resistor prevents arcing and burning of the distributor contact points from excessive current flow. It does this by allowing full battery voltage to reach the coil primary winding only during cranking, for easier starting. During engine operation, the resistor reduces the voltage to 5 to 8 V.

One system uses a temperature-sensitive external resistor to act as a current-compensating device. At low engine speeds, the primary current flows for longer periods of time. This heats up the resistor, thereby increasing its resistance and reducing the current flow. At high engine speeds, the current

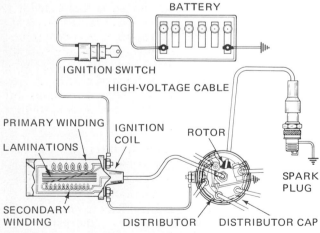

Fig. 2-22. Secondary circuit added to the ignition system of Fig. 2-21.

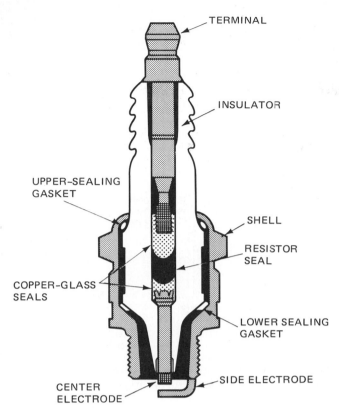

Fig. 2-24. A cutaway view of a spark plug with a built-in resistor. High voltage from the coil causes a spark to jump from the center electrode to the side, or grounded electrode. (*AC Spark Plug Division of General Motors Corporation*)

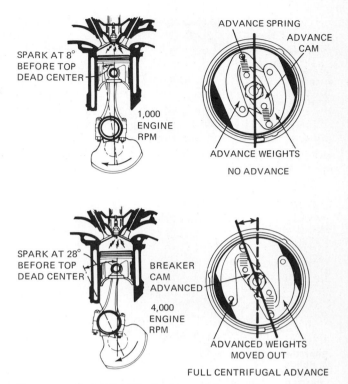

Fig. 2-25. Centrifugal-advance mechanism in no-advance and full-advance positions. In the typical example shown, the ignition is timed at 8° before top dead center on idle. There is no centrifugal advance at 1,000 engine rpm, but there is 28° of total advance (20° centrifugal plus 8° original timing) at 4,000 engine rpm. (*Delco-Remy Division of General Motors Corporation*)

flows for shorter periods of time. This lets the resistor cool, increasing the current flow.

NOTE: Many electronic ignition systems (⊘ 2-15) do not use a primary resistor.

⊘ **2-14 Advancing the Spark** When the engine is idling, each spark is timed to appear at the plug gap just as the piston approaches top dead center on the compression stroke. This is shown in Fig. 2-25. At any speed faster than idle, the spark timing is *advanced,* so that the spark occurs earlier in the cycle. This gives the mixture more time to burn. In most distributors, a *centrifugal-advance mechanism* automatically advances the spark as engine speed increases.

There is another condition during which spark advance should occur. This is when the engine operates at part throttle. At part throttle, less air-fuel mixture gets into the cylinders and combustion chambers. With less fuel in the combustion chambers, the mixture burns slower after it is ignited.

Since the mixture burns slower, the piston is past TDC and moving down again before combustion produces a high pressure on the top of the piston. As a result, much of the power in the fuel can be lost. The *vacuum-advance mechanism* is designed to prevent this loss by advancing the spark during part-throttle operation (Figs. 2-26 and 2-27). The vacuum-advance mechanism does improve part-throttle operation; however, under some conditions it can increase the formation of oxides of nitrogen, as we shall explain in a later chapter. We shall also explain the special controls that are used to prevent vacuum advance under conditions that could produce NO_x.

⊘ **2-15 Electronic Ignition Systems** The electronic ignition system does not use contact points. Instead, it uses a magnetic pickup device in the distributor and an electronic amplifying device with transistors. With the cap on, the distributor looks the same as the contact-point distributor. However, when the caps are removed, the difference between the two is apparent. There are various kinds of electronic ignition systems. We shall describe two of them: the Chrysler system and the General Motors system.

⊘ **2-16 Chrysler Electronic Ignition System** An electronic ignition system has been used in all Chrysler Corporation cars made in the United States since 1973. In this system, the distributor has a metal rotor with a series of tips on it. This rotor, called the *reluctor,* is shown in Fig. 2-28. The reluctor takes the place of the cam in the contact-point distributor previously discussed. Notice that the reluctor in Fig.

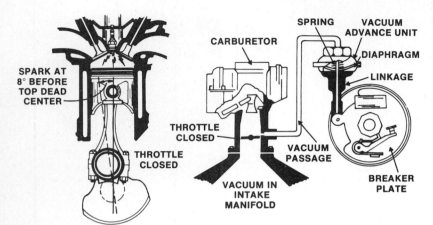

Fig. 2-26. When the throttle is closed, there is no vacuum advance.

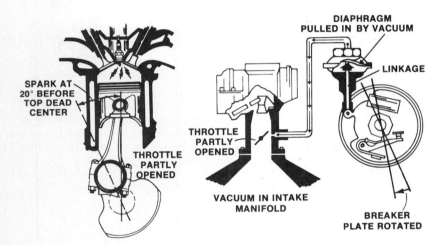

Fig. 2-27. When the throttle is partly opened so that vacuum is applied to the vacuum-advance unit, the breaker plate is rotated, or moved ahead. The cam closes and opens the points earlier, to produce a vacuum advance.

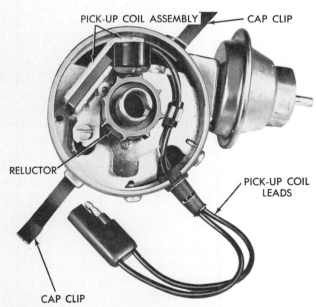

Fig. 2-28. Top view of the Chrysler electronic-ignition distributor. The cap and rotor have been removed so the reluctor and pickup coil can be seen. (*Chrysler Corporation*)

2-28 has eight tips. It is for an eight-cylinder engine, so there is one tip for each cylinder. Notice also that the distributor has a permanent magnet and a pickup coil.

The principle of operation is simple. The reluctor provides a path for the magnetic lines of force from the magnet. Every time a tip of the reluctor passes the pickup coil, it carries the magnetic field through the coil. This magnetic field produces a pulse of electric current in the coil. The current is very small, but it is enough to trigger the control unit into action.

The control unit uses electronic devices—diodes and transistors—to control the flow of current to the ignition coil. When the pulse of current from the pickup coil arrives at the control unit, the control unit stops the flow of current to the ignition coil. This is the same job the contact points do in the distributor discussed earlier. When the current stops flowing in the ignition coil, the magnetic field in the coil collapses. This causes the coil to produce a high-voltage surge. The high-voltage surge is led through the distributor rotor, cap, and wiring to the spark plug that is ready to fire.

The tip of the reluctor now rotates past the pickup coil. The pulse of current from the pickup coil ends. This allows the control unit to close the circuit from the battery to the ignition coil. Primary current flows again, and a magnetic field builds up once more in the ignition coil. Then the next tip of the reluctor passes the pickup coil, and the whole series of events is repeated.

In this system there are no contact points to adjust or wear out. Everything is automatic. The only adjustment required is the ignition timing, which we shall discuss later.

Figure 2-29 shows the wiring for the Chrysler electronic ignition system. The dual ballast is a double resistor. It protects the system from overload but allows maximum current to flow during cranking. This assures a strong spark for good starting performance.

⊘ **2-17 General Motors Electronic Ignition System** General Motors calls the distributor in their electronic ignition system a *magnetic-pulse* distributor. Figure 2-30 shows the distributor. It looks much like the Chrysler unit, and it works in about the same way. The General Motors distributor has a pole piece in the form of a ring. The pole piece has a series of teeth, pointing inward. There is one tooth for each cylinder in the engine. Under the pole piece is a permanent magnet with a pickup coil. The timer core, made of iron, is placed on top of the distributor shaft. It is placed exactly the same way as the cam in the contact-point distributor. The timer core also has one tooth for each cylinder in the engine.

When the engine is running, the teeth on the timer core align with the teeth on the pole piece. They align once per timer-core rotation for each cylinder in the engine. (For an eight-cylinder engine, there are eight teeth on the pole piece and eight teeth

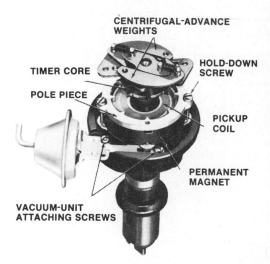

Fig. 2-30. Magnetic-pickup distributor with the cap and rotor removed. (*Delco-Remy Division of General Motors Corporation*)

on the timer core. The teeth align eight times during every revolution of the timer core.) Every time the teeth align, magnetic lines of force are carried through the pickup coil. This produces a pulse of current that flows to the ignition-pulse amplifier (Fig. 2-31). There, the pulse electronically opens the circuit to the ignition-coil primary. The magnetic field in the coil collapses, and a high-voltage surge is produced. This surge is carried by the high-voltage leads, the distributor cap, and the rotor to the spark plug that is ready to fire.

⊘ **2-18 High-Energy Ignition System** In 1972, the Delco-Remy Division of General Motors introduced an ignition distributor that has the ignition coil assembled into it. This combination of coil and distributor is called a unit distributor. With this assembly, the wiring is greatly simplified (Fig. 2-32). Note that there is one lead from the battery (which Delco-Remy calls an "Energizer"). It goes through the ig-

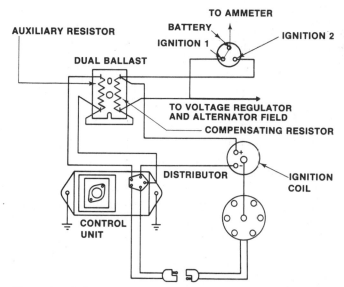

Fig. 2-29. Schematic wiring diagram of the Chrysler electronic ignition system. (*Chrysler Corporation*)

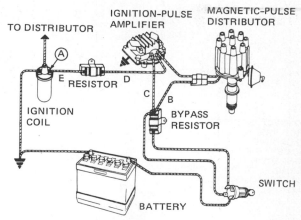

Fig. 2-31. Wiring diagram for an ignition system using a magnetic-pulse distributor and a transistor control unit (ignition-pulse amplifier) to amplify the ignition pulse. (*Delco-Remy Division of General Motors Corporation*)

nition switch to the unit distributor. The only other leads are the high-voltage cables going to the spark plugs. Figure 2-33 shows the distributor assembled, and Fig. 2-34 shows the unit partly disassembled. The ignition coil looks different from the ignition coils on older cars. But it works the same way. All the connections between the coil and distributor are inside the unit distributor, so the wiring is much simpler. The distributor uses the magnetic-pulse principle. This is explained in ⊘ 2-17 and illustrated in Figs. 2-30 and 2-31.

Figures 2-35 and 2-36 show what Delco-Remy calls the "High-Energy Ignition (HEI) System" distributor. It also has the ignition coil built in. This system produces a considerably higher secondary voltage, up to 35,000 V. The HEI system uses spark plugs with a wider gap—as large as 0.080 in [2.03 mm]. A standard plug cannot be used with this system because, to get the wide gap, the side elec-

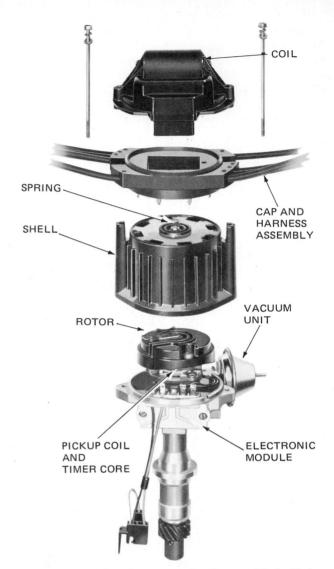

Fig. 2-34. Unit distributor, partly disassembled. (*Delco-Remy Division of General Motors Corporation*)

trode would have to be bent at a severe angle. Instead, special plugs, made for the HEI system, must be used. The wide gap (and, thus, longer spark) helps to fire the leaner mixtures used in modern engines. Leaner mixtures help to reduce HC and CO in the exhaust gas; they are discussed later in this book.

⊘ **2-19 The Fuel System** Figure 2-37 shows a simplified automotive fuel system. The carburetor mixes air and gasoline to supply the cylinders with combustible air-fuel mixture. The gasoline comes from the fuel tank, usually located at the rear of the car. A fuel line connects the tank to the carburetor, through a fuel pump. The fuel pump draws gasoline from the fuel tank and delivers it to the carburetor.

When the engine is running, air passes down through the carburetor on its way to the engine cylinders. The air first passes through the air cleaner, a cylindrical metal case that sits on top of the carburetor. The air cleaner filters dirt and dust out of the

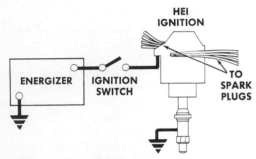

Fig. 2-32. Basic wiring diagram of the General Motors High-Energy Ignition System. (*Delco-Remy Division of General Motors Corporation*)

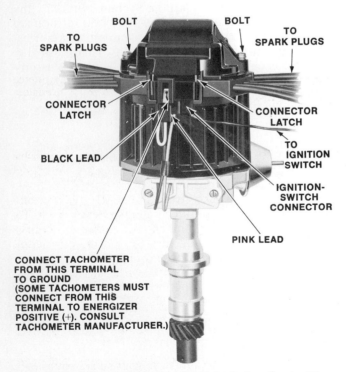

Fig. 2-33. Unit distributor, which includes the ignition coil. (*Delco-Remy Division of General Motors Corporation*)

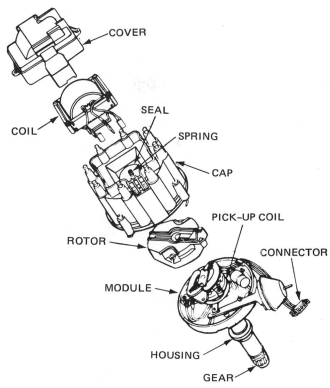

Fig. 2-35. Partly disassembled view of the high-energy distributor. (*Delco-Remy Division of General Motors Corporation*)

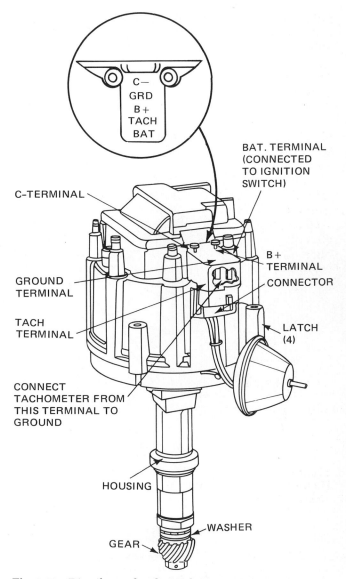

Fig. 2-36. Distributor for the High-Energy Ignition System, which includes the ignition coil. (*Delco-Remy Division of General Motors Corporation*)

air, so they will not enter the engine and cause wear. As the air rushes through the carburetor, the carburetor mixes in the correct "charge" of gasoline. What is correct depends on the engine operating speed and load. The liquid gasoline droplets discharged by the carburetor quickly turn to vapor in the intake manifold. This mixture of air and gasoline vapor enters the cylinders and is called the *air-fuel mixture*, or *air-fuel charge*.

A thorough discussion of automotive emission control systems requires detailed study of the fuel-system components. The fuel tank, carburetor, and air cleaner are covered more fully in later chapters.

⊘ **2-20 The Lubricating System** All the moving parts in the engine must be lubricated. That is, they must be coated with oil so they will slide easily and will not wear excessively. The engine lubricating system takes care of this. It includes an oil pan which holds a supply of lubricating oil, an oil pump that draws oil from this supply, an oil filter that removes dirt particles from the oil, and oil lines that carry the oil to the various moving parts in the engine. Figure 2-38 shows a simplified lubricating system for a V-8 engine.

In any piston engine, small amounts of compression and combustion gases escape past the pistons and rings into the crankcase (see Fig. 2-8). This is called blow-by, because the gases leak, or blow, by the rings. These blow-by gases must be removed from the crankcase to prevent a harmful

pressure buildup. In older engines, blow-by gases were released to the outside air through an open crankcase ventilation, or breather, tube (Fig. 2-39).

But blow-by gases from automotive piston engines add to the air-pollution and smog problem. To control this source of atmospheric pollution, crankcase emission control systems were added to automotive engines. Several variations of these systems have been used by different manufacturers. However, they all seal the open crankcase breather tube and send the crankcase blow-by gases back into the engine to be burned. Details of the different types of crankcase emission control systems are covered later.

Crankcase emission control systems place an added load on the lubricating oil. With the open-crankcase system, the highly acidic blow-by and combustion gases escaped into the atmosphere

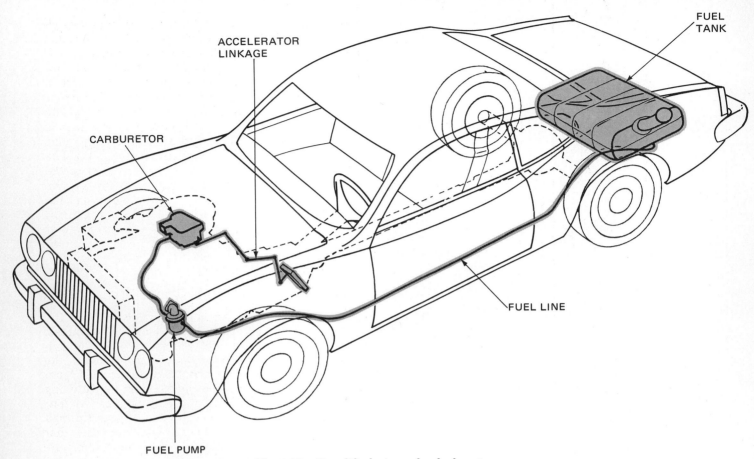

Fig. 2-37. Simplified view of a fuel system.

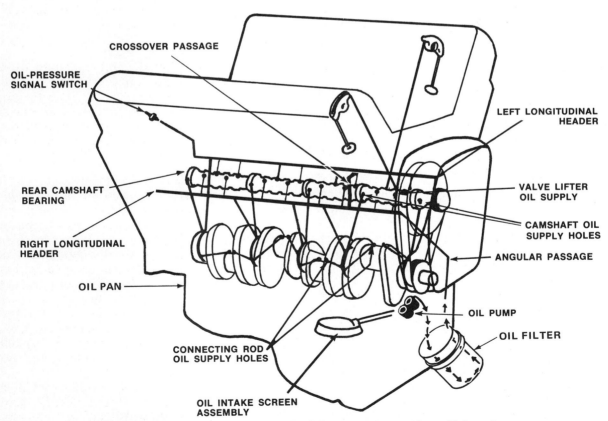

Fig. 2-38. Simplified drawing of the lubricating system for a V-8 engine.

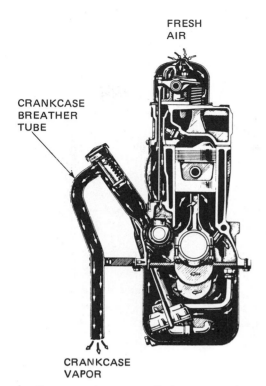

FRESH AIR

CRANKCASE BREATHER TUBE

CRANKCASE VAPOR

Fig. 2-39. Open crankcase ventilation system in an overhead-valve engine.

through the breather tube. But with crankcase emission control systems, the blow-by fumes are kept in the crankcase for a longer time. Because of this (and especially after a hose or the control valve is plugged with sludge), the corrosive acids in the blow-by gases settle into the engine oil. Unless the oil is of the proper type, the acids can corrode the piston rings, cylinder bores, and other engine parts.

To prevent such corrosion, automobile manufacturers have, since 1972, specified high-grade oil for their engines. Most late-model engines require the use of oils that have a service rating of SE. These approved engine oils contain a special additive to reduce corrosion in gasoline engines. In addition, the oils have other additives that provide more protection against oil oxidation, high-temperature engine deposits, and rust.

Engine oils affect ease of starting, oil economy, combustion-chamber deposits, and engine wear. So the oil recommended by the engine manufacturer must always be used. Also, a worn engine with high blow-by accumulates sludge in the crankcase. Using a good grade of engine oil and changing the oil frequently help keep the engine clean.

⊘ **2-21 The Cooling System** During the power stroke, the temperature in the cylinder may exceed 4,000°F [2,204°C (degrees Celsius)]. This temperature is hot enough to melt aluminum pistons and cast-iron cylinder heads. However, these high temperatures are only momentary. The power stroke lasts only a fraction of a second, and the exhaust stroke

then clears the high-temperature gases from the cylinder. The job of the cooling system is to carry the heat away from the cylinder walls and head.

The cooling system (Fig. 2-40) includes a series of openings surrounding the cylinder walls and in the cylinder head. These openings are called *water jackets*, and coolant circulates through them. The coolant is a mixture of antifreeze and water. It is forced through the coolant passages or water jackets by a pump, called the water pump (Fig. 2-41). The water pump draws coolant from the bottom of the cooling-system radiator and pushes it through the water jackets. As the coolant circulates through the water jackets, it picks up heat. The heated coolant then returns to the radiator through the upper radiator hose. From the top of the radiator, the hot coolant—as it cools—settles to the bottom of the radiator through a series of tubes or passages.

Figure 2-42 shows the construction of one type of radiator. Metal fins surround the water tubes, as shown in Fig. 2-42. The fins absorb heat from the coolant moving downward through the water tubes. Air, drawn in by the fan or by vehicle movement, flows from the front to the back of the radiator. The air flowing through the radiator picks up heat from the fins. This cools the hot coolant circulating through the radiator. After the cooler coolant reaches the bottom of the radiator, it goes through the engine again. This is a continuous operation that removes the right amount of heat from the engine.

When the cooling system is removing just enough heat to maintain the specified engine temperature, the engine is said to be "normalized" or at "normal operating temperature."

⊘ **2-22 Coolant Flow** In the radiators described above, the coolant flows from the top to the bottom; these are known as *down-flow* radiators (Figure 2-43). In other radiators, the coolant flows from one side to the other; these are called *cross-flow* radiators (Fig. 2-44). The cross-flow radiator, being shorter from top to bottom, permits a lower car hood line.

⊘ **2-23 Expansion Tank** Some cooling systems have a separate expansion tank (Fig. 2-45). The expansion tank is partly filled with coolant and is connected to the radiator cap. The coolant expands in the engine as it heats up. This sends some of the coolant into the expansion tank. Then, when the engine approaches operating temperature, a valve in the radiator cap closes. The cooling system is now sealed, and its internal pressure goes up. This increased pressure permits the cooling system to operate at a higher temperature without causing the coolant to boil. As a result, the cooling system operates more efficiently (see ⊘ 2-25).

When the engine cools off, the coolant in the cooling system contracts. This produces a vacuum in the cooling system. Now, coolant from the reservoir flows back into the engine water jackets and radia-

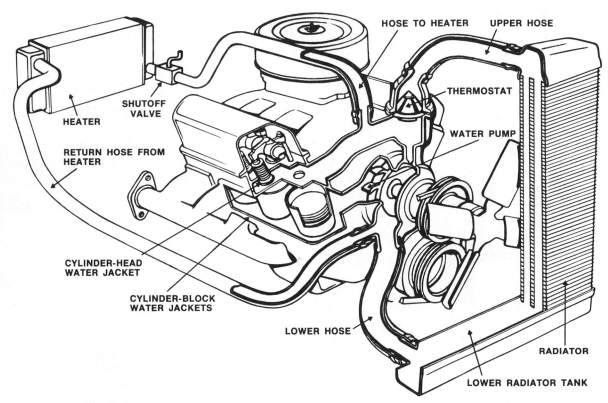

Fig. 2-40. Cutaway view of a V-8 engine, showing the cooling system.

tor. This keeps the cooling system filled to capacity at all times, so the system operates at full efficiency.

⊘ **2-24 Thermostats** The thermostat is located in the coolant passage between the cylinder head and the top of the radiator (Fig. 2-40). Its purpose is to close off this passage when the engine is cold. This prevents coolant circulation and cooling action. Heat is thus retained in the engine, so that it heats up fast. This is desirable because a cold engine wears rapidly. Also, a cold engine burns fuel inefficiently, and more HC and CO come out of the tail pipe.

Figure 2-46 shows three types of thermostats. The wax-pellet type is the most common. Figure 2-47 shows this thermostat in sectional view. When cold, the wax pellet shrinks so that it pulls the valve closed. As it heats up, the wax pellet expands and raises the valve to allow coolant to flow to the radiator.

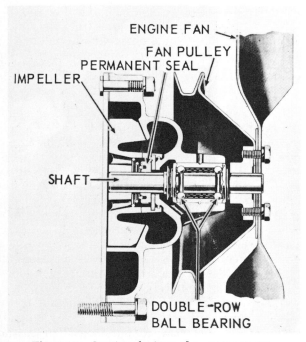

Fig. 2-41. Sectional view of a water pump.

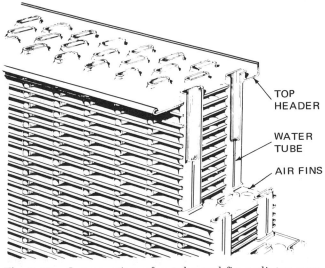

Fig. 2-42. Construction of a tube-and-fin radiator core.

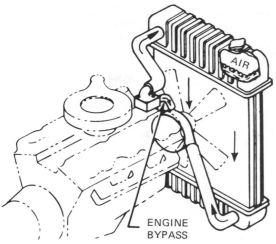

Fig. 2-43. Cooling system using a down-flow radiator. (*Harrison Radiator Division of General Motors Corporation*)

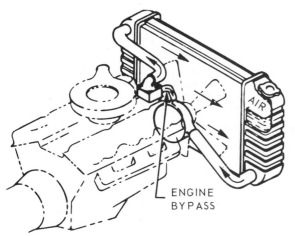

Fig. 2-44. Cooling system using a cross-flow radiator. (*Harrison Radiator Division of General Motors Corporation*)

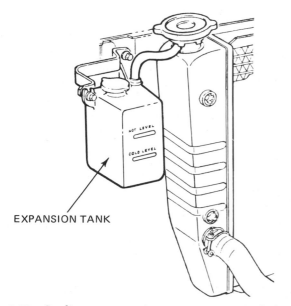

Fig. 2-45. Cooling system using an expansion tank. (*Ford Motor Company*)

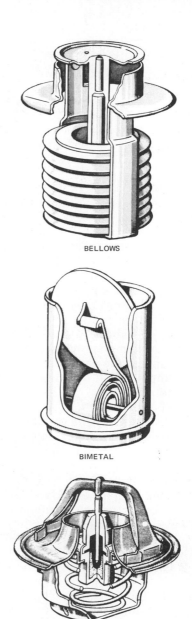

BELLOWS

BIMETAL

WAX PELLET

Fig. 2-46. Three types of cooling-system thermostats. (*Ford Motor Company*)

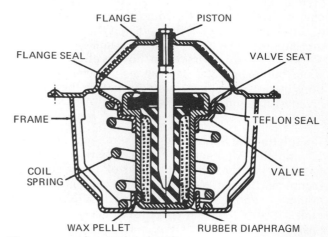

Fig. 2-47. Sectional view of a wax-pellet thermostat. (*Chevrolet Motor Division of General Motors Corporation*)

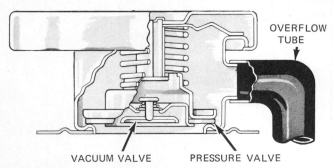

OVERFLOW TUBE

VACUUM VALVE   PRESSURE VALVE

Fig. 2-48. Radiator pressure cap. (*Ford Motor Company*)

◊ **2-25 Radiator Pressure Cap**   The radiator pressure cap (Fig. 2-48) has two valves. One is a pressure valve that stays closed until a preset pressure against the valve is reached. When this pressure is reached, the valve is forced open. This relieves the pressure and prevents damage to the system. The second valve is a vacuum valve. It opens in case vacuum develops in the system, to prevent atmospheric pressure from collapsing the radiator. Vacuum can develop, for example, when the engine cools off and the coolant contracts.

The use of a pressure cap on the radiator increases the pressure within the cooling system. Thus, the coolant may be circulated at higher temperatures without boiling. The coolant therefore enters the radiator at a higher temperature, so the difference in temperature between the air and the coolant is greater. Heat then is more quickly transferred from the coolant to the air passing through the radiator, improving cooling efficiency.

Chapter 2 Checkup

NOTE: Since the following is a chapter review test, you should review the chapter before taking the test.

The basic operation of the piston engine is not too difficult to understand. But when engine systems such as the ignition, fuel, lubricating, and cooling systems are added, it gets more complicated. In this chapter, we reviewed the four-stroke cycle, the parts of the engine and what they do, and the operation of the support systems required to make the engine work. To check yourself on how well you understand the engine and its systems, answer the questions below. Then check your work with the answers given at the end of the book.

Completing the Sentences   The sentences below are incomplete. After each sentence there are several words or phrases, but only one of them correctly completes the sentence. Write each sentence in your notebook, ending it with the word or phrase that makes it correct. When you have finished, turn to the answers at the end of the book, and check your work. Restudy any text sections that contain material on questions you missed.

1. The sequence of events in the four-stroke-cycle engine is: (*a*) intake, compression, venting, exhaust, (*b*) intake, compression, power, exhaust, (*c*) intake, ignition, power, exhaust, (*d*) exhaust, intake, power, compression.
2. The period during which the intake and exhaust valves are both open is called the: (*a*) valve underlap, (*b*) valve duration, (*c*) valve overlap, (*d*) valve timing.
3. The intake valve opens before the end of the: (*a*) intake stroke, (*b*) compression stroke, (*c*) power stroke, (*d*) exhaust stroke.
4. The exhaust valve closes after the beginning of the: (*a*) intake stroke, (*b*) compression stroke, (*c*) power stroke, (*d*) exhaust stroke.
5. The spark must jump the spark-plug gap as the piston nears the end of the: (*a*) intake stroke, (*b*) compression stroke, (*c*) power stroke, (*d*) exhaust stroke.
6. The spark plug is part of the: (*a*) primary circuit, (*b*) secondary circuit, (*c*) intermediate circuit, (*d*) cranking circuit.
7. The spark occurs at the spark plug when the distributor contact points: (*a*) close, (*b*) bounce, (*c*) float, (*d*) open.
8. The ignition condenser aids in the collapse of the magnetic field and: (*a*) times the spark, (*b*) prevents radio interference, (*c*) prevents battery discharge, (*d*) reduces arcing of the contact points.
9. The ignition primary resistor is bypassed during: (*a*) cruising, (*b*) idling, (*c*) cranking, (*d*) acceleration.
10. The timing of the spark is advanced to: (*a*) give the mixture more time to burn, (*b*) give the mixture less time to burn, (*c*) give the spark time to get hotter, (*d*) increase dwell.

Purpose and Operation of Engine Systems   The following questions ask for explanations of the purpose and operation of engine systems and components. Write each explanation in your notebook. If you have any difficulty recalling an explanation, turn back in the chapter and reread the pages that give you the answer. Then write down the explanation. Do not copy directly from the book. Try to answer each question in your own words. This is a good way to fix the ideas firmly in your mind.

1. How does the contact-point type of ignition system create a spark at the spark plug?
2. How does the electronic ignition system create a spark at the spark plug?
3. In the contact-point ignition system, what is the difference between the primary circuit and the secondary circuit?
4. How does the ignition coil work?
5. What jobs are performed by the ignition condenser?
6. How does advancing the spark allow more time for the mixture to burn?
7. Describe how gasoline gets from the fuel tank to the carburetor.
8. What is the job of the engine lubricating system?

9. Why must the proper oil be used in late-model engines?

10. How does the cooling system operate?

Definitions In the following, you are asked to define certain terms. Write the definitions in your notebook. Writing the definitions will help you remember them. It will also provide you with a quick way to locate the meanings when you need them. If you cannot remember the meanings of the terms, look them up in the chapter you have just studied, or in the glossary at the back of the book.

1. Define "blow-by."
2. What are atmospheric pollutants?
3. Define "reciprocating motion."
4. Define "rotary motion."
5. What is a valve train?
6. Define "port."
7. What is valve overlap?
8. Define "high-voltage surge."
9. What is an open-crankcase breather tube?
10. What is an expansion tank?

Suggestions for Further Study

There are several ways to do some further studying about automotive engines. First, you can inspect your own and your friends' cars. However, we do not suggest that you get out your toolbox and start tearing them apart; you are not quite ready for that yet.

Also, you can go to your school automotive shop or to a friendly service shop where automotive engine work is done. By watching what goes on in a service shop, you will learn a great deal about the various types of engines, how to identify them, and how to service them.

You may be able to borrow a manufacturer's service manual from a dealer service shop or from your school automotive-shop library. These manuals are sometimes available, for a price, from manufacturers. Your school automotive shop may have cutaway parts and engines on exhibit. Studying these will help you understand how automotive engines are constructed and how they work.

This chapter provides a brief review of the various actions in the running engine. Its purpose is to set the stage for the discussion of automotive pollutant sources in the next chapter.

For more detailed information on the construction and operation of automotive engines and accessories, refer to the following books. They are all published by the McGraw-Hill Book Company.

The Auto Book
Automotive Electrical Equipment
Automotive Engine Design
Automotive Engines
Automotive Fuel, Lubricating and Cooling Systems
Automotive Mechanics

chapter 3

SOURCES OF AUTOMOTIVE POLLUTION

The internal-combustion engine produces power by burning an air-fuel mixture in the combustion chambers. As the piston moves from the top to the bottom of the cylinder on the intake stroke, atmospheric pressure forces air-fuel mixture into the cylinder. Then the piston moves up on the compression stroke, compressing the mixture. Next, with the piston at the top of the cylinder, the compressed mixture is ignited by the spark plug. The resulting rapid burning produces the high pressure which drives the piston down on the power stroke. Finally, the piston travels back up to the top of the cylinder on the exhaust stroke. As it moves up, it forces the burned gases, containing exhaust pollutants, out of the cylinder. These gases travel through the exhaust system and are released to the atmosphere as they leave the tail pipe. This series of events goes on continuously, in each cylinder, to produce the power to move the vehicle.

If piston rings sealed perfectly, there would not be any crankcase blow-by gases to escape into the atmosphere. If combustion were absolutely complete, there would not be any atmospheric pollution from the exhaust system. Water and carbon dioxide are the products of perfect, complete combustion. However, as we shall see, these ideal conditions cannot be achieved by internal-combustion piston engines. Therefore, automotive engineers must continue to make design and specification changes. They must add mechanical devices to control the known sources of automotive pollution.

⊘ **3-1 Automobile Pollution Sources** There are four basic sources of air pollution from the automobile (Fig. 3-1). They are the engine crankcase, tail pipe or exhaust system, carburetor, and fuel tank. As you can see in Fig. 3-1, hydrocarbons (HC) escape into the atmosphere from each of these sources on a precontrolled car—that is, a car without any emission-control devices. Figure 3-1 shows the percentage that each source contributes to the total hydrocarbon emissions from a typical car.

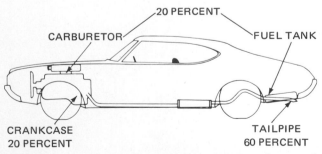

20 PERCENT
CARBURETOR
FUEL TANK
CRANKCASE
20 PERCENT
TAILPIPE
60 PERCENT

Fig. 3-1. Percentage of hydrocarbon emissions from each source on a car without emission-control devices.

⊘ **3-2 Controlling Automobile Pollution Sources** In the modern automobile, each of these pollution sources is controlled by a separate emission-control system. For example, crankcase pollution is controlled by the crankcase emission control system, as shown in Fig. 3-2.

Exhaust emissions are controlled by a variety of techniques and devices. The air-injection reactor (AIR), or air pump (Fig. 3-3), was one of the first devices widely used to control hydrocarbons and carbon monoxide in the engine exhaust gas. Another approach to controlling exhaust emissions is the engine modification, or controlled-combustion system (CCS), shown in Fig. 3-4. It is a combination of several engine modifications and calibrations. This system (Fig. 3-4) does not use an air pump.

To control the amounts of nitrogen oxides that form in the engine during the combustion process, most late-model engines are equipped with an exhaust-gas recirculation (EGR) system. (See Fig. 3-5.) A small amount of exhaust gas is returned to the intake manifold, so that air-fuel mixture burns at a lower temperature. This reduces the formation of nitrogen oxides (NO_x). The most recent exhaust

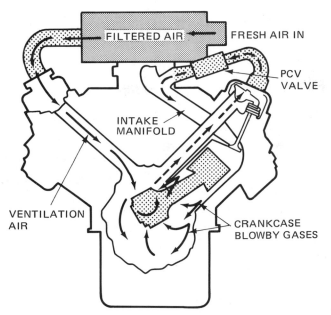

Fig. 3-2. Positive crankcase ventilation (PCV) system on a V-8 engine. This system permits no crankcase emissions to enter the atmosphere. (*Motor Vehicle Manufacturers Association*)

emission control system to be used on new cars is the catalytic-converter system (Fig. 3-6).

Fuel evaporation from the carburetor and fuel tank is controlled by the evaporative control system shown in Fig. 3-7. We shall study each of these systems in detail, and learn how to test and service each component, in later chapters. Now we need to discuss more fully the smog and air pollution caused by automobile emissions.

⊘ **3-3 Photochemical Smog** The most common type of air pollution in southern California is called *photochemical* smog. It is the result of sunlight reacting with hydrocarbons and nitrogen oxides in the atmosphere.

Now, let's review these terms. Hydrocarbons (HC) are unburned gasoline vapors. Nitrogen oxides (NO_x) are products of the combustion process and are formed *only* when combustion takes place.

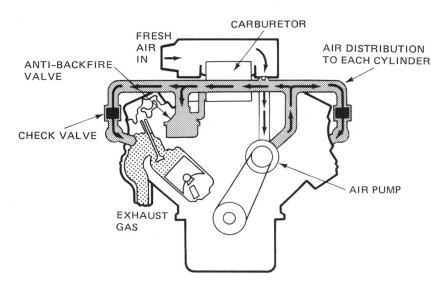

Fig. 3-3. Air-injection-reactor(AIR)or air-pump system of exhaust-emission control. With the use of the air pump, hydrocarbons and carbon monoxide in the exhaust gas are burned harmlessly in the engine exhaust manifold. (*Motor Vehicle Manufacturers Association*)

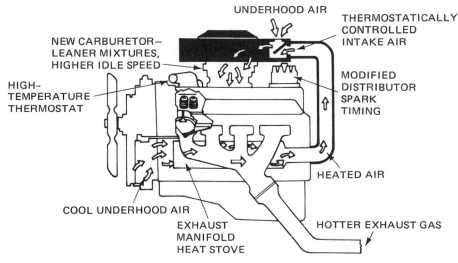

Fig. 3-4. Engine-modification or controlled-combustion system (CCS) of exhaust-emission control. It is a combination of several engine modifications and calibrations. (*Motor Vehicle Manufacturers Association*)

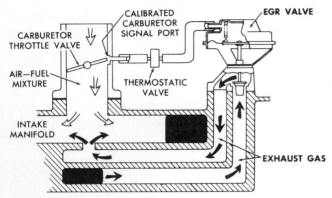

Fig. 3-5. Exhaust-gas recirculation (EGR) system. Recirculating some of the exhaust gas through the engine reduces the formation of NO$_x$. (*Cadillac Motor Car Division of General Motors Corporation*)

NOTE: Remember also that CO is another atmospheric pollutant produced by the engine (⊘ 1-4).

Nitrogen oxides (NO$_x$) are formed by the automobile mainly as a result of high combustion temperatures in the engine. However, other factors affect the engine's formation of NO$_x$. These include the air-fuel ratio, spark timing, intake-manifold vacuum, coolant temperature, combustion-chamber deposits, and distribution of the air-fuel charge to each cylinder. We describe these factors in later chapters.

Carbon monoxide (CO) is a tasteless, odorless, colorless, poisonous gas. The percentage of CO in the exhaust gas varies with the air-fuel ratio. The richer the mixture, the higher the percentage of CO.

Carbon monoxide is not involved in smog or smog formation, either as a smogmaker or as a catalyst. We are concerned about CO because it is a dangerously poisonous gas that is emitted into the air in relatively large quantities by the automobile

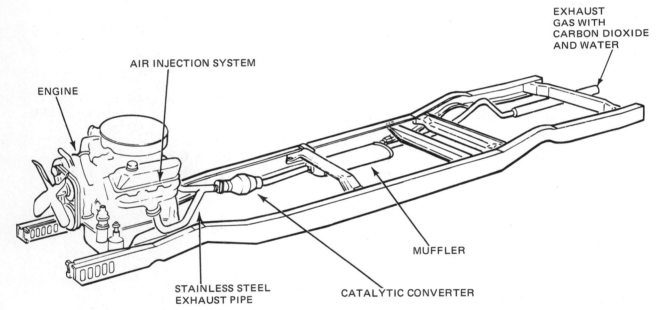

Fig. 3-6. Exhaust-emission control system using a catalytic converter. (*Ford Motor Company*)

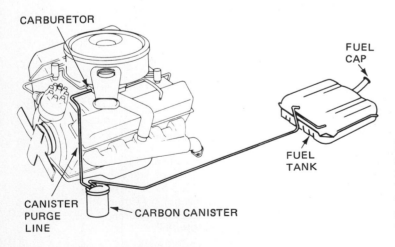

Fig. 3-7. Evaporative control system showing fuel-vapor recovery from the carburetor and fuel tank. (*Buick Motor Division of General Motors Corporation*)

engine. Atmospheric pollution levels of CO must be controlled, because our lives depend on having clean air to breathe.

⊘ **3-4 The Crankcase and Its Contaminants** The crankcase (Fig. 3-8) is the name given to the lower part of the cylinder block of the automotive engine. It supports and encloses the revolving crankshaft in an oiltight area. This is the area between the lower ends of the pistons and the cylinder block above, and the oil pan below.

During engine operation, blow-by enters the crankcase (Fig. 2-8). Remember, blow-by is the leakage of compressed air-fuel mixture and burned gases past the piston rings into the crankcase.

In addition to blow-by, small amounts of gasoline, in the form of liquid droplets, may leak down into the crankcase. This effect is more pronounced when the engine is cold. It results from the condensation of fuel vapor on the cold metal surfaces of the cylinder and combustion chamber. These surfaces are cold, for example, when the engine is first cranked and started in the morning. Then, some of the fuel vapor condenses back into drops of liquid. These small drops run down the cylinder walls, past the pistons and rings, and into the crankcase.

Water (H_2O) collects in the crankcase of a running engine in two ways. First, water is formed as a product of combustion. Recall that gasoline is a hydrocarbon (HC), made up of hydrogen and carbon. During combustion, the hydrogen unites with oxygen in the air to form hydrogen oxide, which has the chemical formula H_2O and the common name water. Some of this water is contained in the blow-by gas that escapes into the crankcase. Second, the crankcase ventilation system carries fresh air through the crankcase. And the fresh air has moisture in it. If the crankcase or other engine parts are cold, the water vapor from both sources condenses to a liquid and drops down into the crankcase.

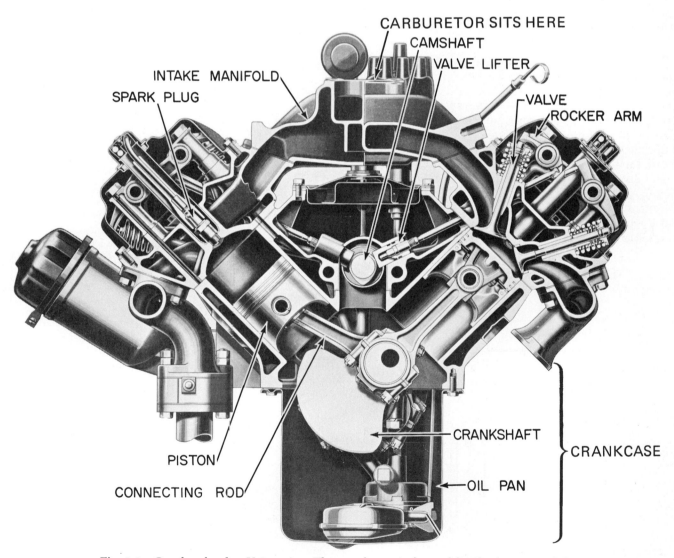

Fig. 3-8. Overhead-valve V-8 engine. The crankcase is formed by the bottoms of the pistons and cylinders, and the oil pan. (*Chrysler Corporation*)

⊘ **3-5 Crankcase Ventilation** The unburned and partly burned gasoline, and the combustion gases and water, must be cleared out of the crankcase. Otherwise, serious engine trouble can occur. The churning action of the rotating crankshaft can whip the water and engine oil into a thick, black, gooey substance called *sludge*. The combustion gases can form acids in this sludge and oil that will corrode the metal parts of the engine. To prolong engine life, these trouble-causing substances must be removed from the crankcase. On early-model cars, the crankcases were ventilated by an opening at the front and another opening at the back (Fig. 3-9). The forward motion of the car created a road draft under the car. In addition, the rotating crankshaft acted like a fan. Together, they kept fresh air passing through the crankcase. The air swept out the potentially damaging substances before they had a chance to do any harm.

However, this crankcase ventilation system, using a road-draft tube, vented the fumes and gases into the atmosphere. This polluted the air. Crankcase emission controls are installed to prevent or control this air pollution.

⊘ **3-6 Crankcase Emission Control Systems** All automobile engines built today are equipped with a positive crankcase ventilation (PCV) system of crankcase emission control. In this system (Fig. 3-10), fresh air flows through the crankcase and mixes with the crankcase fumes. From the crankcase, the fumes and air travel to the intake manifold and are mixed with the fresh incoming air-fuel charge. The mixture then enters the engine cylinders. This gives the previously unburned gasoline contained in the blow-by another chance to burn, instead of being wasted by escaping into the atmosphere. Chapter 5 describes crankcase emission controls in detail.

⊘ **3-7 Crankcase Emission Controls Required** In 1961, auto manufacturers began installing crankcase

Fig. 3-10. Positive crankcase ventilation (PCV) system on a six-cylinder engine. The arrows indicate the path taken by the fresh air. (*Ford Motor Company*)

emission control systems on cars built for registration in California. The early systems were known as *open* systems (Fig. 3-11), because the oil-filler cap was open, or vented to the atmosphere. Two years later, beginning with 1963 model vehicles, crankcase emission controls were required on all new cars manufactured for sale anywhere in the United States. All California cars built in 1964 and later, and all cars built in this country in 1968 and later, used the closed PCV system (Fig. 3-12). Figure 3-13 is a chart showing the years in which these systems were first required.

⊘ **3-8 The Exhaust System** The exhaust system is the source of the pollutants that are most harmful to human life and most difficult to control. There are three exhaust pollutants for which state and federal emission levels are set. These pollutants are un-

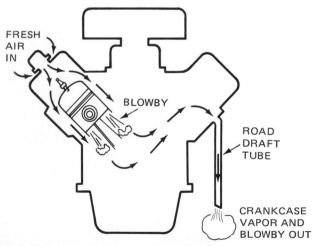

Fig. 3-9. Road-draft-tube system of crankcase ventilation. (*Chrysler Corporation*)

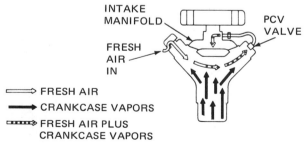

Fig. 3-11. Early open-type crankcase emission control system. (*AC-Delco Division of General Motors Corporation*)

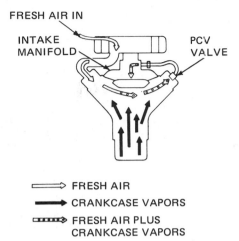

FRESH AIR IN

INTAKE MANIFOLD

PCV VALVE

⇨ FRESH AIR
➡ CRANKCASE VAPORS
⇒ FRESH AIR PLUS CRANKCASE VAPORS

Fig. 3-12. Closed-type crankcase emission control system. (*AC-Delco Division of General Motors Corporation*)

PRODUCTION YEAR	SYSTEM USED	WHERE REQUIRED
1961–63	OPEN	CALIFORNIA ONLY
1964 and later	CLOSED	CALIFORNIA ONLY
1964–1967	OPEN	NATIONWIDE EXCEPT CALIFORNIA
1968 and later	CLOSED	NATION WIDE

Fig. 3-13. Chart showing the years in which open and closed crankcase emission control systems were first installed by car manufacturers in this country.

burned hydrocarbons (HC), partly burned HC or carbon monoxide (CO), and nitrogen oxides (NO_x). See ⊘ 1-4 for an explanation of the combustion process which results in these three pollutants.

⊘ **3-9 Incomplete Combustion** Why does the gasoline fail to burn completely at the time of combustion? After all, it is this failure that results in unburned gasoline (HC), and partly burned HC or

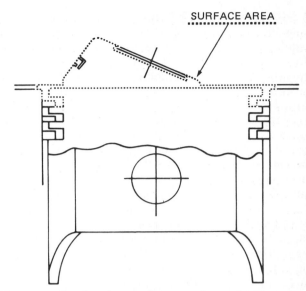

SURFACE AREA

Fig. 3-14. Combustion surface area in combustion chamber. The surface area is shown in dotted lines.

carbon monoxide (CO), in the exhaust gas. If we could get perfect combustion, then only carbon dioxide (CO_2) and water vapor would come out of the tail pipe, along with any air that was not needed for combustion. Why this failure to obtain perfect combustion? There are several reasons.

The combustion chamber is enclosed by relatively cool metal surfaces (Fig. 3-14). The bottom of the combustion chamber is sealed by the head of the piston. (See Fig. 3-8.) Above is the cylinder head with its intake and exhaust valves. The combustion starts at the spark plug when it produces a high-temperature electric spark. The flame spreads outward from the spark-plug electrodes in a rapidly expanding wall of fire. The top row in Fig. 3-15 shows flame travel during normal combustion. The lower row in Fig. 3-15 shows the effects of abnormal combustion or detonation.

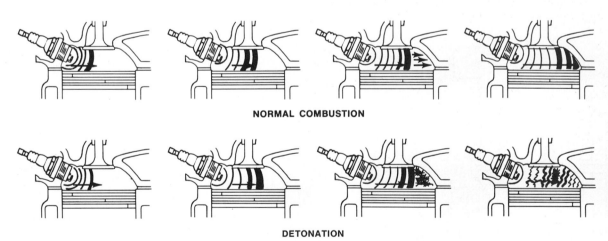

NORMAL COMBUSTION

DETONATION

Fig. 3-15. Normal combustion without detonation is shown in the top row. The fuel charge burns smoothly from beginning to end, providing an even, powerful thrust to the piston. Detonation is shown in the bottom row. The last part of the fuel explodes, or burns, almost all at once to produce detonation, or spark knock. (*General Motors Corporation*)

⊘ **3-10 Flame Quench** As the wall of flame approaches the cool metal surfaces (top row, Fig. 3-15), something happens that prevents the flame from actually getting to these surfaces. The layers of air-fuel mixture next to the metal surfaces are chilled by the cooler metal. These layers become too cool to burn (Fig. 3-16). The cooler metal surfaces take heat away from the layers of air-fuel mixture faster than the combustion process can add it. The result is that these layers of air-fuel mixture do not burn. This process is known as *quench*. Quench puts out the flame close to the combustion-chamber surfaces by the continual removal of heat. When the exhaust stroke starts, the cylinder is swept out by the up-moving piston. The unburned fuel, including that in the quench area, leaves along with the other exhaust gases. The result is that unburned gasoline vapor (HC) and partly burned gasoline or carbon monoxide (CO) come out the tail pipe.

⊘ **3-11 Combustion Temperature** You might think that an easy way to lower HC and CO in the exhaust would be to raise the engine operating temperature. Then the unburned and partly burned gasoline vapor in the quench area would burn. As you can see in Fig. 3-17, raising the engine operating temperature does lower the amount of unburned hydrocarbons in the exhaust gas. However, any increase in engine temperature increases the combustion temperature. That creates another problem. Nitrogen oxides form more readily at higher temperature (Fig. 3-18). Therefore, combustion temperatures must be kept down to prevent the formation of an excessive amount of NO_x.

In the engineering world there is seldom one simple solution to a problem. The solution to one difficulty may introduce another difficulty. Engineering is often a search for the best compromise, one that will minimize the negative and maximize

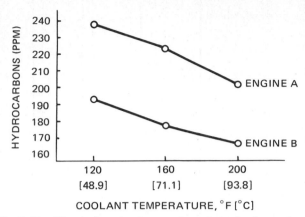

Fig. 3-17. Chart showing how exhaust-gas hydrocarbons decrease as the engine coolant gets hotter. (*Chrysler Corporation*)

the positive. Nowhere is this truer than in trying to engineer emission-control systems for motor vehicles.

Check Your Progress

Progress Quiz 3-1 The following quiz allows you, once again, to check up on yourself. You have made a good start in studying this book. If you have taken the previous progress quizzes, you know how well you are absorbing the information you are studying. You cannot expect to remember everything, but you probably do not have too much difficulty recalling

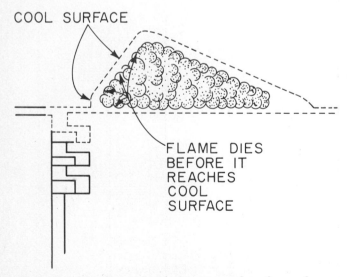

Fig. 3-16. The flame dies before it reaches the cool surface, thus preventing complete combustion of the fuel.

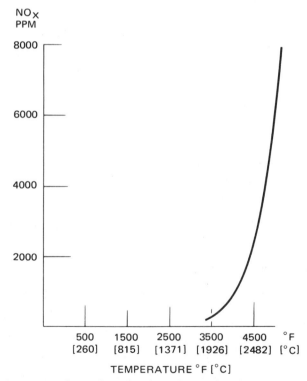

Fig. 3-18. Chart showing the relationship between combustion temperature and the formation of nitrogen oxides (NO_x). (*Chrysler Corporation*)

the essential facts. These essential facts are referred to in the questions below. Answering these questions helps you to fix the facts more firmly in your mind. If you find questions that stump you, turn back to the pages that help you answer them.

Correcting Lists The purpose of this exercise is to help you spot an unrelated item in a list. For example, look at the list "distributor, coil, spark plugs, fuel pump, ignition switch." You can see that "fuel pump" does not belong, since it is the only part that is not in the ignition system. There is one unrelated item in each of the lists below. Write each list in your notebook, but do not write the item that does not belong.

1. Sources of atmospheric pollution from the automobile are the carburetor, fuel pump, crankcase, fuel tank, and tail pipe.
2. Sources of HC pollution from the automobile are the fuel tank, tail pipe, crankcase, carburetor, and ignition distributor.
3. Exhaust-emission control systems include the air-injection reactor, controlled-combustion system, positive crankcase ventilation, exhaust-gas recirculation, and catalytic converter.
4. The formation of photochemical smog requires sunlight, carbon monoxide, hydrocarbons, and nitrogen oxides.
5. Carbon monoxide gas is tasteless, odorless, healthful, colorless, and poisonous.

Completing the Sentences The sentences below are incomplete. After each sentence there are several words or phrases, but only one of them correctly completes the sentence. Write each sentence in your notebook, ending it with the word or phrase that makes it correct.

1. The number of sources of air pollution from the automobile is: (a) one, (b) two, (c) three, (d) four.
2. The sources of air pollution from the automobile are the: (a) crankcase, exhaust, carburetor, and fuel tank, (b) crankcase, exhaust, carburetor, and air cleaner, (c) crankcase, tail pipe, exhaust, and carburetor, (d) crankcase, tail pipe, carburetor, and fuel pump.
3. Photochemical smog is the result of sunlight reacting with: (a) hydrocarbons and nitrogen oxides, (b) carbon monoxide and hydrocarbons, (c) nitrogen oxides and carbon monoxide, (d) nitrogen oxides and the atmosphere.
4. Hydrocarbons are: (a) burned gasoline vapors, (b) unburned gasoline vapors, (c) products of combustion, (d) odorless, colorless, poisonous gases.
5. Carbon monoxide is: (a) evaporated gasoline, (b) an element in smog formation, (c) a tasteless, odorless, colorless, poisonous gas, (d) a catalyst in smog formation.
6. Nitrogen oxides are formed by: (a) evaporating gasoline, (b) carbon monoxide and air, (c) high combustion temperatures, (d) sunlight.

7. The principal crankcase contaminants are: (a) oil and water, (b) dirt and water, (c) carbon monoxide and water, (d) blow-by and water.
8. Gasoline is a hydrocarbon made up of: (a) helium and hydrogen, (b) hydrogen and carbon, (c) hydrogen and water, (d) water and oxygen.
9. On old engines, the crankcase ventilation system used a: (a) PCV valve, (b) road-draft tube, (c) sealed oil-filter cap, (d) sealed crankcase.
10. Crankcase emission control systems were first required on cars built for registration in California in (a) 1960, (b) 1961, (c) 1962, (d) 1963.

⊘ **3-12 Air-Fuel Mixtures** Another reason for incomplete combustion is that a perfect air-fuel-mixture ratio cannot be achieved in every cylinder of a multicylinder engine each time a cylinder fires. With a perfect mixture, the cylinder contains just enough oxygen to completely burn all the gasoline in the air-fuel charge. This is called a *stoichiometric* mixture; it is the same as the familiar ideal air-fuel ratio of 14.7:1 (Fig. 3-19). This means that it takes 14.7 pounds [6.67 kg] of air to burn completely 1 pound [0.45 kg] of gasoline.

A mixture that is too rich has more gasoline vapor than can be burned completely by the available oxygen. When such a mixture is ignited, some of the excess gasoline will not burn. A high percentage of carbon monoxide will be formed during combustion (Fig. 3-19); there will be excess amounts of both HC and CO in the exhaust gas. A mixture that is too lean (that is, has insufficient gasoline vapor) will not burn completely.

As shown in Fig. 3-20, to fire the cylinder charge every time a spark occurs, the air-fuel ratio must lie in a fairly narrow range. A combustible mixture must not be richer than about 8.0:1 (Fig. 3-20), and not leaner than about 18.5:1 (Fig. 3-20). Mixtures outside these limits will misfire. In either case, the result is the same—unburned gasoline vapors (HC) coming out the tail pipe.

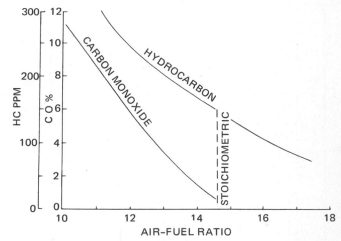

Fig. 3-19. Chart showing the relationship between the air-fuel-mixture ratio and exhaust emissions. (*California Motor Vehicle Pollution Control Board*)

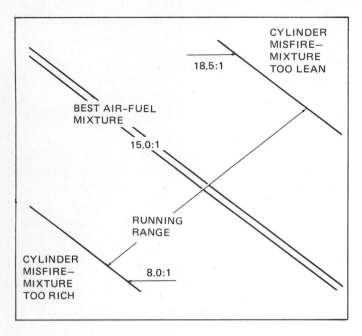

Fig. 3-20. Chart showing the mixture limits for a combustible air-fuel mixture. (*Chevrolet Motor Division of General Motors Corporation*)

You may wonder why we discuss the fuel and air in terms of weight (pounds and kilograms), instead of the more usual gallons or liters. One reason is that we would introduce some awkward numbers if we compared volumes (gallons or liters) of fuel and air. For instance, a 15:1 air-fuel ratio (by weight) is about 9,000 gal (gallons) [34,069 liters] of air to 1 gal [3.78 liters] of gasoline (Fig. 3-21). If we used volume ratios, we would have to refer to the air-fuel ratio as 9,000:1. The weight ratio (15:1, for example) gives us figures that are much easier to handle.

It would appear, from this discussion, that the engine demands a greatly varying air-fuel ratio for different operating conditions. This is not quite true. For example, the mixture must be very rich for starting. This is because the fuel vaporizes very

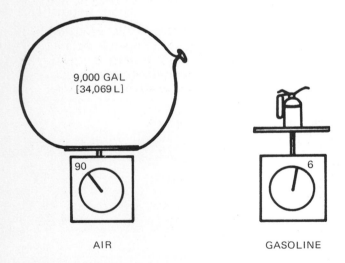

9,000 GAL [34,069 L] ARE NEEDED TO BURN 1 GAL [3.78 L]
90 LB [40.82 KG] ARE NEEDED TO BURN 6 LB [2.72 KG]
15 LB [6.80 KG] ARE NEEDED TO BURN 1 LB [0.45 KG]

Fig. 3-21. Air-fuel ratios based on volume and on weight.

poorly when the engine and carburetor are cold and the air speed is low. Thus, extra fuel must be delivered by the carburetor so that enough will vaporize for starting. Likewise, sudden opening of the throttle for acceleration allows a sudden inrush of air. Extra fuel must enter at the same time (that is, the mixture must be enriched), because only part of the fuel will vaporize and mix with the incoming air to provide the proper proportions of air and fuel to the engine.

In later chapters, we describe the systems that vary the air-fuel mixture for different operating conditions.

⊘ 3-13 Mixture Distribution   Now look at a typical six-cylinder in-line engine (Fig. 3-22). The carburetor sits in the middle of the row of cylinders, between the No. 3 and No. 4 cylinders. The air-fuel mixture passes from the carburetor through the intake manifold to the intake-valve ports in the cylinder head. The ideal arrangement would be for the exact same amount of air-fuel mixture, with all fuel vaporized, to be delivered to each cylinder. Also, the mixture should be identical in richness as it enters each cylinder. As discussed in ⊘ 3-12, "richness" refers to the proportion of vaporized fuel in the mixture. A rich mixture would have a ratio of approximately 12:1, or 12 parts of air to 1 part of fuel, by weight. If the proportion is changed to increase the amount of air, the mixture becomes leaner. A lean mixture would have a ratio of about 16:1, or 16 parts of air to 1 part of fuel, by weight. For normal cruising on the highway, the best ratio would be around 15:1. There are systems in the carburetor that alter the proportions of air and fuel to suit different operating conditions.

The intake manifold can affect the proportions of air and fuel in the mixture reaching the different cylinders. As mentioned, the ideal would be for all fuel to vaporize, and for all cylinders to receive the

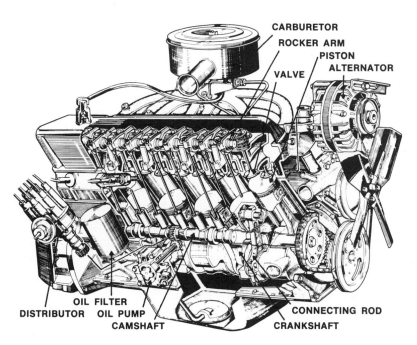

Fig. 3-22. Six-cylinder, in-line, overhead-valve engine, cut away to show internal parts. The carburetor is located at the center of the engine, so that the two end cylinders are equally distant from it. (*Chrysler Corporation*)

CARBURETOR
ROCKER ARM
PISTON
ALTERNATOR
VALVE

OIL FILTER
DISTRIBUTOR **OIL PUMP** **CONNECTING ROD**
CAMSHAFT **CRANKSHAFT**

same amount of mixture of the same richness. However, the intake manifold sometimes acts as a sorting device, supplying some cylinders with a richer mixture than others. Figure 3-23 shows how this can happen. If the fuel does not completely vaporize, there will be droplets (liquid particles) in the mixture. These particles, being relatively heavy, cannot turn the corner as easily as the vaporized fuel. Therefore, they continue moving in a fairly straight line until they hit the walls of the manifold.

In Fig. 3-23, the intake valve in cylinder No. 5 is open, and the air-fuel mixture is flowing toward and into this cylinder. (The vaporized fuel and air can turn the corner and enter cylinder No. 5.) However, the fuel droplets continue on until they strike the wall of the manifold. Now, when the intake valve for cylinder No. 6 opens, the mixture flows into cylinder No. 6. As it enters, it picks up some of the fuel on the manifold walls. This enriches the mixture.

The result is that the center cylinders, closest to the carburetor, may receive a relatively lean mixture. At the same time, the mixture entering the end cylinders may be relatively rich. This results

from the failure of all the fuel to vaporize, and from the sorting effect of the intake manifold. If sufficient heat is supplied to the intake manifold during engine warm-up, and the carburetor vaporizes the fuel sufficiently, the mixture will be reasonably uniform.

In addition, air-fuel ratios change with (1) different engine speeds; (2) different manifold-passage shapes; and (3) varying air speeds through these passages, in response to changing engine speed and throttle opening. In a typical engine, one cylinder can be receiving a relatively rich mixture at low speeds, and a relatively lean mixture at higher speeds. Meanwhile, another cylinder in the same engine may get just the opposite—a relatively lean mixture at low speeds, and a relatively rich mixture at higher speeds. This condition is shown in Fig. 3-24.

Even distribution of the air-fuel charge is very important if our engines are to operate without polluting excessively. Intake-manifold design is the subject of increasing attention by automotive engineers concerned with automotive emission control.

CYLINDER NO. 5
INTAKE VALVE OPEN

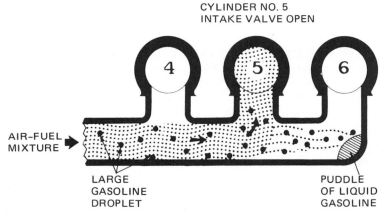

AIR-FUEL MIXTURE

LARGE GASOLINE DROPLET

PUDDLE OF LIQUID GASOLINE

Fig. 3-23. Distribution pattern in an intake manifold. The gasoline particles tend to continue to the end of the manifold, thus enriching the mixture going to the end cylinders. (*Chevrolet Motor Division of General Motors Corporation*)

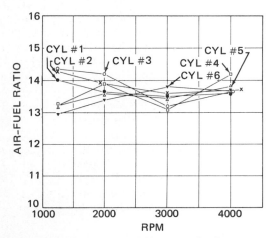

Fig. 3-24. Air-fuel ratios to different cylinders at varying engine speeds in a six-cylinder, in-line engine. Note that the ratios vary from 13:1 (rich) to 14.5:1 (comparatively lean). Cylinder No. 6, for example, receives a mixture of 13:1 at low speeds, which leans out to a little under 14:1 at 4,000 rpm.

⊘ **3-14 Exhaust-Emission Controls Required** Exhaust-emission control systems control HC and CO in the exhaust gases. They were required on all 1966 and later model American-manufactured vehicles first sold and registered in California. Federal regulation required auto manufacturers to add an exhaust-emission control system to all 1968 and later model American-manufactured vehicles.

Then later, in 1971, California law required that new automotive vehicles sold and registered in California must not exceed the state's nitrogen-oxides standards. To meet these standards, some vehicle manufacturers redesigned engines and added new features to the exhaust-emission control systems. Other manufacturers introduced the exhaust-gas recirculation (EGR) system, shown in Figs. 3-5 and 3-25, to reduce NO_x. Federal regulations imposed NO_x exhaust-emission standards on all 1973 model passenger vehicles, and the EGR system came into wide use. The EGR system is described later.

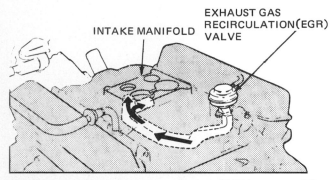

Fig. 3-25. Exhaust-gas recirculation (EGR) system. The EGR valve meters the volume of exhaust gas that is recirculated back into the intake manifold. (*Buick Motor Division of General Motors Corporation*)

⊘ **3-15 Fuel Evaporation** The last two major sources of air pollution that we shall discuss here are the carburetor and the fuel tank (Fig. 3-26). As you know, gasoline is a highly volatile liquid—meaning that it evaporates easily. On older cars, gasoline vapors could escape from the fuel tank through its atmospheric vent (Fig. 3-27). When this vent became plugged, the engine would stop (see ⊘ 3-17).

⊘ **3-16 The Fuel Tank** When the fuel tank is full and the engine is operating, gasoline is forced to the carburetor by the fuel pump (Fig. 3-26). There is atmospheric pressure approximately 14.7 psi (pounds per square inch) [1.03 kg/cm² (kilograms per square centimeter)], above the fuel in the tank, because the tank is vented to the atmosphere. The fuel

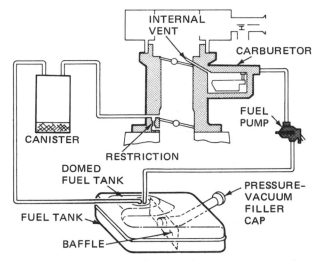

Fig. 3-26. Schematic view of an evaporation control system. (*Pontiac Motor Division of General Motors Corporation*)

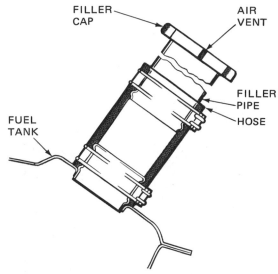

Fig. 3-27. Open type of fuel-tank filler-pipe assembly, showing the air-vent hole through the filler cap. (*Ford Motor Company*)

pump creates a much lower pressure at its vacuum, or inlet, side. This difference in pressure pushes fuel from the tank to the pump.

⊘ **3-17 Fuel-Tank Venting** If the fuel-tank vent is not open, a vacuum is created inside the tank as liquid fuel is pumped out of the tank. Without a vent, air cannot get into the tank to replace the gasoline. When the vacuum in the tank equals the vacuum produced by the fuel pump, no additional gasoline can reach the engine. It starves for fuel and stops. A high vacuum in the fuel tank can cause atmospheric pressure to collapse the tank. To prevent this vacuum from forming, automobiles of the past used fuel tanks that were open to the atmosphere (Fig. 3-27). That is, the filler cap had a small hole that let air in or out. Some tanks had an open vent tube, in the filler pipe, that served the same purpose.

⊘ **3-18 Fuel-Tank Vapor Losses** The air vent in the cap, or the vent tube, also relieves the pressure buildup inside the tank. A pressure buildup can occur, for example, while the car is parked in the hot sun. The heat causes the gasoline to expand and to vaporize more readily. However, if the tank is too full and doesn't have room for the fuel to expand, gasoline runs out the filler-cap vent hole (Fig. 3-27). It then dribbles down the side of the vehicle to the ground.

The spilled liquid gasoline quickly evaporates. When you add its fumes to the fuel vapor coming from the fuel-tank vent of an uncontrolled car, you can easily understand our concern with fuel evaporation. It is a big source of atmospheric hydrocarbon (HC) pollution.

⊘ **3-19 Fuel-Tank Breathing** There is another way in which fuel vapors escape into the atmosphere from the fuel tank. When air is heated, it expands. When air is cooled, it contracts. This is what happens to the air inside the fuel tank. When the temperature goes up, the air inside the tank expands.

Some of it is forced out of the tank through the atmospheric vent (Fig. 3-27). When the temperature goes down, the air in the tank contracts. Now, fresh outside air enters the fuel tank. Thus, the fuel tank "breathes." When you breathe, your lungs draw in relatively dry air. When you expel this air, it contains additional moisture. Breathe on a cool surface, and you'll see this moisture condense as a mist on the surface.

The air that the fuel tank breathes out also contains "moisture," in the form of gasoline vapor. The tank takes in fresh air when the temperature drops. It breathes out air loaded with gasoline vapor when the temperature goes up. If the car is parked in a hot location, the gasoline in the fuel tank evaporates more readily. Then the loss of gasoline vapor is even greater.

⊘ **3-20 Carburetor Vapor Losses** The carburetor can lose gasoline in a somewhat similar way. During normal operation of the engine, gasoline is pumped from the fuel tank to the carburetor by the fuel pump (Fig. 3-26). The carburetor has a small chamber, called the *float bowl,* which holds several fluid ounces of liquid gasoline. In this way, the float bowl serves as a constant-level reservoir of fuel for the carburetor metering jets and nozzles (Fig. 3-28). An engine must have a steady fuel level in the carburetor. This is essential if the air-fuel mixture is to be within the proper range.

⊘ **3-21 Carburetor Vents** Fuel vapors can escape from the float bowl through external vents (Fig. 3-28), internal vents (Fig. 3-26), and carburetor fuel passages and air bleeds. External vents (Fig. 3-28) have been the most common cause of carburetor fuel-vapor loss. Modern carburetors no longer have external float-bowl vents.

Internal vents (Fig. 3-26) are usually tubes that carry the gasoline vapor from above the fuel in the float bowl to the carburetor air horn. When the engine is running, any vapor that forms is discharged into the stream of air passing through the carburetor.

The situation is quite different when the engine

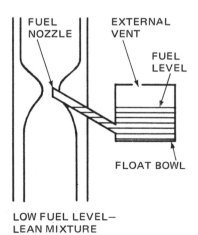

LOW FUEL LEVEL—
LEAN MIXTURE

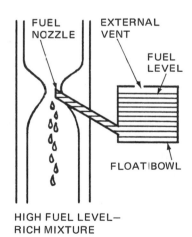

HIGH FUEL LEVEL—
RICH MIXTURE

Fig. 3-28. Simplified carburetor, showing the effects on the air-fuel mixture of a low fuel level in the float bowl (left); and a high fuel level in the float bowl (right).

is stopped after a run. When the engine is hot, it gives off heat. This heat acts on the gasoline in the float bowl. The gasoline begins to vaporize. The vapor passes from the float bowl, through the internal vent, to the air cleaner where most of the vapor is trapped. However, some vapor can still escape into the atmosphere through the air cleaner.

⊘ **3-22 Fuel-Vapor Recovery** The loss of gasoline vapor (HC) from the fuel tank and carburetor produces air pollution. To prevent this, new cars are equipped with a fuel-vapor recovery system, or evaporative control system (Fig. 3-26). This system traps the gasoline vapor escaping from the fuel tank and carburetor and burns the vapor in the engine. We shall discuss this system in detail in Chap. 6.

⊘ **3-23 Evaporative Emission Controls Required** Evaporative emission control systems were required on all 1970 model cars first registered in California. Beginning with the 1971 model year, an evaporative emission control system was required on every new car sold in the United States.

CHAPTER 3 CHECKUP

NOTE: Since the following is a chapter review test, you should review the chapter before taking the test.

In this chapter, we have pointed out the four sources of air pollution from the automobile. This chapter forms the basis for all that follows on automotive emission control. To become competent in servicing emission controls, you must know where the pollutants come from, what they are, how they are formed, and how they can be controlled. Begin using the chemical symbols for the pollutants in your everyday study and work. Short definitions of each are given in the text and in the glossary at the back of the book.

Once again, you will want to test your knowledge of the subjects covered in the chapter you have just completed. The questions that follow have two purposes. One is to test your knowledge. The other is to help you review the chapter and fix the facts more firmly in your mind.

You may not be able to answer all the questions first time through. If you miss a question, turn back into the chapter and restudy the pages that give you the answer. For example, under "Definitions" you are asked to give the meanings of certain words and phrases. If you cannot remember them all, turn back to the chapter to find the definitions, or turn to the glossary at the back of the book. Refer to the text material while writing the definitions. The act of writing down the definitions will help you remember them.

NOTE: Write your answers in your notebook. Then, later, when you finish *Automotive Emission Control,*

your notebook will be filled with valuable information to which you can quickly refer.

Completing the Sentences The sentences below are incomplete. After each sentence there are several words or phrases, but only one of them correctly completes the sentence. Write each sentence in your notebook, ending it with the word or phrase that completes it correctly.

1. When an engine is equipped with a PCV system, the crankcase blow-by fumes are returned to the: (*a*) air cleaner, (*b*) carburetor, (*c*) exhaust manifold, (*d*) intake manifold.
2. The pollutants most dangerous to human life and most difficult to control come from the: (*a*) exhaust system, (*b*) fuel tank, (*c*) carburetor, (*d*) crankcase.
3. State and federal automotive emission standards have been set for: (*a*) H_2O, HC, and CO, (*b*) HC, CO, and CO_2, (*c*) C, H, and H_2O, (*d*) HC, CO, and NO_x.
4. The products of perfect complete combustion are: (*a*) carbon dioxide and water, (*b*) carbon monoxide and water, (*c*) hydrocarbons and water, (*d*) oxides of nitrogen.
5. The process that prevents the combustion flame from burning the layer of air-fuel mixture next to the combustion-chamber surface is called: (*a*) pinging, (*b*) detonation, (*c*) quench, (*d*) turbulence.
6. In most engines, a richer air-fuel mixture gets to the: (*a*) middle cylinders, (*b*) end cylinders, (*c*) nearest cylinders, (*d*) even-numbered cylinders.
7. Federal regulations required an exhaust-emission control system on all new vehicles starting in: (*a*) 1966, (*b*) 1967, (*c*) 1968, (*d*) 1970.
8. The two sources of hydrocarbon pollution controlled by the evaporative control system are the: (*a*) fuel pump and carburetor, (*b*) carburetor and air cleaner, (*c*) air cleaner and fuel tank, (*d*) fuel tank and carburetor.
9. Carburetor fuel-vapor losses increase most with an increase in: (*a*) humidity, (*b*) barometric pressure, (*c*) temperature, (*d*) tank size.
10. Internally vented carburetors are part of the: (*a*) evaporative control system, (*b*) PCV system, (*c*) air-pump system, (*d*) NO_x control system.

Definitions In the following, you are asked to define certain terms. Write the definitions in your notebook. Writing the definitions in your notebook will help you remember them. It will also provide you with a quick way to locate the meanings, if you need them again. If you cannot remember the meaning of a term, look it up in the chapter you have just studied, or in the glossary at the back of the book.

1. What is an air-injection reactor?
2. Define "nitrogen oxides (NO_x)."
3. What is photochemical smog?
4. Define "catalyst."
5. What is blow-by?
6. What is a road-draft tube?
7. Define "PCV."

8. What is quench?
9. What is a stoichiometric mixture?
10. Define "fuel-tank breathing."

SUGGESTIONS FOR FURTHER STUDY

If you would like to learn more about automotive emission controls, raise the hood of a late-model car. Use the illustrations in this chapter to identify the various emission-control systems on the car. By locating each part of each system and identifying it, you are learning things that will be very valuable to you once you get "on the job." After you have identified every part of a system, draw a sketch of the system in your notebook, and label each part. Then, if time permits, follow the same procedure on a different year, make, and model of car. Eventually, you will know instantly the name of every major part of each automotive emission-control system. But even more important, you will know how to identify which systems are on the car, what each part looks like, and where it is usually located.

chapter 4

ALTERNATIVE ENGINES AND POWER SYSTEMS

Ever since the internal-combustion engine got its start more than a century ago, there have been challengers to its supremacy. Engineers have proposed (and sometimes developed) power sources that, in some respect, could rival the gasoline-burning internal-combustion engine. This engine is often referred to as the IC engine or as the ICE (Internal-Combustion Engine). But so far, none of the rivals has been able to beat out the IC engine in the marketplace. We shall discuss several reasons for this. First, however, let us name some of the most frequently discussed rivals. They include the diesel, Wankel rotary-combustion engine, gas turbine, steam engine, Stirling engine, electric cars, hybrid power systems, and the kinetic-energy wheel, commonly known as "flywheel propulsion." These possible alternatives are considered in this chapter.

⊘ **4-1 Diesel Engines** More than one automotive expert predicts that the diesel engine may be the ultimate winner in the clean-air race. Let's examine the characteristics of the diesel and the types of exhaust emissions from diesel engines.

Dr. Rudolf Diesel patented and built his first compression-ignition engine in 1892. It must have looked similar to the early diesel engine shown in Fig. 4-1. What makes the diesel engine different is that it uses no separate electric ignition system. Also, the diesel engine uses a special grade of oil as fuel, instead of gasoline. The oil is sprayed (injected) into the engine cylinders by a high-pressure fuel-injection system (Fig. 4-2). The heat created by compressing air in the cylinder raises the air temperature to about 1,000°F [538°C]. At this temperature, the fuel ignites as soon as it is injected. Combustion results from this heat of compression. When Dr. Diesel tried to start his first engine, it actually blew up. But by 1897, diesel engines were running and were pronounced a scientific success.

A popular four-cylinder diesel engine used in passenger cars today is shown in Fig. 4-2. The diesel four-stroke cycle follows this sequence of events in the cylinder (Fig. 4-3): As the piston travels from the top to the bottom of the cylinder on the intake stroke (A in Fig. 4-3), the cylinder completely fills with air. No throttle valve or inlet air restriction is required in the diesel engine. Next, the compression stroke compresses the air (B in Fig. 4-3) at a compression ratio of 16:1 or higher. This high compression creates high air temperatures. As the piston reaches TDC at the end of the compression stroke, fuel is forced into

Fig. 4-1. An early diesel engine. (*Smithsonian Institution*)

the hot compressed air by a high-pressure fuel-injection system (C in Fig. 4-3).

The fuel starts burning as it sprays from the injector nozzle into the hot air in the combustion chamber. The pressure resulting from the burning of

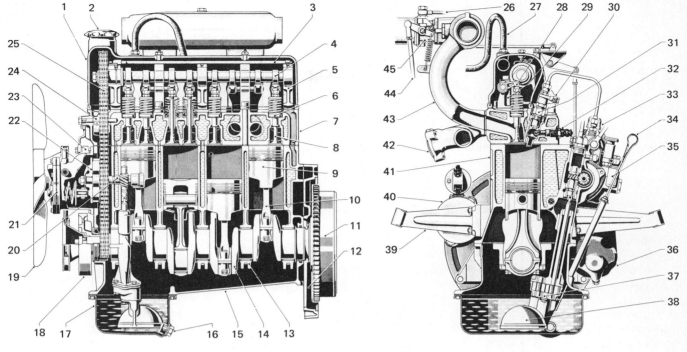

Fig. 4-2. Sectional views of a four-cylindrical diesel engine for passenger cars. (Mercedes-Benz)

1 CYLINDER HEAD COVER
2 OIL FILLER NECK
3 OIL PIPE (CAMSHAFT LUBRICATION)
4 CAMSHAFT
5 CAMSHAFT BEARING
6 ROTOCAP (VALVE TURNING DEVICE)
7 CYLINDER HEAD
8 EXHAUST VALVE
9 PISTON
10 CONNECTING ROD
11 FLYWHEEL
12 INTERMEDIATE FLANGE
13 CRANKSHAFT BEARING COVER
14 CRANKSHAFT
15 OIL SUMP, UPPER PART
16 OIL DRAIN PLUG

17 OIL SUMP, LOWER PART
18 COUNTERWEIGHT
19 FAN
20 DRIVE SHAFT (INJECTION PUMP–OIL PUMP)
21 VACUUM PUMP
22 INJECTION TIMER
23 WATER PUMP
24 TIMING CHAIN SPROCKET BEARING
25 DOUBLE ROLLER CHAIN
26 VACUUM LINE
27 BREATHER LINE
28 ROCKER ARM
29 ROCKER ARM SUPPORT
30 FUEL OVERFLOW LINE

31 INJECTION NOZZLE
32 GLOW PLUG
33 INJECTION PUMP
34 OIL DIPSTICK
35 FUEL FEED PUMP
36 OIL FILTER
37 OIL PUMP
38 STRAINER
39 ENGINE BRACKET
40 STARTER
41 CYLINDER CRANKCASE
42 EXHAUST MANIFOLD
43 RAM MANIFOLD
44 CONTROL LINKAGE
45 MIXTURE CONTROLLER

the fuel forces the piston down the cylinder on the power stroke. At the end of the power stroke, the piston moves up on the exhaust stroke; it forces the exhaust gases out of the cylinder (*D* in Fig. 4-3). Then the cycle is repeated: air intake, air compression, fuel injection and the power stroke, and then the exhaust stroke.

Dr. Diesel gained fame and made a fortune from

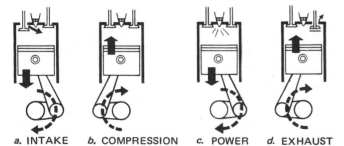

a. INTAKE   *b.* COMPRESSION   *c.* POWER   *d.* EXHAUST

Fig. 4-3. Action in a four-cycle diesel engine during the four piston strokes.

his diesel-engine patents in the years following 1892. One night in the fall of 1913, he disappeared from a steamship traveling from Antwerp to London. His disappearance remains a mystery to this day. But his engine survived to become the backbone of the heavy-transportation and construction industries (Fig. 4-4). The diesel engine has powered everything from airplanes to submarines. It has even appeared several times at Indianapolis, for example in a Cummins-powered car starting the race in the pole position in 1952. Today, Mercedes-Benz and other foreign manufacturers sell diesel-powered passenger cars in the United States. Many other foreign companies build diesel-powered vehicles that are not imported here.

In the United States, automotive manufacturers are moving toward diesel engines. The Oldsmobile Division of General Motors Corporation has announced a diesel-powered car. Other car companies are also showing interest in modern versions of the diesel engine.

Fig. 4-4. A V-8 diesel engine for use in heavy trucks and construction equipment. (*Detroit Diesel Allison Division of General Motors Corporation*)

⊘ **4-2 Diesel-Engine Emissions** The diesel engine does not require a throttle valve to control intake air, as does a carbureted gasoline engine. Thus, plenty of air is always available in the cylinder to burn the fuel. This reduces carbon monoxide emissions to a very low level.

There is less unburned HC in diesel-engine exhaust than in gasoline-engine exhaust. Diesel fuel does not have many of the light hydrocarbons, found in gasoline, that evaporate rapidly and contribute to the smog problem. Diesel fuel is burned almost as soon as it is injected. Therefore, no quench area (see ⊘ 3-10) of unburned hydrocarbons can form between the burning fuel and the cool combustion-chamber walls.

The diesel is little cleaner than the gasoline

engine in terms of nitrogen oxide emissions. NO_x forms readily in the diesel, where combustion takes place under high temperature and pressure, in the presence of excess oxygen. In other words, as the load on a diesel engine increases, so does its emission of NO_x.

Exhaust-emission levels from diesel engines also vary widely with variations in combustion-chamber design and fuel-injection systems. Two different types of combustion-chamber design are used in the diesel engine—the precombustion chamber (Figs. 4-2 and 4-5) and the open chamber (Fig. 4-3). The precombustion chamber is a small chamber next to the main combustion chamber. The fuel is injected into this chamber, where it starts burning before entering the main chamber. Diesel fuel is

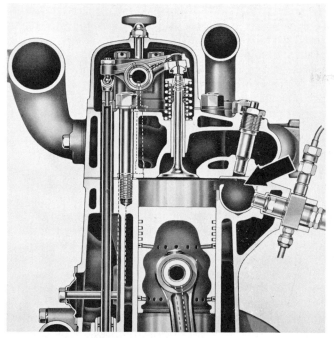

Fig. 4-5. A type of precombustion chamber called a *turbulence* chamber (indicated by arrow) and fuel injector in a Hercules diesel engine. (*Hercules Motor Corporation*)

injected directly into the open chamber (Fig. 4-3). The fuel starts burning later, and finishes burning sooner, than in a precombustion-chamber engine.

When a precombustion chamber (Figs. 4-2 and 4-5) is used, CO, HC, and NO_x emission levels are substantially reduced [as compared to direct-injection diesel engines (Fig. 4-3)]. But both designs are relatively high producers of NO_x. Exhaust-gas recirculation, retarded injection timing, and water induction can be used with some success to control diesel NO_x emissions.

Public objection to the diesel engine is caused by the visible smoke and odor from the exhaust. As you can see by studying Fig. 4-6, smoke can be a diesel-engine problem. Smoke and odor are usually

considered nuisances with questionable ill effects on human health, rather than serious contributors to smog formation.

Many other factors, such as cost, size, weight, noise, vibration, and driveability, must be considered when comparing the gasoline and diesel engines. Does the diesel engine have a future as an alternative to the gasoline engine in passenger-car use? Remember, the gasoline engine gives us three atmospheric pollutants to clean up. The diesel-engine problem is primarily that of controlling NO_x.

4-3 Wankel Rotary Engine The date July 13, 1968, may go down in history as the start of the great engine revolution. On that date the Japanese-built Mazda R-100 compact coupe, with a Wankel rotary-combustion engine (Fig. 4-7), was introduced in the United States. In the next few years the manufacturer of the Mazda, Toyo Kogyo of Japan, built hundreds of thousands of Wankel engines. The Wankel became the first serious modern-day challenger to the piston engine.

The Wankel engine is the result of the life work of the German engineer Felix Wankel. After more than 30 years of study and development, his first successful rotary engine ran in 1957. In 1958, an American firm, the Curtiss-Wright Corporation, obtained the first unrestricted license to manufacture rotary engines based on Wankel's patents. In 1961, a Japanese company, Toyo Kogyo, obtained a license to build Wankel engines for land vehicles. In 1968, after having tested the rotary-engine concept in a small car and found American consumers willing to buy, Toyo Kogyo launched a massive American marketing campaign for the Mazda.

In 1970, General Motors announced the planned purchase—for $50 million—of a license to manufac-

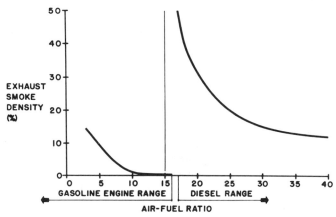

Fig. 4-6. Chart showing the relationship between exhaust smoke and air-fuel ratio in gasoline and diesel engines. (*Cummins Engine Company, Inc.*)

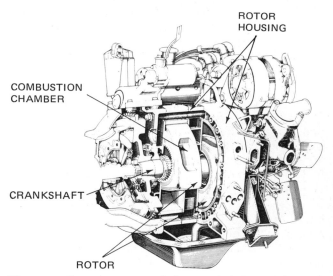

Fig. 4-7. Cutaway view of the Wankel-designed rotary engine used in the Mazda car. Note the two rotors and housings where cylinders and pistons would normally be located (at center of cutaway). (*Toyo Kogyo Company, Ltd.*)

ture Wankel engines for every purpose except aircraft. When conservative General Motors took this step toward the Wankel, the world took its first serious look at the engine that rotates instead of reciprocates. Today, the list of those purchasing licenses or entering negotiations to build Wankel engines includes many major vehicle and engine manufacturers.

In recent years, the American automotive industry has cooled toward the Wankel engine. General Motors, after spending many millions in advanced research, decided to reduce their Wankel activities. Reasons cited for the loss of interest in the Wankel include design problems such as rotor sealing, high pollution emissions, and operating inefficiency. One factor may have been the lack of a clear understanding of what federal pollution standards would be in the future. Without firm standards for the next several years, no one could predict what the maximum allowable HC and CO would be in 5 years. If the standards were liberal enough to permit the Wankel to pass the emission tests, the Wankel might be a good bet. But if the standards were tight, then the Wankel might be acceptable only with several modifications and special emission controls.

The Wankel or rotary-combustion (RC) engine operates on the conventional four-stroke-cycle of intake, compression, power, and exhaust. This familiar sequence of events, as applied to the Wankel engine, is shown in Fig. 4-8. The RC engine has three chambers that vary in size as the rotor rotates. Figure 4-8 shows the complete series of actions that occur during one revolution of the rotor. There are four stages in the action cycle. Let's start at A (upper center in Fig. 4-8). Here, the rotor has moved around so that one of the rotor lobes has cleared the intake port, as shown at 1. As the rotor continues to rotate (clockwise in Fig. 4-8), the space between the rotor and housing increases, as shown at 2 in B. This produces a partial vacuum which causes air-fuel mixture to enter, as shown by the small arrow under 2. This is the same action as in the piston engine when the piston moves down on the intake stroke. As the rotor moves farther around, the space between it and the housing continues to increase. (See 3 in C and 4 in D.) When the rotor reaches the point shown in D, the trailing lobe passes the intake port. Now the mixture is sealed between the two lobes of the rotor, as shown at 5 in E.

Now let's follow the mixture as the rotor continues to turn. Look at F. Here, the mixture (6 in F) is starting to be compressed. The compression continues through 7 in A. At 8 in B, the mixture is nearing maximum compression. This is the same as the piston approaching TDC on the compression stroke.

Next, combustion takes place. At 9 in C, the spark plugs fire, and the compressed mixture is ignited. Now the hot gases push against the rotor and turn it farther around, as shown at 10 in D. The hot gases continue to expand, as shown at 11 in E and 12

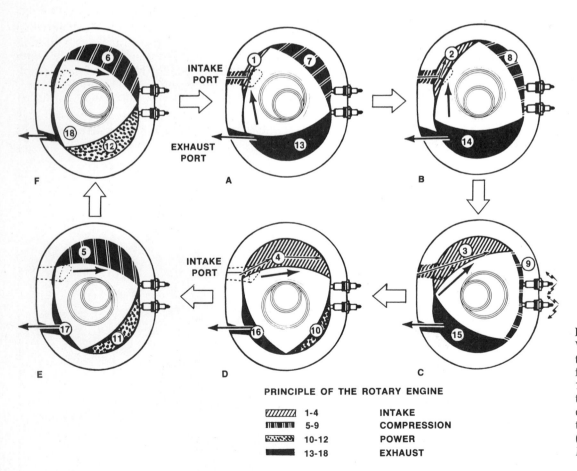

PRINCIPLE OF THE ROTARY ENGINE

/////	1-4	INTAKE
‖‖‖	5-9	COMPRESSION
░░░	10-12	POWER
▓▓▓	13-18	EXHAUST

Fig. 4-8. Principle of Wankel-engine operation. Follow the actions from A to F and from 1 to 18. This takes you through the complete cycle of events between two apexes of the rotor. (*Toyo Kogyo Company, Ltd.*)

in *F*. This is the same as the power stroke in the piston engine.

Note that the engine uses two spark plugs. This gives more complete burning of the air-fuel mixture, thereby reducing exhaust emissions. The combustion chamber, formed by the housings and rotor, is long and narrow. The two plugs give more complete burning of the air-fuel mixture, because combustion is started at two points in the mixture. However, other Wankel engines operate satisfactorily with a single spark plug.

At 13 in *A*, the leading lobe of the rotor is clearing the exhaust port in the housing. Now the burned gases begin to exhaust from the space between the rotor lobes. This exhaust continues through 14 in *B*, 15 in *C*, 16 in *D*, 17 in *E*, and 18 in *F*. By that time, the leading rotor lobe is clearing the intake port, as shown at 1 in *A*. Now the whole chain of events takes place again.

We have looked at the actions taking place between one pair of rotor lobes. But there are three lobes, and three chambers between the lobes. Therefore, there are three sets of actions going on at the same time in the engine. In other words, there are three power thrusts for every rotor revolution. With a two-rotor engine, there are six power thrusts for every revolution of the two rotors.

The Wankel eccentric shaft, or crankshaft, makes three revolutions for every one revolution of the triangular rotor (Fig. 4-8). For a single rotor, the engine delivers one power stroke per revolution of the eccentric shaft. This is twice as many power strokes per crankshaft revolution as in a single-cylinder four-stroke-cycle piston engine. The four-stroke-cycle engine delivers a power stroke only once in every two revolutions of the crankshaft. For a given output, the Wankel is about half the size and weight of a piston engine. The Wankel has neither valves nor any other valve-train parts, and only one or two spark plugs per rotor (Fig. 4-9).

Three different events of the four-stroke-cycle (one in each rotor chamber) occur simultaneously, at 120° intervals. Two or more rotors can be attached together to build two-, three-, or four-rotor engines of widely varying power output.

⊘ **4-4 Wankel-Engine Emissions** How does the Wankel compare with the piston engine in exhaust emissions? All petroleum-fueled engines give off the same three pollutants—hydrocarbons, carbon monoxide, and nitrogen oxides. However, hydrocarbon emissions are higher in the rotary engine. Here's why.

The Wankel engine has a large combustion-chamber surface (see *C* in Fig. 4-8). This entire surface is a quench area. Recall from ⊘ 3-10 that, in a quench area, a thin layer of unburned air-fuel mixture is cooled by the metal combustion-chamber walls so much that it will not burn. In the Wankel engine, there is a trailing rotor-tip seal forming each chamber. It scrapes the unburned HC from the rotor housing as each chamber exhausts. This action can be understood by studying Fig. 4-8 once again.

Another source of unburned hydrocarbons is the crevice effect. That is, the effect of the small dead space, or crevice, formed between the side seals and edge of the rotor, and the rotor housing (Fig. 4-10). The mixture trapped in this space during each cycle fails to burn and passes into the exhaust as additional HC emissions.

As in the piston engine, hydrocarbon emissions from the Wankel can be controlled. The engine in the Mazda is equipped with a crankcase emission control (PCV) system. It also uses an air pump and a thermal reactor (Fig. 4-11) for hydrocarbon control. (See ⊘ 9-1 for an explanation of the thermal reactor.)

Incomplete combustion of the air-fuel mixture in the quench area, and the sweeping of these gases

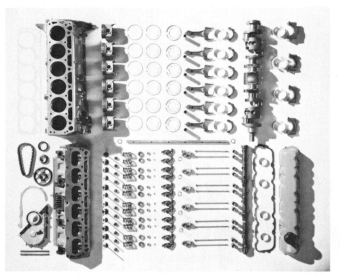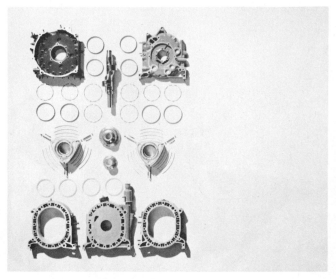

Fig. 4-9. Parts in a six-cylinder piston engine (left), compared with the parts in a two-rotor Wankel engine (right). (*Toyo Kogyo Company, Ltd.*)

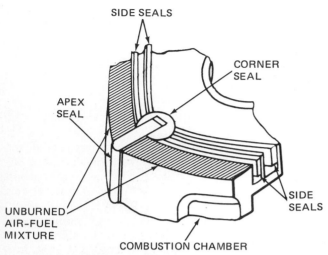

Fig. 4-10. Section of a rotor with seals, showing areas of unburned air-fuel mixture. (*Toyo Kogyo Company, Ltd.*)

into the exhaust, add to the high CO emissions of the Wankel. But, as with hydrocarbons, CO emissions are controllable by the same techniques used for the piston engine (see ⊘ 9-1).

Less nitrogen oxides are created by the combustion process in the Wankel engine. Remember, nitrogen oxides are formed in engines with high combustion temperatures. In a rotary engine, combustion temperatures are lower than in the piston engine. The Mazda automobile with the Wankel engine, equipped with the emission controls mentioned above, meets all federal and state emission standards. Aside from the diesel engine, it is the only alternative engine that has reached passenger-car production.

⊘ **4-5 The Gas Turbine** The gas turbine (Fig. 4-12) has developed rapidly since its introduction in jet aircraft during World War II. Today its applications include all sizes of airplanes and helicopters, racing cars, trucks, stationary power plants, and railroad locomotives. So it seems logical that the gas turbine should become the replacement for the automotive piston engine. One problem, more than any other, has limited its automotive production. The gas-turbine engine runs best under heavy load at high speed for long periods of time. This type of operation is very seldom needed in the average automobile. The average car starts and stops frequently, is used for short trips, and spends most of its running time idling or carrying light loads. Only occasionally must it deliver short spurts of maximum power. And this is just the kind of operation that the gas-turbine engine does most poorly—start and stop frequently, idle, accelerate and decelerate, and make short trips with light loads.

However, there are many advantages to the gas turbine as an automotive powerplant. It has multi-fuel capability which means it can run on natural gas, leaded or unleaded gasoline, kerosene, diesel, or any similar fuel. The basic gas-turbine engine is simple in design and reliable in operation. But its control systems are no simpler than those of the piston engine.

Here's how the gas turbine works (see Figs. 4-12 and 4-13): The turbine has two basic sections, a gasifier section and a power section. A stream of air is taken into the gasifier-section inlet through the air intake and compressed by the air-compressor impeller. Mounted in the air intake, the impeller has a series of curved blades around its outer edge. As it rotates, the air from between the blades is thrown out by centrifugal force. This compresses the air and forces it into the combustion chamber, or combustor (Figs. 4-12 and 4-13). Fuel is sprayed into this air and ignited by a flame from an ignition system, or ignitor. The resulting combustion produces gases at high pressure and temperature. The hot expanding gases flow rapidly from the gasifier section into the power section (Figs. 4-12, and 4-13). This section contains another rotor, with curved blades, called the *power-turbine rotor,* or *wheel.* The gases hit the power-turbine rotor, causing it to spin as the energy of the gases is converted into mechanical rotary

Fig. 4-11. Location of the thermal reactor used to control hydrocarbon emissions on a Mazda Wankel engine. (*Toyo Kogyo Company, Ltd.*)

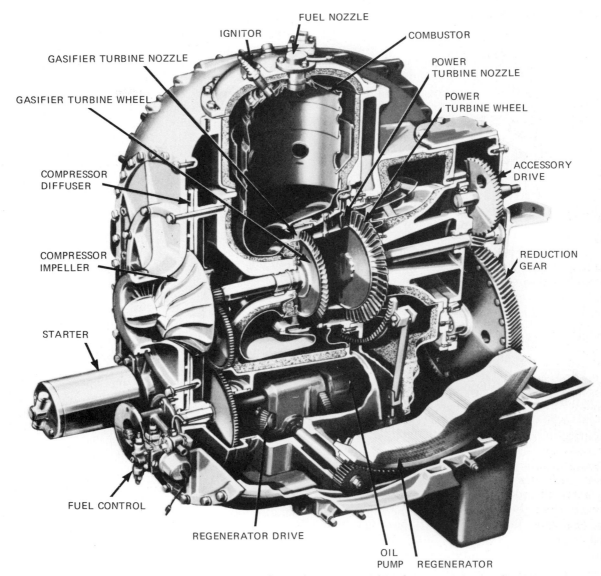

Fig. 4-12. Cutaway view of a turbine engine. (*Ford Motor Company*)

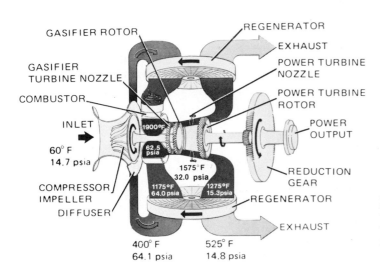

Fig. 4-13. Schematic view showing the locations of the components in a turbine engine. (*Ford Motor Company*)

motion (Fig. 4-13). Turbine speeds may be as high as 40,000 rpm. The power-turbine rotor is attached to the engine power output shaft. The rotary motion of the power output shaft is carried to the wheels through suitable gear reduction and the normal automotive drive train. The burned gases are exhausted to the atmosphere.

The first automobile powered by a gas turbine was demonstrated by the British Rover Company in 1950. A turbine-powered car appeared at Indianapolis in 1961 but did not compete. A turbine-powered Rover/BRM raced at Le Mans in 1963. That same year, Chrysler placed 50 turbine-powered sedans in the hands of the motoring public to obtain consumer evaluations. The turbine reappeared at Indianapolis in 1966, but again did not race. Then, in the 1967 Indianapolis race, Parnelli Jones, driving Andy Granatelli's STP Paxton Turbocar, made "gas turbine" a household word by almost winning the race. The Turbocar was forced out because of a gearbox ball-bearing failure, while leading the 200-lap race on the 197th lap.

In 1971, General Motors Corporation and Ford Motor Company began limited production of gas-turbine engines suitable for certain heavy-duty trucks and other special applications. These turbines may someday challenge the diesel engine. But today, the gas turbine is not in competition with the spark-ignition gasoline-fueled automobile engine.

⊘ **4-6 Gas-Turbine Emissions** The gas-turbine engine exhaust is almost free of hydrocarbons and carbon monoxide emissions (Fig. 4-14). No quench area or layer of unburned fuel surrounds the combustion chamber, as in the piston engine. Carbon monoxide formation is minimal, since the gas turbine runs on lean air-fuel mixtures with excess air. This condition produces very little CO in the combustion process. Further control of CO and HC is provided in cars and trucks by using an automatic fuel-flow shutoff during deceleration.

With no objectionable smoke or odor from the turbine exhaust, only the NO_x emission level is difficult to control (Fig. 4-14). NO_x is formed in the turbine combustion process. It results from high combustion temperatures and a lean air-fuel mixture—the same lean mixture that is needed to reduce HC and CO emissions. However, just like the piston engine, the automotive gas turbine must comply with federal and state emission standards if the vehicle is driven on the highways.

High fuel consumption, poor acceleration, high initial cost of manufacture, and high NO_x emission levels are the basic reasons for delays in the use of gas-turbine engines in automobiles.

⊘ **4-7 Steam Engines** In 1769, a French Army engineer, Nicholas Cugnot, built the first steam-powered road vehicle (Fig. 4-15) at the Paris Arsenal. Designed as a tractor to tow artillery, Cugnot's vehicle had a top speed of about 2 mph (miles per hour) [3.22 km/h (kilometers per hour)]. When it overturned in 1771, the idea of a steam road vehicle was temporarily abandoned. But Cugnot's setback didn't stop the spreading idea of using machines instead of people and animals to do heavy work. Thanks to other people of vision, the stationary steam engine went on to power the world during the Industrial Revolution.

As the twentieth century began, steam engines were considered a strong competitor of internal-combustion engines for use in automobiles. An example of an early steam carriage is shown in Fig. 4-16. In 1932, Doble built the last steam car in the United States, joining Locomobile, Stanley, and White as unsuccessful steam-car manufacturers who wrote an early chapter in automotive history. The internal-combustion engine won out over the steam engine because it was more flexible and simple in many ways to manufacture, operate, and service.

However, in recent years, there has been renewed interest in the steam engine for automobiles. For one thing, since it is an external-combustion engine, it will burn almost any hydrocarbon fuel. The fuel doesn't explode periodically in the cylinders, as in the gasoline piston engine. Burning takes place continuously in a burner outside the cylinders, with consistent flame, combustion, and low-emission characteristics. This makes emission control with the steam engine much easier than with the conventional engine.

A steam engine (Fig. 4-17) needs a continuous supply of water and a source of heat. The heat evaporates the water from a boiler (sometimes called a

	1976 Federal Regulation (Grams Per Mile)	Conventional Turbine Engine (Grams Per Mile)
HC	0.41	0.15
CO	3.4	1.37
NO_x	0.4	4.13

Fig. 4-14. Chart showing the emissions of an automotive gas turbine. Note that, under federal regulations, emissions are measured by weight. (*General Motors Corporation*)

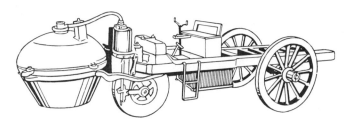

Fig. 4-15. The first steam-powered road vehicle, built in Paris in 1769 by Nicholas Cugnot.

Fig. 4-16. Charles Randolph's steam carriage of 1872. This vehicle, built in Glasgow, weighed 4½ tons [4,082 kg] and had a top speed of 6 mph [9.66 km/h]. It carried eight passengers, the driver, and the engineer. (*A History of Technology, vol. 5, Oxford*)

steam generator), turning the water into steam. The high-pressure steam is then used to drive the pistons up and down in the engine (Fig. 4-17). Figure 4-18 shows a 160-hp (horsepower) [120-kW (kilowatt)] steam engine built by General Motors and installed in a Pontiac passenger car. General Motors reported fuel consumption to be 3.8 mpg (miles per gallon) in city driving. Moreover, the steam engine weighs 450 lb [204.12 kg] more than the engine it replaced, and it produces less than half the horsepower.

Another type of steam engine uses the steam to spin a high-speed rotor (Fig. 4-19). This engine is called a *steam turbine* and is usually very large. Steam turbines are used in ships and electric generating plants. They are too inefficient and expensive when made small enough for passenger-car use.

Automotive piston-type steam engines also have many disadvantages for passenger-car use. The first steam cars used the wasteful open steam system. In the open steam system, the steam pushed the piston from one end of the cylinder to the other, transmitting power to the crankshaft. Then the exhaust valve opened, and the steam exhausted into the outside air. Since steam is vaporized water, this meant that the car lost its water quickly. Water had to be added

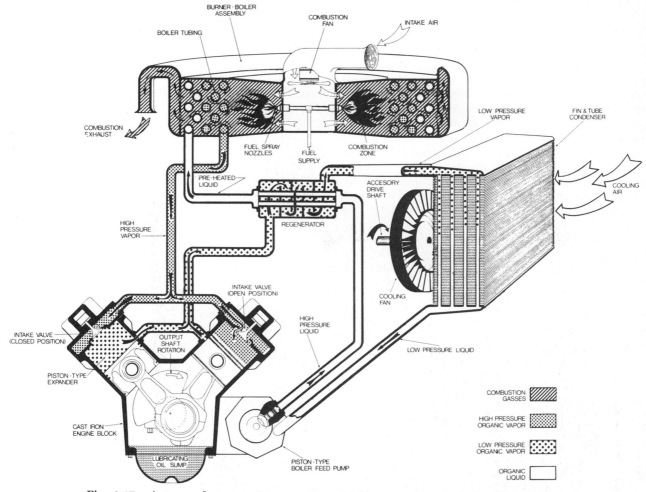

Fig. 4-17. A type of steam piston engine which uses a liquid chemical instead of water to prevent parts corrosion. (*Thermo Electron Corporation*)

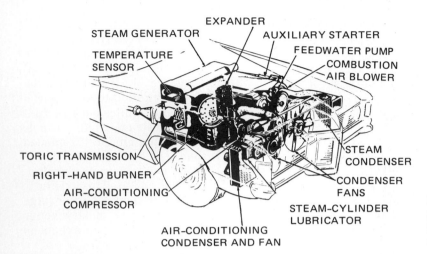

STEAM GENERATOR EXPANDER AUXILIARY STARTER FEEDWATER PUMP COMBUSTION AIR BLOWER TEMPERATURE SENSOR STEAM CONDENSER TORIC TRANSMISSION RIGHT-HAND BURNER AIR-CONDITIONING COMPRESSOR CONDENSER FANS STEAM-CYLINDER LUBRICATOR AIR-CONDITIONING CONDENSER AND FAN

Fig. 4-18. A piston-type steam engine installed in a passenger car. (*General Motors Corporation*)

at frequent intervals. This created yet another problem. If the fresh water had a high mineral content, it left a scaly deposit as it evaporated; the boiler tubes soon became clogged shut.

Scaling is greatly reduced by using a closed steam system. In this system, after the used steam comes out the exhaust valve, it is condensed back to water in a condenser or heat exchanger. The water is therefore saved for reuse within the engine, instead of being exhausted to the outside air. The closed steam system requires a heat exchanger or condenser. This is a tube-and-fin device somewhat like the radiator in a typical automobile cooling system. As the steam passes through the tubes, it is cooled by air flowing around the tubes. As the steam cools, it condenses to water. One problem with the condenser or heat exchanger is that it must be quite large. One design (Fig. 4-20) covers the entire roof of the car.

Another problem with almost all steam engines is that it takes time to "get up steam." To start the engine, the boiler has to be lit. That doesn't take long. But then there is a wait—now usually less than 1 min (minute)—until sufficient steam pressure has built up to move the car.

Two men who have worked on the automotive steam engine are the multimillionaire industrialist William P. Lear and Wallace L. Minto, the Sarasota,

Florida, inventor. Lear's company, Lear Motors of Reno, Nevada, built one of three steam buses tested in California in 1972. A schematic of the engine compartment is shown in Fig. 4-21.

Minto's engine, shown in Fig. 4-20, uses Freon as the working fluid instead of water. Freon is the refrigerant used in most air-conditioning systems. The evaporated Freon, at high pressure, drives a rotary type of engine. This engine has meshing gears, somewhat like an oil pump. The high-pressure Freon gas rotates the gears; this rotary motion is carried through the transmission and drive shaft to the differential and wheels.

⊘ **4-8 Steam-Engine Emissions** Congressional hearings in 1968 aroused public interest in steam cars. To determine if a modern steam engine could serve as an alternative power plant for the piston engine, contracts were awarded to three different companies to build new steam engines for buses. After acceptance testing, the buses were placed in limited service on routes in Los Angeles, Oakland, and San Francisco. Tests indicated that the bus emission levels easily bettered the 1975 California exhaust-emission standards for the diesel engines they replaced. But there were many other problems.

General Motors designed, built, and tested two

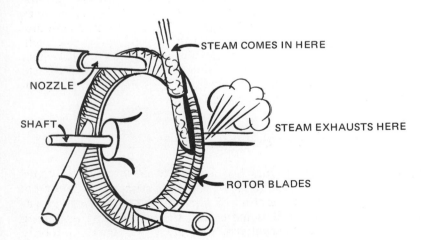

STEAM COMES IN HERE
NOZZLE
SHAFT
STEAM EXHAUSTS HERE
ROTOR BLADES

Fig. 4-19. A simple steam turbine. The steam, hitting the curved blades of the rotor, cause the rotor to spin.

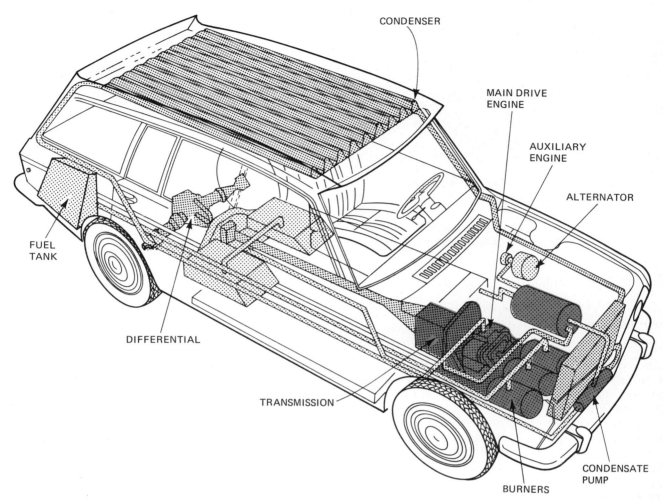

Fig. 4-20. An experimental steam engine which burns kerosene to vaporize Freon which drives the steam engine. Note that the large condenser covers the entire roof of the car.

steam-powered passenger cars. One of these is shown in Fig. 4-18. In the vehicles, NO_x levels exceeded federal passenger-car-engine standards, the engines used almost three times as much fuel as a conventional engine, production costs were much higher, maintenance requirements were also high,

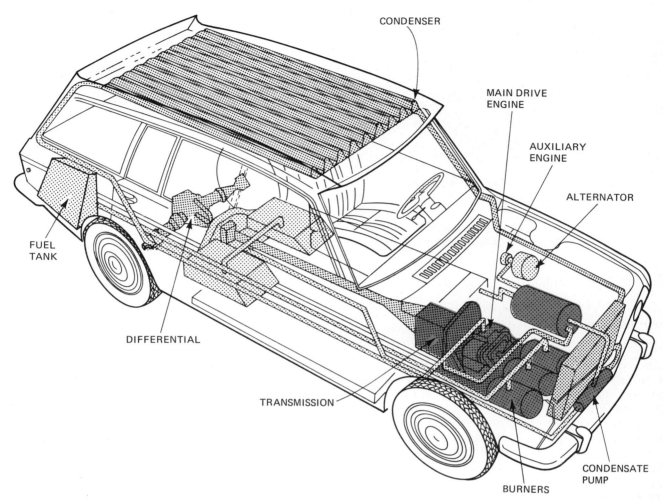

Fig. 4-21. Schematic of the engine compartment of a steam bus. (*General Motors Corporation*)

and vehicle performance was so poor as to be unacceptable to the average driver.

Why today's interest in steam power for automobiles? A continuous-combustion process—like that of the steam engine—has the potential to burn almost any fuel completely, thereby producing fewer exhaust emissions. Proponents claim that cleaner air would result if steam engines replaced the internal-combustion engines·in millions of cars. Most tests indicate that HC and CO levels are very low in the steam engine. But experienced automotive engineers have learned one thing only too well: Success in designing an ideal engine—steam or any other kind—and getting it into mass production to replace the conventional piston engine are two entirely different things.

Check Your Progress

Progress Quiz 4-1 Today, no discussion of cleaner air and automotive emission control is complete without mention of alternative engines and power systems. It is important, though, to note one thing about alternatives. That is, all the most commonly discussed engines and power plants release energy by burning fossil fuels. The air pollutants from burning fossil fuels are almost always the same. What does vary is the emission level from different fuels, engines, and combinations of fuel and engine. This depends on how the engine or vehicle is used. Basically, the emission-control systems for any combustion engine are similar to those used on the conventional piston engine, which you are studying. The service procedures on these emission-control systems are also similar.

Check your understanding by doing the exercise below. If you have any trouble, reread the previous few pages, and then take the quiz again. Remember, the quiz is designed to help you recall the important facts about alternative engines and power systems.

Completing the Sentences The sentences below are incomplete. After each sentence there are several words or phrases, but only one of them correctly completes the sentence. Write each sentence in your notebook, ending it with the word or phrase that completes it correctly.

1. For ignition, a diesel engine uses: (*a*) a spark plug, (*b*) a fuel injector, (*c*) a supercharger, (*d*) the heat of compression.
2. Public objection to diesel-engine exhaust is caused by: (*a*) high HC emissions, (*b*) visible smoke and odor, (*c*) noise and vibration, (*d*) high NO_x emissions.
3. The Wankel rotary engine first ran in: (*a*) 1957, (*b*) 1958, (*c*) 1961, (*d*) 1968.
4. Wankel HC emissions are high because of: (*a*) the fuel used, (*b*) a large combustion surface area, (*c*) the use of an air pump, (*d*) the use of a thermal reactor.
5. The first automobile powered by a gas turbine was demonstrated in: (*a*) 1950, (*b*) 1961, (*c*) 1963, (*d*) 1966.
6. In a gas turbine, the pollutant most difficult to control is: (*a*) HC, (*b*) CO, (*c*) H_2O, (*d*) NO_x.
7. An advantage of the steam engine is that it burns: (*a*) only gasoline, (*b*) almost any hydrocarbon fuel, (*c*) only wood, (*d*) almost any liquid.
8. Steam-bus emission levels were lower than: (*a*) comparable gasoline engines, (*b*) comparable diesel engines, (*c*) comparable Wankel engines, (*d*) no other engines.
9. The type of steam engine most suitable for automotive use is the: (*a*) steam turbine, (*b*) steam piston engine, (*c*) steam internal-combustion engine, (*d*) steam shovel.
10. HC emissions from a gas turbine are low because the engine operates with: (*a*) light loads, (*b*) varying engine speed, (*c*) unleaded gasoline, (*d*) an excess of air.

⊘ **4-9 The Stirling Engine** Society's continuing quest for the perfect engine includes the consideration that no one be injured in any way by the engine's operation. Low noise, low smoke, low odor,

and low exhaust emissions are necessary standards for such an engine. Only one known engine comes close to meeting the standards, and that is the Stirling engine.

This engine, shown in Fig. 4-22, was patented in 1816 by Robert Stirling, a minister of the Church of Scotland. Like the steam engine, it is a hot-air engine for converting heat energy into mechanical energy by using the closed-cycle, continuous external-combustion process.

Since 1938, the N. V. Philips Company of the Netherlands has been experimenting with the engine, trying to refine and simplify its design. In 1960, General Motors and Philips announced a joint development agreement, a project that was terminated in 1970. Then, in 1972, Ford announced a licensing and development agreement with Philips for the Stirling engine.

Neither American car maker (nor any other manufacturer) has a Stirling engine in production. However, the engine has been built in small sizes and power outputs for experimental and development work. Some significance must be attached to both General Motors and Ford research into the potential of the Stirling engine. So let us look at how this engine operates.

The pressure of gas in a container goes up when the gas is heated; it goes down when the gas is cooled. This is the principle of the Stirling engine (Fig. 4-22). A small amount of working gas is sealed inside the Stirling engine. This gas is alternately heated and cooled. When heated, its increased pres-

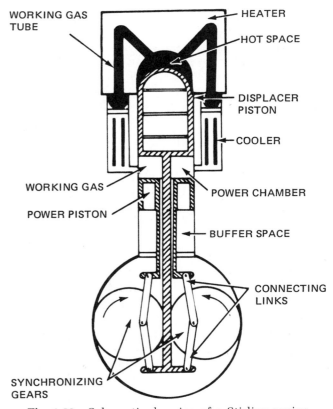

Fig. 4-22. Schematic drawing of a Stirling engine.

sure pushes a power piston down. When cooled, its lowered pressure, in effect, pulls the power piston up.

The working gas is moved between a cold space and a hot space (Fig. 4-22) in four overlapping phases. In the first phase, the gas is compressed in the cold space by the working, or power, piston. This compressed gas is moved into the hot space with the help of a transfer, or displacer, piston; there, it receives heat from an outside external-combustion burner. In the third phase, the gas expands and pushes against the power piston, turning the output shaft. Then, the displacer piston moves the gas back into the cold space. A regenerator, or heat exchanger, is located between the hot space and the cold space. It removes and stores heat as the hot gas passes into the cold space. It returns the heat as the cold gas moves back into the hot space.

The displacer piston does not produce power, but causes the gas to displace (move) between the heater and the cooler section of the engine (Fig. 4-22). The power piston moves up and down between the power chamber and the buffer space.

Experimental engines have operated at 3,000 rpm with an efficiency of 30 percent. This is a little better than the efficiency of most conventional piston engines. Stirling engines have less backwork or pumping losses (compression- and exhaust-stroke power losses) than conventional piston engines. With two synchronized pistons for each cylinder, a two-gear rhombic drive (Fig. 4-22) or a swash-plate drive system (Fig. 4-23) is required to transmit power from the power piston to the output shaft.

Some engineers have proposed Stirling engines for such small-engine applications as lawn mowers. They are easy to start, silent in operation, and simple in design. Other engineers believe that they will appear first for large stationary or pumping stations. One possibility is that they will be used to power space satellites and space stations. The Stirling engine requires a source of heat. On earth, heat can come from burning almost any form of fossil fuel or from a nuclear source. In space, no source of heat other than the sun would be needed. With a large reflector to gather heat from the sun and a large radiator to radiate the heat away, a Stirling engine could operate without any fuel at all.

Figure 4-23 is a cutaway view of a four-cylinder experimental Stirling engine proposed for automotive applications. The design shown in Fig. 4-23 will produce 180 hp [134.28 kW]. It fits into an automobile as shown in Fig. 4-24. Note that this design does not use the rhombic drive. Instead, it uses a swash plate. A swash plate, also called a *wobble plate,* is a metal disk that is set at an angle to the shaft on which is it mounted. The swash plate changes the reciprocating motion of the pistons to rotary motion.

⊘ **4-10 Stirling-Engine Emissions** Exhaust emissions of HC and CO from a Stirling engine are so low that almost any standard can be met. However, the high combustion temperatures when petroleum fuel is used cause high NO_x emission levels. As with the piston engine, exhaust-gas recirculation lowers the NO_x formation, but it also lowers the engine thermal efficiency.

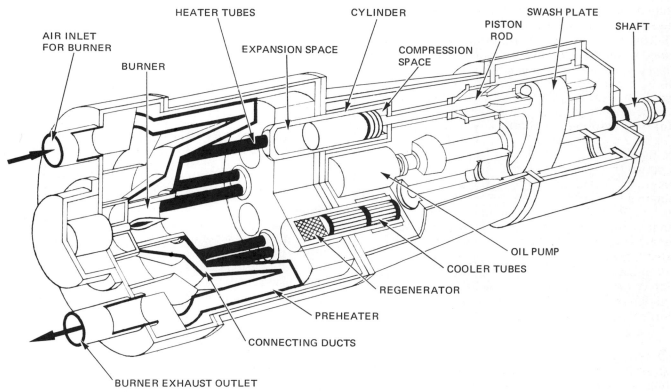

Fig. 4-23. Cutaway view of a four-cylinder, 180-hp Stirling engine.

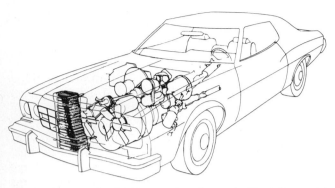

Fig. 4-24. How the Stirling engine shown in Fig.4-23 would fit into an automobile.

The Stirling engine is a reality. It shows a potential for low emissions and noise levels. With further development in mechanical simplification and size, weight, and cost reduction, the Stirling engine might someday become an alternative to the conventional piston engine.

⊘ **4-11 Electric Cars** Years ago, there were many electric cars in use throughout the United States. (An early electric car is shown in Fig. 4-25.) They were powered by the same type of conventional lead-acid storage battery used in the electric system of every car today. But instead of just one battery per car, each old-time electric vehicle needed a dozen or more batteries. These old-time electric cars were very simple in design. As Fig. 4-25 shows, most had no gears, simple brakes, and tiller steering. They gave off no smog-producing pollutants and were almost silent in operation. Their acceleration and speed were very low. They had a range of 40 to 50 mi (miles) [64 to 80 km] of around-town driving before they had to be garaged for a long battery recharging. These old electric cars were ideal for the purpose for

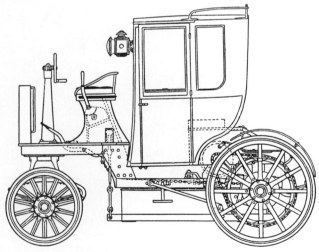

Fig. 4-25. Bersey electric cab of 1897. A number of these cabs operated for several years in London. They had a range of up to 50 mi [80 km] between battery recharges. (*A History of Technology, vol. 5, Oxford*)

which they were designed—to provide limited low-speed transportation in town.

For many years, the electric car has been a museum piece. Its lack of range and performance make it unacceptable in today's world. But concern with the air-pollution problem and the search for possible solutions are causing many individuals and states, the federal government, and automobile manufacturers to take a fresh look at electric cars. In England, an estimated 50,000 electric vans are in daily use for short-mileage delivery service in towns and cities. This is exactly the type of service performed by millions of air-polluting internal-combustion-engine vehicles here in the United States.

The problem that plagues the electric-car designer today is the same problem that the designer fought at the turn of the century. The familiar lead-acid battery is heavy. After enough batteries are loaded on a vehicle to provide acceptable speed and range (Fig. 4-26), little power is available to move a payload of either packages or people.

Many different kinds of batteries are being investigated by scientists and engineers. But no other type of battery has proved as reliable or as cheap to manufacture as the lead-acid battery. The fuel cell has been thought to have some possibilities for automotive applications (Fig. 4-27). In the fuel cell, fuel is burned in such a way that the energy is directly converted into electricity. But the cost is high, the crash hazards are great, and the problems of refueling a fuel cell are complicated. Note, in Fig. 4-27, that the fuel cell and batteries take up almost all the space in the van, and even part of the roof. As a result, a fuel-cell-powered van is strictly a two-passenger vehicle.

General Motors built an electric car called the Electrovair, using a silver-zinc battery. This car, shown in Fig. 4-26, had fair acceleration but an operating range between charges of only 40 to 80 mi [64 to 129 km]. Because of the amount of silver and zinc required per car, the cost of the battery is prohibitive.

The electric car still awaits a major breakthrough in battery design and construction. Until that happens, mass production of a modern electric car is not likely. Present estimates indicate that an electric car built today would cost much more than the current production-model piston-engine vehicle. In addition, an electric car is essentially a one-purpose car. The family owning an electric car today still needs a second car for longer-distance and high-speed trips.

Any serious discussion of electric-car production using lead-acid batteries requires an economic analysis of the availability of lead. A car that would range 100 mi [161 km] on a single battery charge would require more than 1,000 lb [454 kg] of lead in the battery pack. Total world lead production is slightly more than 3 million short tons per year. Before electric cars can be produced in volume, the problem of getting the lead for the batteries must be solved.

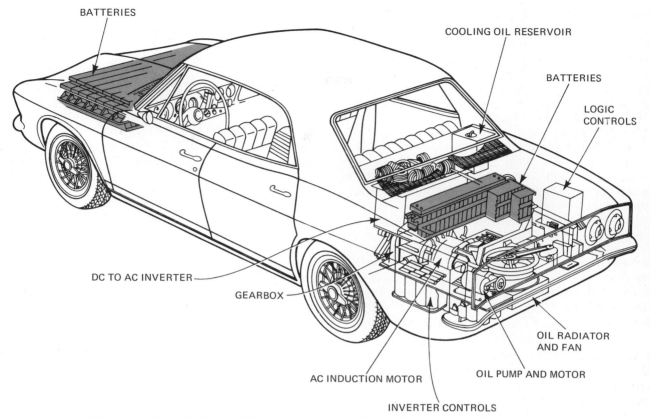

Fig. 4-26. General Motors Electrovair, an experimental electric car that uses silver-zinc batteries. (*General Motors Corporation*)

Another problem would arise if many people began driving electric cars. Recharging the batteries in thousands of electric cars would require the electric companies to build new and larger generating plants. Probably these new plants would burn fossil fuel—coal or oil. According to some experts, burning greater amounts of these fuels would add more pollutants to the air than if we continued to drive our conventional gasoline-engine cars.

⊘ **4-12 Electric-Generating-Plant Emissions** As we mentioned, one problem with the electric car is where to get the electricity to recharge the batteries. One estimate indicates that the United States uses about 2,000 billion kilowatt-hours of electricity a year. According to one estimate, present usage of automotive horsepower runs to about the same amount of energy. Each electric car would need some sort of battery charger, either built into the

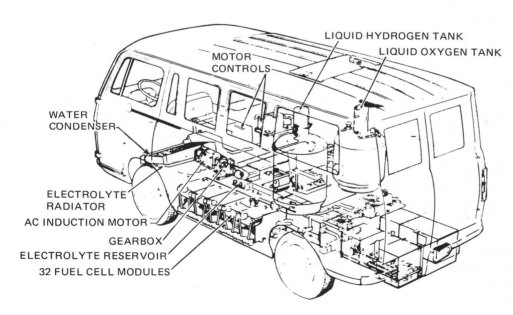

Fig. 4-27. Phantom view of the Chevrolet Electro-Van, powered by a fuel cell, showing the arrangement of major components. (*General Motors Corporation*)

home garage or at a convenient public recharging station. A tremendous increase in electric generating capacity would be needed to handle the battery-recharging requirements of millions of electric cars. However, if electric cars were gradually phased in over a period of years, then additional generating plants could be built over the same period of years.

The construction of additional electric generating plants does not complete the discussion of the electric car. It is often said that an electric vehicle is pollution-free and emits no smog-producing elements in operation. This statement fails to cover the air-pollution characteristics of the generating plants themselves.

Large electric generating plants usually use some form of fossil fuel as an energy source, to produce the power to turn the huge generators. Any form of coal, oil, or natural gas is a fossil fuel. When it burns, varying amounts of particulates, sulfur dioxide (SO_2), and nitrogen oxides (NO_x) are created. About 80 percent of the electric generating plants in the United States use fossil fuel as the power source. With automotive emissions declining, these generating-plant emissions cause an increasingly large percentage of our air pollution.

Nuclear-fueled electric generating plants are expected to produce approximately 20 percent of the electricity in the United States by 1980. However, estimates for 1980 also show that approximately two-thirds of the electricity generated will be in conventional fossil-fueled plants.

The introduction of electric cars would transfer the air-pollution source from the moving vehicle to the stationary generating plant. While the large plant is easier to identify as a pollution source, controlling its emissions is a very expensive process. The problem of cleaning up the generating plants needed to recharge electric cars makes their widespread use improbable.

⊘ **4-13 Hybrid Cars** There has been much research on hybrid cars—usually cars that are part electric and part combustion-powered. These are interesting from the engineering standpoint. But, at present, no practical combination competes well with the internal-combustion engine.

There are many interesting design concepts for hybrid cars (Fig. 4-28). One frequently used design is to add a small combustion engine to an electric car. The purpose of the small engine is to power a built-in battery charger. With the engine running all the time, or at least when needed, the batteries remain charged longer. This improves both vehicle speed and range. In some proposed designs, the charging engine can be mechanically connected to the drive wheels for high-speed freeway driving or hill climbing.

Figure 4-28 shows a hybrid gasoline-electric vehicle built by General Motors. The power system consists of a small gasoline engine coupled with a dc series electric motor through an electromagnetic

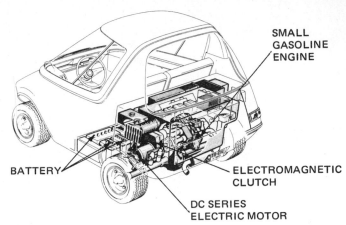

Fig. 4-28. A hybrid gasoline-electric vehicle. (*General Motors Corporation*)

clutch. Figure 4-29 shows another hybrid car, combining a Stirling engine with an electric motor. Also built by General Motors, this car is called the Stir-Lec II. In this vehicle, an 8-hp [5.97 kW] single-cylinder Stirling engine runs at constant speed. It drives an alternator to charge a lead-acid battery pack of 14 batteries connected in series. A 20-hp [14.92 kW] dc motor drives the vehicle.

Another system frequently found in hybrid-car designs is a regenerative braking and charging system. With this system, the deceleration and braking energy of the vehicle could be used to power the battery charger. Regenerative braking also charges the batteries when the vehicle is coasting or going downhill.

Analysis of the hybrid vehicle shows that it may combine the best advantages of several power systems. But it also usually combines the serious disadvantages of those same systems. On-board battery packs and recharging systems have the same shortcomings discussed in ⊘ 4-11 and 4-12. Hybrid-car performance, speed, and range characteristics are similar to those discussed for the electric car.

One advantage in most hybrid-car designs is that controlling emissions from the small constant-speed-and-load engine is simpler and cheaper than for a conventional-size piston engine. Often, the auxiliary power source is a fuel cell or a steam or Stirling engine, as discussed. A basic disadvantage of the hybrid car is that there are two separate power systems, instead of one. This increases the complexity, cost, and manufacturing and service problems tremendously. Emission controls must be applied to both power systems. Therefore, total hardware costs may exceed the cost of controlling emissions from the typical automobile engine.

Many experimental designs of hybrid cars have been proposed or built by General Motors and others. These one-of-a-kind vehicles usually serve as research and development prototypes. They are used for testing and evaluating advanced designs in power plant, drive train, and transportation systems. No major automotive manufacturer is expected to produce a hybrid car in the immediate future.

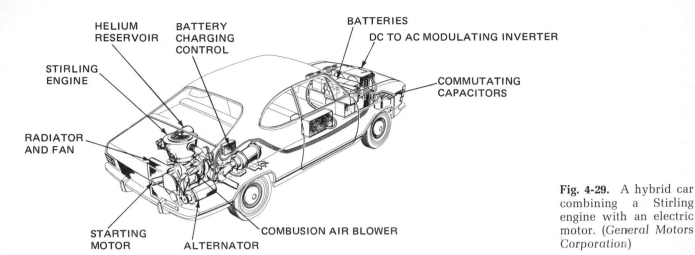

Fig. 4-29. A hybrid car combining a Stirling engine with an electric motor. (*General Motors Corporation*)

⊘ **4-14 Flywheel Propulsion** This concept for operating an automobile has been studied and tried out in Europe. The idea is as simple as a child's wind-up toy. A large flywheel weighing several hundred pounds is mounted in a vehicle, somewhat as shown in Fig. 4-30. It is "charged" by electrically spinning the flywheel at high speed. The energy thus stored in the flywheel operates a generator to produce electric current that then powers electric motors at the car wheels. Johns Hopkins Applied Physics Laboratory made a study of this concept of storing kinetic energy in a vehicle to power it. They concluded that cars capable of traveling 100 mi [161 km] on a single charge are possible. Theoretically, these cars could accelerate to 60 mph [97 km/h] in 15 s (seconds) and have a top speed of 70 mph [113 km/h].

In 1953, the 70-passenger Oerlikon bus was introduced in Europe (Fig. 4-31). It was driven by a 3,300-lb [1,497 kg] flywheel and was considered a technical success. However, it had to pull up to a utility pole about every half mile. Then electrical connections were made to "recharge" the flywheel, that is, to speed up the flywheel again. Since each recharge took about 2 min, passengers were hardly pleased about the bus. After use in Switzerland, Germany, and Leopoldville, the last Oerlikon bus was removed from service in 1969.

In 1972, Lockheed Missiles & Space Company announced a project planned in connection with the San Francisco Municipal Railway. This project called for Lockheed to build a flywheel- or kinetic-energy-powered trolley coach. Figure 4-32 shows a cutaway view of the proposed installation.

The trolley coach is a type of electric bus that has rubber tires. It gets its power from overhead streetcar wires. The bus is to be compatible with the trolley-coach system operated by the San Francisco Municipal Railway in the city of San Francisco. An advantage of the proposed bus would be the ability to recharge or speed up its flywheel from the overhead or underground streetcar power lines. Once charged, the flywheel bus would leave the normal wire route for limited operation in areas not served by either streetcars or trolley coaches.

With relatively heavy flywheels spinning at supersonic speeds, and relatively light vehicles, the theoretical predicted performance for buses and cars might be achieved. But other problems await solution. For example, in areas where streetcar or trolley-coach wiring does not exist, a system of recharging stations would have to be built. And some people are concerned about the hazard that exists in a collision, when a flywheel weighing several hundred pounds is spinning at high speed in the back of the

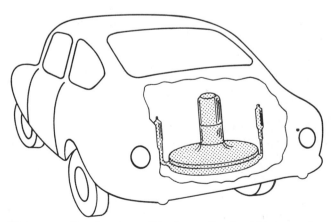

Fig. 4-30. Flywheel car. The large flywheel is located at the back of the car.

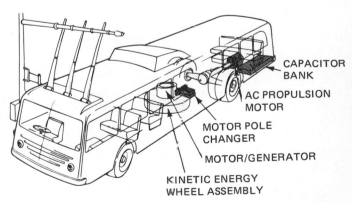

Fig. 4-31. The flywheel-powered Oerlikon bus. (*Lockheed Missiles and Space Company, Inc.*)

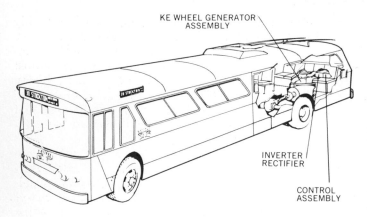

KE WHEEL GENERATOR
ASSEMBLY

INVERTER
RECTIFIER

CONTROL
ASSEMBLY

Fig. 4-32. Electric coach powered by a kinetic-energy wheel and generator. (*Lockheed Missiles and Space Company, Inc.*)

Fig. 4-33. A 370-lb [168-kg] aluminum V-8 racing engine. This engine develops 410 hp [306 kW] at 9,000 rpm from a displacement of 182 in³ [2,982 cc] with an 11:1 compression ratio. It has four overhead camshafts, four valves per cylinder, and fuel injection into eight inlet ports. (*Ford Motor Company of England, Ltd.*)

vehicle. Also, charging stations require extra electric generating capacity. This means building more generating plants that will probably burn fossil fuel. The problems of controlling electric generating-plant emissions were covered in ⊘ 4-12. In summary, the use of flywheel propulsion may create as many problems as it solves.

⊘ **4-15 Cost and Effects of Conversion** Consider the general economic problems that could result from changing to a different type of automotive power plant. For example, suppose some genius announces a new type of power plant which burns standard gasoline, is pollution-free, highly efficient, relatively simple in design, and potentially free of bugs—in other words, an ideal engine. How long would it take for the automotive industry to start mass production of this new engine? How much would it cost to put the new engine into production? Would the public quickly accept the new engine and immediately start buying cars powered by it? Who would pay the massive costs of conversion—the major retooling of one of the world's largest industries? Unfortunately, the answer to the last question is probably you, the car buyer.

These important questions have to be answered before any manufacturer can market a new type of engine. No manufacturer can afford to invest the years of time and billions of dollars required to prove out the new design, and gamble on future public acceptance in the marketplace. The truth is that the public is very slow to accept engineering innovations in their cars.

Just think of the modern piston-type internal-combustion engine used in today's automobiles. Almost 100 years have gone into redesigning, refining, and improving this engine. The peak of piston-engine development is typified by the high-performance racing engine shown in Fig. 4-33. And there is still room for improvement. But there is hardly any comparison between the old-time cranky, balky engine of 50 years ago and the light, flexible, highly reliable servant that the modern engine has become.

A world without the internal-combustion engine, in our present technological situation, is almost unthinkable. Without automobiles, trucks, buses, railroads, and airplanes, our civilization would collapse overnight. Until now, engineers believe that the internal-combustion engine is the best bet, considering all factors.

One prediction stands out above all other considerations of alternatives to the piston engine: During the next 10 years, 350 million more internal-combustion piston engines will be built to power passenger cars and trucks. How to service the emission control systems of these vehicles—today's cars as well as those yet to be built—is the subject we shall study in the following chapters.

⊘ **4-16 Prediction of Future Engines** In 1975, the Eaton Corporation completed an intensive study of all existing forms of internal-combustion engines. They predicted that the turbine and Stirling engines, along with the Wankel, would take an increasing part of the market in future years. Eaton produced the graph shown in Fig. 4-34. As you can see, they expect the use of reciprocating engines to fall off to only about 50 percent of the total by 1989. And most or all of those in use will be of the stratified-charge design. Stratified charging, which permits the use of a leaner mixture and reduces the HC and CO in the exhaust, is covered in ⊘ 8-3. Note that the Stirling and turbine engines approach one-third of the total market by 1989. Use of the Wankel is shown as increasing more gradually over the years. It will be interesting to look at this graph in 1989 and see how close the predictions are.

CHAPTER 4 CHECKUP

NOTE: Since the following is a chapter review test, you should review the chapter before taking the test.

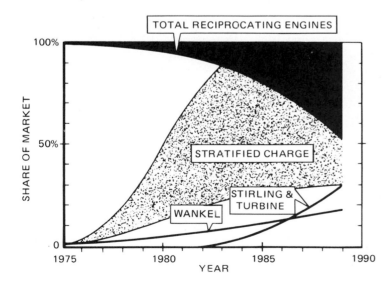

Fig. 4-34. Graph showing the predicted percentage of total production of various types of engines to the year 1989. (*Eaton Corporation*)

You are making good progress in your study of automotive emission control. The chapter you have just completed gives you a good background on the various alternative engines and power systems that you may be servicing someday. Now, check yourself on how well you understand the alternatives to the conventional piston engine, by working through the following checkup. Review the chapter before taking the test. If the questions seem hard to answer, review the chapter again. Remember, most successful students review assignments several times, to make sure they have fixed the essential facts in their minds.

Completing the Sentences   The sentences below are incomplete. After each sentence there are several words or phrases, but only one of them correctly completes the sentence. Write each sentence in your notebook, ending it with the word or phrase that completes it correctly.

1. In addition to low exhaust-emission levels, the Stirling engine has very low: (*a*) operating temperatures, (*b*) fuel consumption, (*c*) noise levels, (*d*) operating speeds.
2. Most electric cars are powered by: (*a*) fuel cells, (*b*) silver-zinc batteries, (*c*) lead-acid batteries, (*d*) dry-cell batteries.
3. Most electric generating plants are fueled by: (*a*) fossil fuel, (*b*) nuclear energy, (*c*) waterfalls, (*d*) windmills.
4. Fossil-fueled electric generating plants have a high output of: (*a*) HC and CO, (*b*) CO and NO_x, (*c*) SO_2 and NO_x, (*d*) HC and SO_2.
5. Hybrid cars usually combine an electric motor and a: (*a*) fuel cell, (*b*) Stirling engine, (*c*) flywheel, (*d*) combustion engine.
6. Flywheels were used in Europe to power (*a*) cars, (*b*) trucks, (*c*) trains, (*d*) buses.
7. The number of internal-combustion piston engines that will be built in the next 10 years is: (*a*) 1 million, (*b*) 10 million, (*c*) 350 million, (*d*) 1 billion.
8. Possible alternatives to the internal-combustion piston engine include: (*a*) diesels, gas turbines, and steam engines, (*b*) gas turbines, Stirling engines, and bicycles, (*c*) Stirling engines, hybrid cars, and horses, (*d*) bicycles, tricycles, and horses.
9. Types of alternative power systems that usually include the use of electric motors are: (*a*) diesel, Wankel, and gas turbine, (*b*) Wankel, gas turbine, and steam engine, (*c*) gas turbine, electric car, and hybrid car, (*d*) electric car, hybrid car, and flywheel-powered vehicle.
10. The cost of the automotive industry converting to an alternative power plant would ultimately be paid by the: (*a*) federal government, (*b*) car buyer, (*c*) state government, (*d*) auto manufacturer.

Questions   Here are questions that deal with alternative engines and power systems. Write the answer to each question in your notebook. Use your own words. If you do not know the answer, turn back to the pages covering that engine or power system. Be sure to refer to the illustrations. It is often said that "a picture is worth a thousand words." Studying the illustrations will give you a greater understanding of the various engines and power systems, and how each can be used in an automobile.

1. Explain the difference between an open combustion chamber and a precombustion chamber.
2. Describe the difference between a Wankel rotary-combustion (RC) engine and a conventional IC engine.
3. Discuss the advantages and disadvantages of the gas-turbine engine for passenger-car use.
4. What was the first engine widely used to replace people and animals in performing work?
5. What is meant by the phrase "multifuel capability"?
6. What engine was invented in 1816 by a Scottish minister?
7. Describe the type of driving that can be performed practically by an electric car.
8. How does the flywheel bus transfer the energy stored in the rotating flywheel to the tires on the ground?
10. Discuss the possible economic effects of a total, immediate conversion to the use of electric cars for all trips of less than 50 mi [80 km].

Definitions   In the following, you are asked to define certain terms. Write the definitions in your notebook. Writing the definitions will help you remember them. It will also provide you with a place where you can quickly locate the meanings when you need them. If you cannot remember the meanings of the terms, look them up in the chapter you have just studied, or in the glossary at the back of the book.

1. What is a diesel engine?
2. Define "fuel injection."
3. What is a precombustion chamber?
4. Define "rotary engine."
5. What is an eccentric shaft?
6. Define "alternative engine."
7. What is a gas-turbine engine?
8. Define "gasifier section."
9. Define "steam engine."
10. What is a continuous combustion process?

SUGGESTIONS FOR FURTHER STUDY

If you would like to know more about alternative engines and power systems, read and clip out newspaper and magazine articles dealing with the subject. Add the clippings to your notebook for future reference.

PART TWO

CONTROLLING CRANKCASE EMISSIONS AND FUEL EVAPORATION

Part Two of *Automotive Emission Control* discusses three of the four sources of automotive emissions—the crankcase, the fuel tank, and the carburetor. As explained previously, emissions that pollute the air can come from these three sources and from the tail pipe in uncontrolled automobiles. Part Three of this book discusses the steps that have been taken to clean up the exhaust gases. Part Two contains two chapters.

⊘ **CHAPTER 5** Crankcase Emission Control ⊘ **CHAPTER 6** Evaporative Control Systems

chapter 5

CRANKCASE EMISSION CONTROL

In Chaps. 1 and 3 we discussed air pollution and smog, and the part that the automobile plays in creating them. We noted that gasoline evaporating from the fuel tank and carburetor add to the smog problem. We also noted that incomplete combustion of gasoline in the engine, combined with the formation of nitrogen oxides, produces most automotive emissions. Some estimates say that, nationwide, about 45 percent of air pollution is caused by the automobile. Vehicles produce approximately 90,000,000 tons of atmospheric pollution annually. All other sources combined produce approximately 110,000,000 tons of additional atmospheric pollution each year.

Remember, there are four sources of air pollution from the automobile: the crankcase, the tail pipe or exhaust system, the carburetor, and the fuel tank. In this chapter we study crankcase emission control systems. Following chapters describe controls for the other emission sources. The engine crankcase was the first source of vehicle emissions to be completely controlled.

⊘ **5-1 Crankcase Ventilation** Air must circulate through the crankcase when the engine is running. The reason is that water and liquid gasoline appear in the crankcase during certain phases of engine operation. During the compression and combustion strokes, highly corrosive blow-by gases are forced past the piston rings into the crankcase. Blow-by gases contain burned and unburned fuel and water vapor from the combustion chamber. As shown in Fig. 2-8, engine blow-by results from high combustion-chamber pressures, necessary working clearance of piston rings in their grooves, normal ring shifting that sometimes lines up the clearance gaps of two or more rings, and reduction in ring sealing contact area with changes in the direction of piston travel.

The water is a product of combustion. For every gallon (or liter) of gasoline burned, more than a gallon (or liter) of water is formed by the combustion process. When the engine is cold, some of the water vapor in the blow-by and in the fresh ventilating air condenses on the cylinder walls and crankcase. It forms into droplets and runs down into the oil pan. Gasoline vapor also condenses on cold engine parts and drips down into the oil pan. This gasoline dilutes and thins the oil, reducing its lubricating ability. Fortunately, in normal operation these liquids in the oil evaporate as the engine warms up. Then, they are removed from the crankcase through the crankcase ventilation system.

If the water is not removed from the crankcase,

it can cause serious trouble. Whipped by the churning effect of the rotating crankshaft, the water reacts with the oil in the crankcase to form thick, gummy sludge. The acidic compounds from the blow-by gets in the sludge and cause corrosion and faster wear of engine parts. Sludge can also clog oil passages and prevent normal engine lubrication, thereby leading to early engine failure.

NOTE: For a crankcase ventilating system to be effective, the engine must be warm enough to vaporize the liquid gasoline and water in the crankcase. That means the car must be driven far enough for the engine to warm up. If a car is used for short trips, in start-and-stop operation, the engine may not reach a temperature high enough to vaporize the water and gasoline in the crankcase. This is especially true in cold weather. It takes upward of 10 mi [16 km] of driving to vaporize the water and gasoline. If a car is operated so that the engine never really warms up, the crankcase oil should be changed frequently, to remove the water and gasoline in the crankcase.

⊘ **5-2 Relieving Crankcase Pressure** Blow-by also causes pressure in the crankcase. If this pressure is allowed to build up, engine oil is forced past the oil seals and gaskets, and out of the engine. To help control the effects of blow-by, there must be a way to relieve the crankcase pressure it causes. This is another job for the crankcase ventilating system: to prevent pressure buildup in the crankcase.

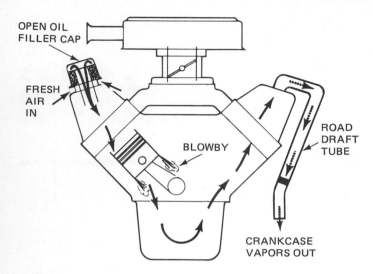

Fig. 5-1. Road-draft-tube type of crankcase ventilation, used on engines before crankcase emission control devices were required. (*Ford Motor Company*)

⊘ **5-3 The Road-Draft Tube** In early engines, the crankcase ventilating system was very simple (see Fig. 5-1). It provided crankcase breathing by passing fresh air through the crankcase. On almost all American-made automobile engines built prior to 1961, the fresh air entered through an air inlet at the top front of the engine (Fig. 5-1). The fresh air mixed with the blow-by fumes and other vapors in the crankcase. These vapors were routed out of the crankcase through a large, hollow tube called the *road-draft tube,* which discharged under the car into the atmosphere.

The fresh-air inlet was usually the crankcase breather cap (Fig. 5-2). On most engines, it also served as the cap for the crankcase oil-filler tube. The cap was open, or vented. That is, it was hollow, with holes on both sides to let fresh air pass through. The cap was filled with oil-soaked steel wool or a similar material, to serve as an air filter. The filter prevented dust particles in the air from getting into the crankcase oil and causing engine wear.

The road-draft tube (Fig. 5-1), or crankcase outlet, was a thin-walled tube about 1 in [25.4 mm] in

diameter. It usually extended down the side or back of the engine until its open end was in the road draft. The road draft is the wind or airstream that passes under the car while the car is moving. This air movement around the tube created a low-pressure area (a slight vacuum, or venturi effect) at its discharge end, which helped draw fumes from the crankcase.

⊘ **5-4 Road-Draft-Tube Operation** In operation, the road-draft-tube system of crankcase ventilation was simple and effective above about 25 mph [40 km/h]. With the car in motion, air was trapped under the hood in the engine compartment, causing a high-pressure area around the open breather cap. This forced outside air to pass through the breather cap and into the engine. Inside the crankcase of a running engine, the crankshaft acts like a fan. It whips and mixes the fresh air and crankcase fumes as it rotates (see Fig. 5-3). The road-draft-tube opening into the crankcase was usually designed to benefit from this crankshaft fan effect. The ventilating air

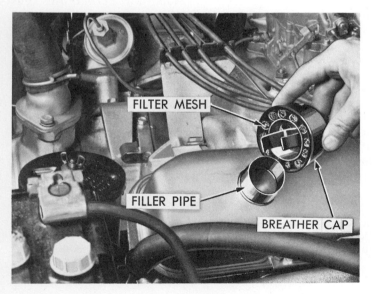

Fig. 5-2. Open type of crankcase breather cap.

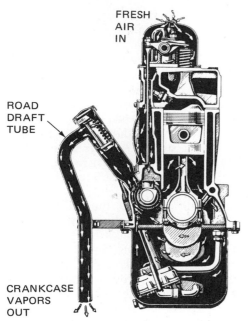

Fig. 5-3. Typical open crankcase ventilation system using a road-draft tube. The flow of ventilating air through the engine is shown by the arrows.

passing through the crankcase removed the water and fuel vapors. A low pressure or vacuum under the moving car pulled the ventilating air and vapors from the engine through the road-draft tube. The flow of ventilating air inside an engine is shown by the arrows in Fig. 5-3.

The crankcase opening for the road-draft tube was usually well shielded; it frequently had a baffle in front of it. This prevented oil splashing into the tube or being drawn out of the engine by the ventilating air. Without any moving parts, the road-draft-tube system of crankcase ventilation required little service.

⊘ **5-5 Road-Draft-Tube Emissions** The road-draft-tube system worked well to keep the crankcase free of fumes and pressure buildup. However, it discharged all of the crankcase pollutants into the atmosphere. This discharge through the road-draft

tube represented about 20 percent of the total HC emissions from an automobile without any emissions control (Fig. 3-1). When the hood was up and the engine idling, crankcase vapors could often be seen escaping from the open breather cap. Therefore, controlling blow-by was decided on as the first step in eliminating atmospheric pollution from the automobile. In the following sections, we shall see how this is done by each of the four types of crankcase emission control systems.

⊘ **5-6 Type 1: Valve Controlled by Manifold Vacuum** Blow-by is mostly air-fuel mixture that did not burn the first time through the engine. One way to remove and recover this fuel from the crankcase is to route the blow-by back into the intake manifold to be burned in the cylinders.

An early system that partially controlled crankcase emissions was installed on cars built for sale in California in 1961. The system was called the *positive crankcase ventilation* (PCV) system.

In the PCV system, a tube is connected between a crankcase vent and the intake manifold (Fig. 5-4). The road-draft tube is not used, so its opening is plugged. While the engine is running, intake-manifold vacuum is used to pull vapor from the crankcase through the tube into the intake manifold. Fresh ventilating air is drawn into the crankcase through an open oil-filler cap (Fig. 5-4). Once in the intake manifold, the crankcase vapors are mixed with the incoming air-fuel mixture and sent to the cylinders for burning.

However, for the engine to operate properly under all conditions of speed and load, a flow-control valve is required. Without a flow-control valve, excessive ventilation air passes from the crankcase into the intake manifold during idle and low speed. This upsets the engine air-fuel ratio and results in poor idling with frequent stalling.

⊘ **5-7 The PCV Valve** As mentioned above, a flow-control valve is needed to regulate the airflow, and to prevent crankcase oil from being pulled into the intake manifold. Today, almost all cars use a

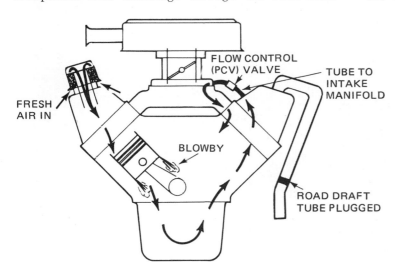

Fig. 5-4. Type-1 open PCV system of crankcase ventilation using a PCV valve and an open oil-filler cap. (*Ford Motor Company*)

positive crankcase ventilation (PCV) valve to regulate the flow of vapors from the crankcase. As shown in Fig. 5-4, the flow-control valve, or PCV valve, is installed in the tube from the crankcase vent (usually in the valve cover) to the intake manifold. The PCV valve is a type of variable-orifice valve. That is, the size of opening in the valve changes to control the flow of crankcase vapors through it. We discuss the operation of the PCV valve in ⊘ 5-8.

Most of the time that a car is traveling on the highway, the PCV valve is open. But it is designed to vary the amount of flow into the intake manifold according to the mode of engine operation—idle, acceleration, cruise, and so on. A sectional view of a typical PCV valve is shown in Fig. 5-5. It consists of a coil spring, a valve, and a two-piece outer body which is usually crimped together. The valve dimensions, spring tension, and internal passage dimensions are designed to allow the rate of crankcase-vapor flow that each engine requires.

⊘ **5-8 PCV-Valve Operation**   Now, let's discuss how the PCV valve works. At idle or low speed, the high intake-manifold vacuum tries to pull the valve closed, or into its minimum-flow position. This is shown in the top of Fig. 5-6. As the valve tries to close, it compresses the valve spring. The small passageway carries the greatly reduced flow of blow-by.

As the manifold vacuum decreases to about 12 to 15 in Hg (inches of mercury) [305 to 381 mm Hg], the compressed spring overcomes the pull of the vacuum on the valve and begins to force it open, toward the maximum-flow position. As the valve moves open (center, in Fig. 5-6), the flow capacity increases. This is to handle the greater volume of blow-by that results from an increase in engine load and speed.

Typical PCV-valve flow rates are 1 to 3 ft³/min (cubic feet per minute) [0.028 to 0.085 m³/min (cubic meter per minute)] with the valve in the low-speed minimum-flow position. At maximum flow, which occurs at approximately 6 in Hg [152 mm Hg] or less of vacuum, the valve will pass 3 to 6 ft³/min [0.085 to 0.170 m³/min].

If the engine backfires, the sudden pressure in the intake manifold forces the valve back and seated against the inlet of the valve body (bottom, in Fig. 5-6). This completely closes the air passage and prevents any possible crankcase explosion. That is, backseating the valve prevents the backfire from traveling through the valve and connecting hose into the crankcase. If the backfire entered the crankcase, the flame and heat could ignite the combustible blow-by gases. This would cause an explosion that could damage engine gaskets and parts.

On engines equipped with the type-1 PCV systems, the additional ventilating air drawn through the crankcase and into the intake manifold tends to lean the air-fuel mixture. However, carburetors are calibrated to take this into account. Should the PCV valve stick in the open, maximum-flow position, the additional ventilating air flowing through the valve causes the idle mixture to get leaner.

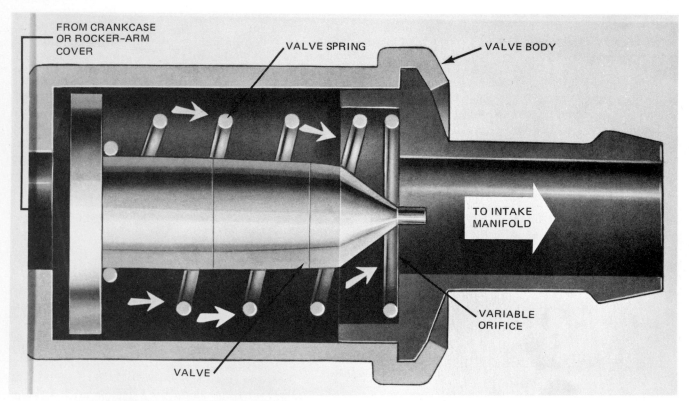

Fig. 5-5.   Sectional view of a PCV valve. The arrows show the flow path through the valve. (*Chevrolet Motor Division of General Motors Corporation*)

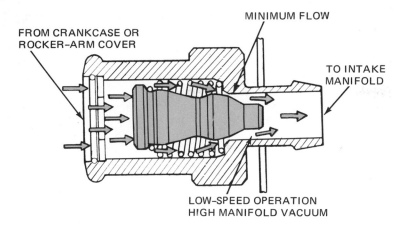

FROM CRANKCASE OR ROCKER-ARM COVER

MINIMUM FLOW

TO INTAKE MANIFOLD

LOW-SPEED OPERATION HIGH MANIFOLD VACUUM

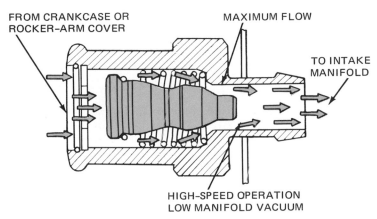

FROM CRANKCASE OR ROCKER-ARM COVER

MAXIMUM FLOW

TO INTAKE MANIFOLD

HIGH-SPEED OPERATION LOW MANIFOLD VACUUM

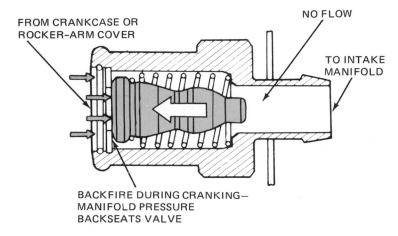

FROM CRANKCASE OR ROCKER-ARM COVER

NO FLOW

TO INTAKE MANIFOLD

BACKFIRE DURING CRANKING— MANIFOLD PRESSURE BACKSEATS VALVE

Fig. 5-6. The three positions of the PCV valve. Top, valve position during low engine speed; center, valve position during high engine speed; lower, valve position during engine backfire. (*Ford Motor Company*)

⊘ **5-9 Type-1 Applications** The type-1, or *open*, PCV system is so called because the oil-filler cap is not sealed. It is of the open type, with a vent through which ventilating air passes into the crankcase. The cap has a filter of rubberized horsehair, or other material, to filter the air before it enters the engine. Typical six-cylinder and eight-cylinder engine applications of the type-1 open PCV system are shown in Fig 5-7.

The type-1 system was first required in 1961 on American-built production cars sold and registered in California. But positive crankcase ventilation was not completely new. It had been used previously on military and commercial vehicles to help control engine sludge formation. Nationwide introduction of the PCV system followed on 1963 model automobiles.

Operating characteristics of the type-1 open PCV system are shown in Fig. 5-8. Notice, in the right column of Fig. 5-8, that, on a good engine, the type-1 open PCV system is 100 percent effective in controlling crankcase emissions at idle and low speed. That is, under these conditions, no crankcase vapor or blow-by escapes into the atmosphere. However, with the engine under load or at high speed, this system is only partially effective.

Once the amount of blow-by in the engine exceeds the flow rate of the PCV valve, pressure begins to build up in the crankcase. This stops the flow of ventilating air through the open oil-filler cap. Then

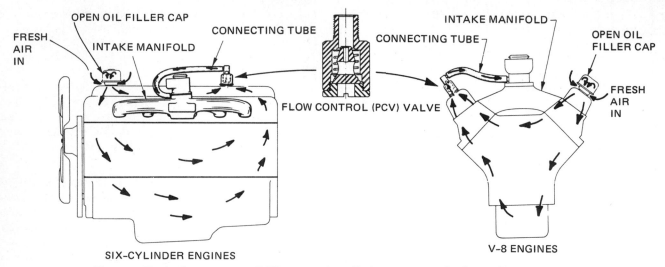

Fig. 5-7. Typical type-1 open PCV-system installations on six-cylinder and V-8 engines. On the V-8 shown, the air circulates from one rocker-arm cover, through the crankcase, and out the other rocker-arm cover to the intake manifold. (*Chrysler Corporation*)

the excess blow-by begins to flow backward, through the vent holes in the oil-filler cap and into the atmosphere.

Check Your Progress

Progress Quiz 5-1 Find out how well the material you just studied has "stuck with you," by answering the questions below. If you are not sure about some of the answers, reread the previous few pages and then try the questions again.

⊘ **Completing the Sentences** The sentences below are incomplete. After each sentence there are several words or phrases, but only one of them correctly completes the sentence. Write each sentence in your notebook, ending it with the word or phrase that completes it correctly.

1. Two unwanted liquids appearing in the crankcase of a cold engine after starting are: (*a*) air and oil, (*b*) oil and gasoline, (*c*) water and oil, (*d*) water and gasoline.

CONDITIONS AFFECTING EMISSION CONTROL	POSITION THROTTLE	AVAILABLE VACUUM	COMPRESSION PRESSURE	AMOUNT OF BLOWBY FROM ENGINE	POSITION OF PCV VALVE	PATH OF BLOWBY	PERCENT (APPROX.) EFFECTIVE IN CONTROLLING CRANKCASE EMISSION
ENGINE OFF ①	CLOSED	NONE	NONE	NONE	OPEN	NONE	
LOW SPEED (IDLE)	CLOSED	HIGH ②	LOW ③	LOW	CLOSED ④	ALL THROUGH VALVE	100
⑤ LOW SPEED (LOAD)	WIDE OPEN	LOW	HIGH	HIGH	FULLY OPEN	HALF THROUGH VALVE	50
						HALF TO ATMOSPHERE	
HIGH SPEED	PARTLY OPEN	MEDIUM	MEDIUM	MEDIUM	PARTLY OPEN	3/4 THROUGH VALVE	75
						1/4 TO ATMOSPHERE	

NOTE: 1 IN CASE OF BACKFIRE, DURING CRANKING, THE VACUUM IN THE INTAKE MANIFOLD WILL CAUSE THE PCV VALVE PLUNGER TO MOVE TOWARD THE CRANKCASE; THUS, SEALING THE PASSAGE TO THE CRANKCASE AND PREVENTING A POSSIBLE EXPLOSION.
NOTE: 2 BLOWBY IS AT A MINIMUM WHEN MANIFOLD VACUUM IS HIGH AT IDLE.
NOTE: 3 BLOWBY IS AT A MAXIMUM WHEN COMPRESSION IS HIGH.
NOTE: 4 PCV VALVE IS ON MINIMUM (CLOSED) FLOW POSITION WHEN MANIFOLD VACUUM IS HIGH.
NOTE: 5 FOR LOW SPEED, OPEN THROTTLE POSITION, AS WELL AS VARIOUS THROTTLE PLATE POSITIONS AND LOAD COMBINATIONS. THE MAIN CONCERN OF EMISSION CONTROL IS AT IDLE AND DURING DECELERATION CONDITIONS.

Fig. 5-8. Operating characteristics of the type-1 open PCV system of crankcase emission control. Notice that the type-1 system controls 100 percent of the crankcase emissions only at idle speed. (*Ford Motor Company*)

2. Water mixed with engine oil forms: (*a*) varnish, (*b*) sludge, (*c*) tar, (*d*) grease.

3. Gasoline mixed with engine oil causes: (*a*) oil dilution, (*b*) corrosion, (*c*) sludge, (*d*) varnish.

4. Before crankcase emission control devices, engine crankcases were vented by a: (*a*) road-draft tube, (*b*) tube to the air cleaner, (*c*) tube to the intake manifold, (*d*) tube to the carburetor.

5. The percentage of the total HC emissions from the automobile that escape into the atmosphere through the road-draft tube is about: (*a*) 10 percent, (*b*) 50 percent, (*c*) 20 percent, (*d*) 75 percent.

6. The PCV valve is controlled by: (*a*) manifold pressure, (*b*) manifold vacuum, (*c*) crankcase pressure, (*d*) crankcase vacuum.

7. At idle, the PCV valve is: (*a*) at its maximum-flow position, (*b*) at its minimum-flow position, (*c*) backseated, (*d*) completely open.

8. At full throttle, the PCV valve is: (*a*) at its minimum-flow position, (*b*) completely closed, (*c*) backseated, (*d*) at its maximum-flow position.

9. Returning the blow-by gases to the intake manifold in a closed PCV system causes the mixture to: (*a*) get richer, (*b*) stay the same, (*c*) get leaner, (*d*) stall the engine.

10. A PCV valve stuck in the maximum-flow position causes the idle mixture to: (*a*) get richer, (*b*) stay the same, (*c*) get leaner, (*d*) increase in temperature.

⊘ **5-10 Type 2: Valve Controlled by Crankcase Vacuum** The type-2 crankcase emission control system (Fig. 5-9) is used primarily as an add-on kit for used cars. It has, however, been installed by some new-car manufacturers. The device is approved in California for local smog-station installation on any 1955 or later model vehicle not factory equipped with a crankcase emission control system.

This device uses a crankcase vacuum-operated control valve to prevent blow-by gases from escaping. This system (Fig. 5-9) operates on the principle that any blow-by past the piston rings creates a slight pressure rise in the crankcase. This pressure rise causes the control valve to open. As the valve opens, more crankcase gases can flow into the intake manifold.

Like the type-1 system, the type-2 system is basically a tube, from the crankcase to the intake manifold, with a variable-orifice control valve installed in it. A variable orifice is a hole that acts as a valve by changing size to vary the flow rate.

⊘ **5-11 Type-2 Valve Operation** Instead of a PCV valve, the type-2 system uses a modulator valve with a flexible teflon diaphragm (Fig. 5-10). The valve is closed when the engine is idling with normal or very little blow-by. This is shown in the top illustration in Fig. 5-10. In the closed position, the valve spring is compressed.

The type-2 valve has a breather hole which permits atmospheric pressure to act against one side of the diaphragm. Through the diaphragm and valve, there is a small passage, called the *idle groove*, which is always open. This passage permits a small flow of crankcase gases into the intake manifold when the engine is idling and the valve is closed. The flow through the small passage is about 3 ft³/min [0.085 m³/min].

As the engine reaches cruising speed, or as blow-by increases, there is less intake-manifold vacuum. Consequently, the valve opens. This position is shown in the lower illustration in Fig. 5-10.

Because of its control by crankcase vacuum, the flow rate through the type-2 valve depends on the amount of blow-by generated by the engine. The valve opening automatically adjusts to the blow-by rate of the engine. This completely controls the blow-by and prevents its escape to the atmosphere, except from engines in very poor condition. Then, the amount of engine blow-by may exceed the capacity of the valve.

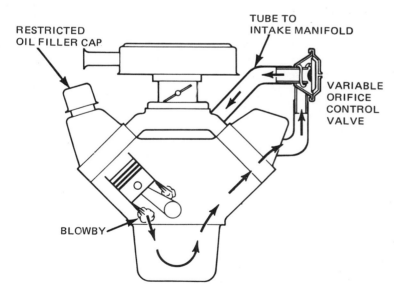

RESTRICTED OIL FILLER CAP

TUBE TO INTAKE MANIFOLD

VARIABLE ORIFICE CONTROL VALVE

BLOWBY

Fig. 5-9. The type-2 valve is controlled by crankcase vacuum. (*Ford Motor Company*)

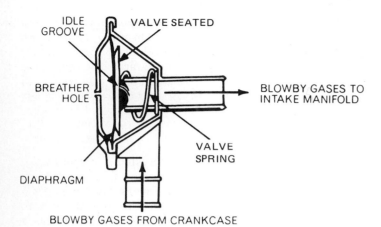

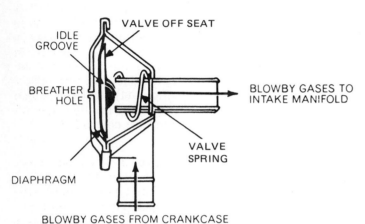

Fig. 5-10. The two positions of the type-2 control valve. Top, the closed position, for minimum flow when the engine is idling; bottom, the open position, for maximum flow when the engine is at cruising speed or has a high blow-by rate.

⊘ **5-12 Airtight Crankcase Required** With the type-2 system, the flow of ventilating air into the crankcase must be limited. It is limited by the use of an airtight crankcase and a special restricted oil-filler cap. The special cap has a small hole in it through which a relatively constant amount of ventilating air enters the crankcase. If the flow of ventilating air is not limited, the diaphragm-type valve tends to open fully. In the full-open position, the valve pulls in ventilating air up to its maximum capacity. This causes excessive lean-out in the air-fuel mixture. Therefore, it is important that the crankcase breather cap be the specified restricted type, and that air leaks into the crankcase be minimized.

Blow-by gases added to the downstream side of the carburetor in the intake manifold (as on type-1 and type-2 devices) have no effect on the engine air-fuel mixture. But on type-1 and type-2 devices, ventilating air introduced through the crankcase into the intake manifold tends to lean out the air-fuel mixture. However, carburetors are calibrated to compensate for this when the devices are installed by the automobile manufacturer. When this type of device is installed in the service shop, a readjustment of the idle mixture screws is often required because of the slightly leaner mixture.

All crankcase blow-by, and the ventilating air, flows to the intake manifold through the variable-orifice control valve (Fig. 5-9). Because of this, high-

dust-capacity breather filters are used. Also, it is important that no part of the system be restricted, or pressure will build up in the crankcase. Should a flow restriction occur, oil and vapor will blow out through the oil-filler cap, rocker-arm cover, and oil-pan gaskets. In addition, oil may be forced out through the timing cover and rear main oil seals.

⊘ **5-13 Type 3: Tube-to-Air-Cleaner Device** The simplest crankcase emission control system is the tube-to-air-cleaner device (Fig. 5-11). Known as the type-3 system, this device consists solely of a tube connecting the crankcase to the carburetor air cleaner. Many different designs of tube-to-air-cleaner device have been used. None of the designs uses any type of flow-control valve. The most common differences among type-3 systems are in the location of the tube and the method of controlling the flow of ventilation air.

⊘ **5-14 Type-3 Operation** While the engine is operating, blow-by entering the crankcase raises the crankcase pressure. But the airflow through the air cleaner causes it to have a lower pressure than the crankcase. Thus, blow-by gases flow from the crankcase, through the tube, and into the carburetor airstream.

⊘ **5-15 Type-3 Disadvantages** One serious disadvantage of the type-3 system caused American man-

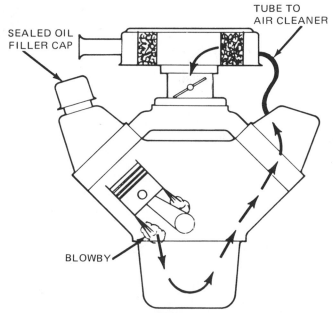

Fig. 5-11. The type-3 vent-tube-to-air-cleaner system. Note that no flow control valve is used. (*Ford Motor Company*)

ufacturers to abandon its use. In a cold engine, the crankcase moisture is carried through the tube to the air cleaner. There, the moisture is either deposited on the air-filter element, restricting its flow, or dropped into the carburetor. In cold climates, moisture in the carburetor can result in carburetor icing.

Another disadvantage of the type-3 device is that it tends to enrich the air-fuel mixture. Notice the flow of blow-by gas in Fig. 5-11. The addition of blow-by gas to the upstream side, ahead of the carburetor, causes a second charge of fuel to mix with the blow-by gas as it flows through the carburetor. When this system is used on new cars, carburetors are calibrated to compensate for the addition of the second fuel charge.

⊘ **5-16 Type-3 Applications** The type-3 system has been used for many years on foreign vehicles. Its

purpose is to provide an escape path from the crankcase for blow-by gases. On many engines, no provision is made for the introduction of ventilation air into the crankcase. These are referred to as *sealed* systems, because a sealed oil-filler cap is used (Fig. 5-11). The type-3 tube-to-air-cleaner system has not been used on any recent American-manufactured vehicles.

⊘ **5-17 Type-4 Combination Systems** None of the three types of crankcase emission control systems already discussed is completely effective in controlling crankcase emissions. In the type-1 system, blow-by in excess of the flow rate of the PCV valve escapes to the atmosphere through the open oil-filler cap (Fig. 5-4). In the type-2 system, blow-by gases may escape to the atmosphere through air leaks in the crankcase or through the ventilating air hole in the oil-filler cap (Fig. 5-9). In the type-3 system, blow-by can escape through air leaks in the crankcase or at the air cleaner (Fig. 5-11). However, when two of these systems are installed on the same engine, all crankcase emissions are controlled.

⊘ **5-18 Type 4: Type 1 plus Type 3** The type-4 combination system (Fig. 5-12) is basically the type-1 PCV-valve system with the type-3 tube-to-air-cleaner system. (Compare Figs. 5-4 and 5-11 with Fig. 5-12.) The blow-by gases are returned to the engine cylinders through the intake manifold and, under some operating conditions, through the carburetor air cleaner. While the PCV valve is usually used as the flow-control valve in the type-4 system, some fixed-orifice valves are also installed (see ⊘ 5-21). A closed oil-filler cap is used rather than the open type. All other possible outlets for blow-by gases, such as the dipstick tube, are sealed. All ventilating air entering the engine crankcase must first be filtered through the carburetor air cleaner or through a separate PCV filter. This PCV filter is located on the inside wall of the air-cleaner housing (Fig. 5-13). Some systems use a special breather cap with a synthetic-rubber flapper-type check valve and re-

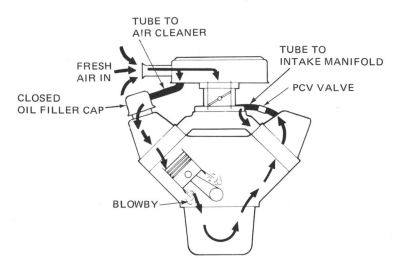

Fig. 5-12. The type-4 positive crankcase ventilation system. (*Ford Motor Company*)

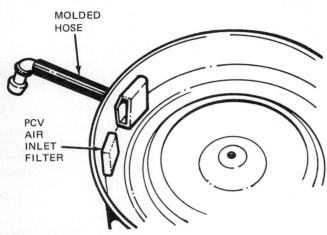

Fig. 5-13. Location of the PCV filter in the air-cleaner housing on a six-cylinder engine. (*American Motors Corporation*)

stricting holes. The check valve prevents blow-by gases from leaking into the atmosphere from the breather cap.

On many type-4 systems, the air-flow tube from the carburetor air cleaner is connected directly to the rocker-arm cover, rather than through the sealed oil-filler cap (Fig. 5-14). On others, the tube is connected to the sealed oil-filler cap (Fig. 5-15). The tube to the air cleaner is usually connected to the clean, or downstream, side of the air cleaner. On some systems, the tube is connected to the unfiltered side of the air cleaner and has a separate filter (Figs. 5-13 and 5-14).

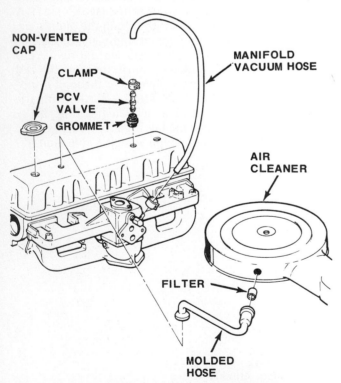

Fig. 5-14. The PCV system on a six-cylinder engine. (*American Motors Corporation*)

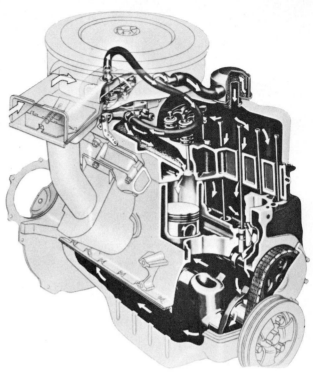

Fig. 5-15. Typical installation of a type-4 closed PCV system on a six-cylinder engine. (*Ford Motor Company*)

⊘ **5-19 Type-4 Operation** During part-throttle operation of the engine, the intake-manifold vacuum draws the blow-by gases from the crankcase through the PCV valve (Fig. 5-12). Normally, the capacity of the valve is sufficient under these conditions to handle the blow-by plus a small amount of ventilating air. The ventilating air is usually drawn from the clean side of the carburetor air cleaner, through the tube-to-air-cleaner connection, and into the crankcase (Fig. 5-12).

Under full-throttle conditions, the intake-manifold vacuum is insufficient to draw all the blow-by through the PCV valve. Therefore, the blow-by flows through the tube-to-air-cleaner connection in the reverse direction (Fig. 5-16). That is, the blow-by flows from the crankcase, through the rocker-arm cover and the air cleaner, and into the carburetor. In engines with excessive blow-by, some of the flow goes through the tube connection to the air cleaner under all conditions.

The PCV valve may stick, or there may be a flow restriction, in a type-4 system. Then the crankcase gases flow back, or backflow, into the carburetor airstream passing through the air cleaner. From there, the gases are returned to the cylinders and burned. Thus, the type-4 system is a completely closed system that prevents any crankcase emissions from reaching the atmosphere (Fig. 5-17). For this reason, it is known as the *closed* PCV system.

In case of a backfire, the valve is forced back and seated against the inlet end of the valve body, thus closing the air passage, as explained previously

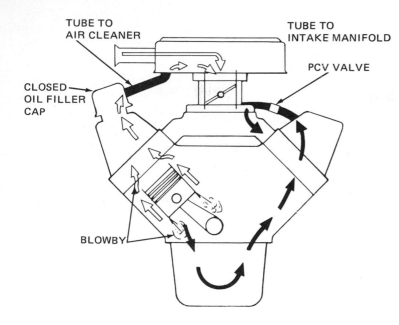

TUBE TO
AIR CLEANER

TUBE TO
INTAKE MANIFOLD

PCV VALVE

CLOSED
OIL FILLER
CAP

BLOWBY

Fig. 5-16. Flow of blowby when the blowby is more than the PCV valve can handle. Note that the blowby is passing up through the tube to the air cleaner. Compare this with Fig. 5-12. (*Ford Motor Company*)

(Fig. 5-6). This prevents the backfire from traveling into the crankcase and causing a crankcase explosion.

⊘ **5-20 Directions of Air and Blow-by Flow** In the six-cylinder engine shown in Fig. 5-15, filtered ventilation air from the carburetor air cleaner enters the oil-filler cap. The air passes down into the valve rocker-arm chamber above the cylinder head. From there it goes through the pushrod holes and through the oil drain holes into the crankcase. Then it flows back up to the valve rocker-arm cover and into the intake manifold. A slight vacuum is maintained in the engine crankcase, by a restriction in the oil-filler cap. The PCV valve is located in the line between the rocker-arm cover and the intake manifold (Fig. 5-14).

In a V-8 engine (Fig. 5-12), the filtered air from the carburetor air cleaner enters one valve rocker-arm cover through the sealed oil-filler cap. From there, it flows down through the crankcase and up to the other valve rocker-arm chamber in the other

CONDITIONS AFFECTING EMISSION CONTROL	POSITION THROTTLE	AVAILABLE VACUUM	COMPRESSION PRESSURE	AMOUNT OF BLOWBY FROM ENGINE	POSITION OF PCV VALVE	PATH OF BLOWBY	PERCENT (APPROX.) EFFECTIVE IN CONTROLLING CRANKCASE EMISSION
ENGINE OFF ①	CLOSED	NONE	NONE	NONE	OPEN	NONE	
LOW SPEED (IDLE)	CLOSED	HIGH ②	LOW ③	LOW	CLOSED ④	ALL THROUGH VALVE	100
⑤ LOW SPEED (LOAD)	WIDE OPEN	LOW	HIGH	HIGH	FULLY OPEN	HALF THROUGH VALVE	100
						HALF TO AIR CLEANER	
HIGH SPEED	PARTLY OPEN	MEDIUM	MEDIUM	MEDIUM	PARTLY OPEN	1/4 TO AIR CLEANER	100
						3/4 THROUGH VALVE	

NOTE: 1 IN CASE OF BACKFIRE, DURING CRANKING, THE VACUUM IN THE INTAKE MANIFOLD WILL CAUSE THE PCV VALVE PLUNGER TO MOVE TOWARD THE CRANKCASE; THUS, SEALING THE PASSAGE TO THE CRANKCASE AND PREVENTING A POSSIBLE EXPLOSION.
NOTE: 2 BLOWBY IS AT A MINIMUM WHEN MANIFOLD VACUUM IS HIGH AT IDLE.
NOTE: 3 BLOWBY IS AT A MAXIMUM WHEN COMPRESSION IS HIGH.
NOTE: 4 PCV VALVE IS ON MINIMUM (CLOSED) FLOW POSITION WHEN MANIFOLD VACUUM IS HIGH.
NOTE: 5 FOR LOW SPEED, OPEN THROTTLE POSITION, AS WELL AS VARIOUS THROTTLE PLATE POSITIONS AND LOAD COMBINATIONS. THE MAIN CONCERN OF EMISSION CONTROL IS AT IDLE AND DURING DECELERATION CONDITIONS.

Fig. 5-17. Operating characteristics of the type-4 closed PCV system of crankcase emission control. Notice that the type-4 system controls 100 percent of the crankcase emissions at all engine speeds. (*Ford Motor Company*)

cylinder bank. Then, the ventilating air flows through the PCV valve and into the intake manifold. The arrows in Fig. 5-12 show the flow. The PCV valve may be on or in the carburetor base or intake manifold (Fig. 5-18).

All 1968 and later model cars are equipped with type-4 closed positive crankcase ventilation systems.

⊘ **5-21 Fixed-Orifice System** Most type-1 open systems and type-4 closed systems use a variable orifice or PCV valve. But, as mentioned earlier, some engines are equipped with crankcase emission control systems that use only a fixed orifice, or restriction, to control blow-by flow to the intake manifold. Figure 5-19 shows the fixed-orifice system that is on most Chevrolet Corvairs. No valve is used with these systems. The oil-filler cap may be sealed or open.

Sometimes the air flow into the crankcase is restricted instead of regulated. In these systems, a fixed orifice in the oil-filler cap controls the amount of ventilating air entering the crankcase. As in other type-3 systems, the crankcase vapors flow from the crankcase through a tube to the air cleaner (Fig. 5-11).

⊘ **5-22 Dual-Action Valve** For several years Oldsmobile used the dual-action valve (Fig. 5-20). The valve is quite large, and it mounts on the valve cover. An open oil-filler cap is used with the dual-action valve.

Notice in Fig. 5-20 that the dual-action valve has both a fixed orifice and a check valve. At low speed, manifold vacuum acting through the fixed orifice draws blow-by from the crankcase through the connecting tube and fixed orifice into the intake manifold.

At high speed, blow-by increases, raising the

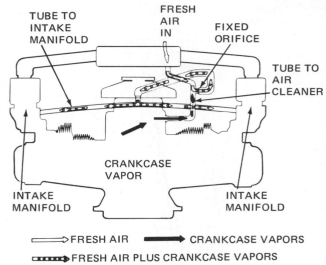

Fig. 5-19. Fixed-orifice system of crankcase emission control, used on most Chevrolet Corvairs. (*AC-Delco Division of General Motors Corporation*)

pressure in the crankcase. As you can see in Fig. 5-20, the blow-by pressure pushes against the underside of the check valve. The top side of the check valve is connected by a tube to the air cleaner. With high engine speed, the air rushing through the air-cleaner inlet causes a slight vacuum in the tube from the valve to the air cleaner. This combination of vacuum above the valve and pressure below the valve causes it to open. Now the excess blow-by flows through the tube into the air cleaner.

⊘ **5-23 Effects of Crankcase Devices** Some motorists, who do not fully understand crankcase devices, are quick to blame them for almost any engine problem. However, crankcase devices, when properly installed and serviced, do more than help reduce air pollution. They provide benefits to the engine and operating economies for the motorist.

A crankcase device keeps the engine free of sludge. This decreases engine wear. By reclaiming the blow-by from the crankcase, gasoline mileage is improved. Thus, installed properly and serviced regularly, crankcase devices promote a cleaner, long-lasting engine that operates with better gasoline economy.

⊘ **5-24 Proper Installation and Maintenance** Correct installation and regular maintenance are essential for proper operation of a crankcase emission control device. The worst thing that a motorist or mechanic can do is to plug up the device, or to allow the system to become plugged from lack of regular maintenance. The blow-by gases must be released, or pressure will build up in the crankcase. This will force oil and blow-by to escape from the engine and may damage the seals and gaskets.

For many years, the California Highway Patrol investigated complaints from motorists about crankcase devices. They reported that, in their investiga-

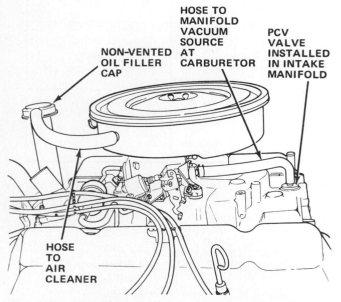

Fig. 5-18. PCV system for a V-8 engine. (*American Motors Corporation*)

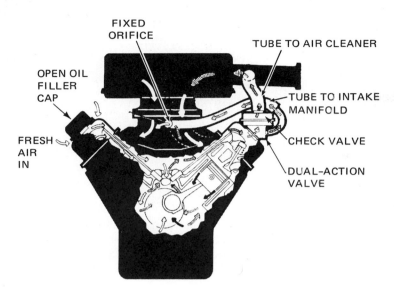

Fig. 5-20. Dual-action valve used for several years by Oldsmobile. (*AC-Delco Division of General Motors Corporation*)

tions, they never found an engine ruined by a properly installed and operating crankcase device. Complaints of a crankcase device causing rough idle or poor performance can usually be traced to improper installation (of a retrofit device) or to improper maintenance. Failure of the motorist to have the engine tuned and the crankcase device serviced as required will also cause these complaints.

Service procedures for crankcase emission control devices are covered in detail in Chap. 14 and in the *Workbook for Automotive Emission Control*, published by the McGraw-Hill Book Company.

CHAPTER 5 CHECKUP

NOTE: Since the following is a chapter review test, you should review the chapter before taking the test.

The study of on-the-car automotive emission control systems begins with this chapter on crankcase emission control devices. Few changes are being made in the design and operation of these crankcase devices. Almost all mechanical, tuneup, or electrical work on the engine requires some knowledge of how these devices are connected. To diagnose customer complaints and troubleshoot engine problems, the skilled mechanic must know how and why crankcase emission control devices operate as they do.

Completing the Sentences The sentences below are incomplete. After each sentence there are several words or phrases, but only one of them correctly completes the sentence. Write each sentence in your notebook, ending it with the word or phrase that completes it correctly.

1. The type-2 valve is controlled by: (*a*) crankcase vacuum, (*b*) crankcase pressure, (*c*) manifold vacuum, (*d*) manifold pressure.

2. The type-3 system has been widely used on: (*a*) American cars, (*b*) American trucks, (*c*) foreign cars, (*d*) tractors.

3. Excessive blow-by flow through the type-3 system causes the intake-manifold mixture to: (*a*) get leaner, (*b*) stay the same, (*c*) overheat the engine, (*d*) get richer.

4. The type-4 combination system takes fresh ventilating air into the crankcase from the: (*a*) intake manifold, (*b*) carburetor, (*c*) air cleaner, (*d*) road-draft tube.

5. The closed PCV system is a combination of type: (*a*) 1 and 3, (*b*) 2 and 3, (*c*) 1 and 2, (*d*) 1 and the road-draft tube.

6. The closed PCV system controls crankcase emissions: (*a*) 25 percent, (*b*) 50 percent, (*c*) 75 percent, (*d*) 100 percent.

7. The closed PCV system is called: (*a*) type 1, (*b*) type 2, (*c*) type 3, (*d*) type 4.

8. The open PCV system is called: (*a*) type 1, (*b*) type 2, (*c*) type 3, (*d*) type 4.

9. The crankcase ventilation system which prevents pressure buildup in the crankcase is: (*a*) a road-draft tube, (*b*) type 1, (*c*) type 4, (*d*) all types.

10. Compared to an engine using conventional crankcase ventilation, crankcase devices should increase: (*a*) oil consumption, (*b*) gasoline mileage, (*c*) atmospheric emissions, (*d*) spark-plug life.

Questions Here are questions that deal with crankcase emission control systems. Remember, this chapter discusses factory-installed crankcase devices, not the add-on type of used-car devices. (They are discussed in detail in Chap. 18.) In your notebook, write the answer to each question in your own words. If you do not know an answer, turn back through the last few pages and restudy the material. Be sure to refer to the illustrations. Study the pictures of each system until you understand the function of each part and the flow of blow-by through the system.

1. What percent of air pollution is caused by the automobile.

2. What was the first source of air pollution from the automobile to be controlled?

3. What causes engine blow-by?

4. What causes water to appear in the crankcase?

5. Why must a crankcase have a ventilation system?

6. How does the road-draft tube work?

7. What is a PCV valve?

8. What is the difference between an open PCV system and a closed PCV system?

9. In the PCV system, what prevents an engine backfire from causing a crankcase explosion?

10. Why must the crankcase ventilating air be filtered?

Definitions In the following, you are asked to define certain terms. Write the definitions in your notebook. This will help you remember them. It will also provide you with a place where you can quickly locate the meanings, when you need them. If you cannot remember the meanings of the terms, look them up in the chapter you have just studied, or in the glossary at the back of the book.

1. What are crankcase emissions?

2. Define "crankcase ventilation."

3. What is crankcase ventilating air?

4. What is a dual-action valve?

5. What is manifold vacuum?

6. What is a variable-orifice valve?

7. Define "PCV system."

8. What is an open oil-filler cap?

9. Define "fixed orifice."

10. What is a closed PCV system?

SUGGESTIONS FOR FURTHER STUDY

If you would like to learn more about crankcase emission controls, borrow Chevrolet, Chrysler, and Ford service manuals from your instructor. Study the section in each on crankcase emission control systems. The manufacturers' manuals cover crankcase devices for each of their models of cars. Then, locate several cars and trucks which have crankcase emission controls. Examine each engine closely, noting the appearance and location of each hose and connection that is part of the crankcase emission control system.

chapter 6

EVAPORATIVE CONTROL SYSTEMS

In this chapter, we look at the various types of evaporative emission controls, also called fuel-vapor recovery systems, used on modern automotive vehicles. Recall that, in Chap. 3, we explained the reasons why a fuel-vapor recovery system is needed. Gasoline vapor escapes from the fuel tank and carburetor if there is no such system. In this chapter, we review these reasons and then describe the various systems in detail.

⊘ **6-1 Need for a Vapor-Recovery System** Both the fuel tank and the carburetor can lose gasoline vapor if the vehicle has no control system. The fuel tank "breathes" as temperature changes. That is, as the tank heats up, the air inside it expands. Some air is forced out through the tank vent tube or through the vent in the tank cap. This air is loaded with gasoline vapor. Then, when the tank cools, the air inside it contracts. Air enters the tank from outside. This breathing of the tank causes a loss of gasoline. The higher the tank temperature goes (for example, when the car is parked in the sun), the more gasoline is lost.

The carburetor can also lose gasoline by evaporation. The carburetor float bowl is full whenever the engine is running. When the engine stops, engine heat evaporates some or all of the gasoline stored in the float bowl. Without a vapor-recovery system, this gasoline vapor would escape into the atmosphere.

A vapor-recovery system captures these gaso-line vapors and prevents them from escaping into the air. It thus helps to reduce atmospheric pollution. All modern cars are equipped with vapor-recovery systems. They are called by various names: ECS (evaporation control system), EEC (evaporation emission control), VVR (vehicle vapor recovery), and VSS (vapor saver system) are a few of the names used. All work in the same general way.

⊘ **6-2 Vapor-Recovery Systems** Figures 6-1 and 6-2 show typical vapor-recovery systems. The canister is filled with activated charcoal or carbon. The purpose of this charcoal is to trap gasoline vapor, as follows. Just after the engine is shut off, heat enters the carburetor. This causes gasoline remaining in the carburetor float bowl to vaporize. This vapor passes through a tube, or pipe, to the top of the canister. As it moves down through the canister, the vapor is adsorbed by the charcoal particles. (They work somewhat like the charcoal filters on cigarettes,

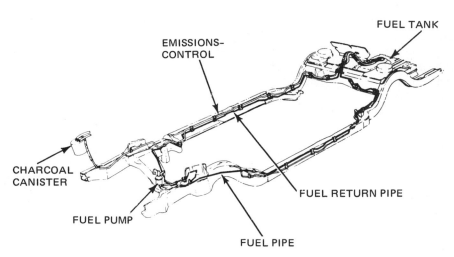

Fig. 6-1. Fuel and emission-control pipes and canister location. (*Pontiac Motor Division of General Motors Corporation*)

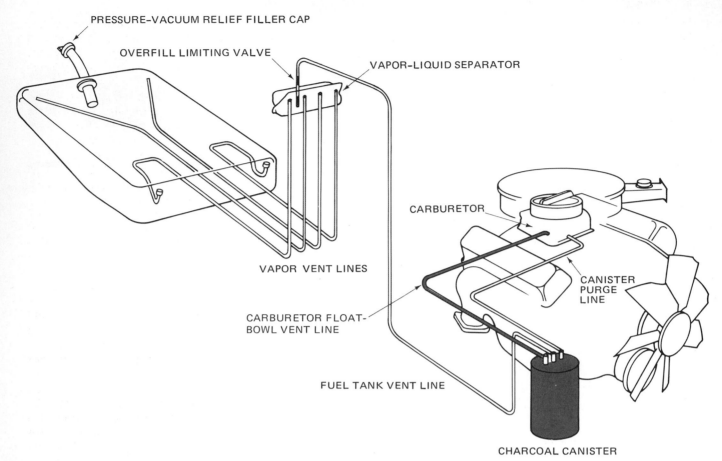

Fig. 6-2. Vapor recovery system. Note the vent line between the carburetor float bowl and the canister. (*Chrysler Corporation*)

which trap particles of tar and other substances to remove them from the smoke.)

Many carburetors have a special vent which is connected by a tube to the charcoal canister (Fig. 6-3). The vent and tube carry the float-bowl vapor directly to the canister. Note that the carburetor shown in Fig. 6-3 has a pressure-relief valve. The purpose of this valve is to prevent gasoline vapors from leaving the float bowl during normal engine operation. However, when the engine is stopped and the gasoline begins to vaporize, the pressure of the vapor lifts the valve. This allows the vapor to flow to the charcoal canister. Many systems have a separate tube to carry vapor from the carburetor float bowl to the canister, as in Figs. 6-2 and 6-3. In other systems, the single purge line from the canister to the carburetor carries the float-bowl vapors to the canister.

At the same time, vapor-laden air from the fuel tank is carried to the canister by a special emission-control pipe or tube (Fig. 6-1). As the air passes down through the canister, the gasoline vapor is trapped by the charcoal particles. The air exits from the bottom of the canister, leaving the gasoline vapor (HC or hydrocarbon vapor) behind. There is a filter at the bottom of the canister. The filter comes into action during the *purge* phase of operation. This occurs when the engine is started. Now, intake-manifold vacuum draws fresh air up through the canis-

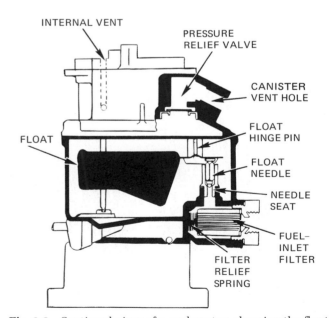

Fig. 6-3. Sectional view of a carburetor, showing the float system. Note the two vents, one internal and the other to the charcoal canister. (*Chevrolet Motor Division of General Motors Corporation*)

ter. The fresh air removes, or purges, the gasoline vapor from the canister. It takes the HC through the canister purge line (Fig. 6-2) to a connection at the carburetor. This HC passes into the stream of air-fuel mixture going into the engine and is burned along with the mixture. There is more about the charcoal canister in ⊘ 6-4.

⊘ **6-3 Fuel-Return Line** Note that, in Fig. 6-1, there is a fuel-return pipe or line that connects the fuel pump and the fuel tank. This fuel-return line is connected to the pressure side of the fuel pump. Figure 6-4 is a sectional view of a fuel pump. The vapor- (or fuel-) return connector is shown to the lower left. If any vapor forms in the fuel pump, it is sent back to the fuel tank through the fuel- or vapor-return line.

To understand why vapor can form in the fuel pump, first note that the fuel pump alternately produces vacuum and pressure. During the vacuum phase, the rocker arm is pulling the pump diaphragm up. This vacuum causes atmospheric pressure at the fuel tank to push gasoline into the fuel pump. Then, when the rocker arm releases the diaphragm, the diaphragm spring pushes the diaphragm down, producing pressure on the gasoline in the pump. This pressure pushes gasoline through the outlet and connecting tube into the carburetor float bowl.

It is during the vacuum phase of the operation that vapor can form. During this phase, the boiling (or vaporizing) temperature of the fuel goes down. The lower the pressure (that is, the greater the vacuum), the lower the temperature at which any liquid vaporizes. For example, water boils at 212°F [100°C] at the sea-level atmospheric pressure of 14.7 psi [1.078 kg/cm^2]. But at 16,000 ft [4,876.8 m] above sea level, where the pressure is around 7 psi [0.492 kg/cm^2], water boils at 185°F [85°C].

The combination of high under-the-hood temperatures and partial vacuum in the fuel pump can cause some of the fuel to vaporize. This causes vapor lock, a condition that prevents normal delivery of fuel to the carburetor. With vapor lock, the vapor just expands and contracts as the fuel-pump pressure changes. There is no liquid pressure to send gasoline to the float bowl, and the engine stalls.

In modern engines, the under-hood temperatures are high. This is particularly true on cars with air conditioners. The air conditioner gives off its heat under the hood. Also, when the engine is idling, the engine cooling system is not very efficient. Thus, vapor lock is more likely to occur during long periods of idling, as in stop-and-start traffic.

As mentioned, the vapor-return line is connected to a special outlet in the fuel pump. It carries any vapor that has formed back to the fuel tank. The vapor condenses into liquid gasoline in the cooler fuel tank. In addition, extra gasoline can be pumped through the fuel pump and then be returned to the fuel tank through the vapor-return line. This excess fuel, in constant circulation, helps keep the fuel pump cool. It thus reduces the tendency for vapor to form. Note that some manufacturers call the line a *fuel-return line,* rather than a vapor-return line, for this reason (Fig. 6-1).

Some cars have a vapor separator connected between the fuel pump and the carburetor (Fig. 6-5). It consists of a sealed can, a filter screen, an inlet and an outlet fitting, and a metered orifice, or outlet, for the return line to the fuel tank. Any fuel vapor that the fuel pump produces enters the vapor separator (as bubbles) along with the fuel. These bubbles rise to the top of the vapor separator. The vapor is then forced, by fuel-pump pressure, to pass through the fuel-return line and back to the fuel tank. There, it condenses into liquid gasoline.

⊘ **6-4 Charcoal Canister** A charcoal canister is shown in Fig. 6-6. This is one of several shapes used for canisters. Figure 6-7 shows a canister in sectional view. The arrows show the flow of air and gasoline vapor. When the engine is turned off, vapor from the fuel tank and carburetor float bowl flows into the canister (Fig. 6-7). The air passes down through the charcoal particles, as shown, and leaves the canister without the gasoline vapor.

Then, when the engine is started, intake-manifold vacuum draws air up through the canister and into the carburetor. This air cleans the gasoline vapor out of the canister (Fig. 6-8).

The charcoal canister shown in Figs. 6-7 and 6-8 is for a V-8 engine. Some canisters for some six-cylinder engines and some V-8 engines have an extra connection and a restrictive valve, also known as a *purge valve.* Figure 6-9 is a sectional view of a canister for a six-cylinder engine. Figure 6-10 is a sectional view of a purge valve. This valve limits the flow of vapor and air to the carburetor during idling. But it allows full flow of vapor and air from the canister during part-throttle and full-throttle operation. A six-cylinder engine can idle very roughly and

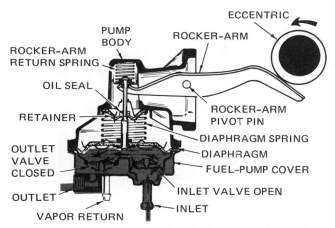

Fig. 6-4. Sectional view of a fuel pump. The rocking motion of the rocker arm moves the diaphragm up and down. This pumping action draws fuel from the fuel tank and sends it to the carburetor float bowl. The vapor-return connector at the lower left is connected to the fuel tank through the vapor-return line.

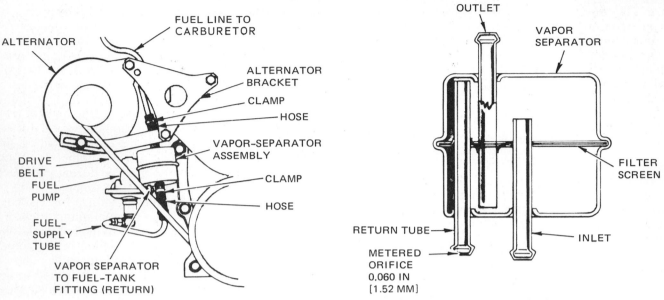

Fig. 6-5. Left, location of the vapor separator, in the line between the fuel pump and the carburetor. Right, enlarged sectional view of the fuel-vapor separator. (*Chrysler Corporation*)

even stall if full vapor-air flow occurs during idling. The valve keeps this from occurring. At higher speeds, however, full vapor-air flow can be tolerated.

The valve is operated by a vacuum signal from a drilled hole in the carburetor air horn. This hole is located just below the throttle valve when the throttle is closed. With the throttle closed and the engine idling, high vacuum develops below the throttle. This causes the purge valve to limit the vapor-air

flow. But when the throttle opens, the vacuum is reduced; this allows the purge valve to open so that the vapor-air flow can increase. Thus, during part-throttle and full-throttle operation, the canister is purged of gasoline vapor.

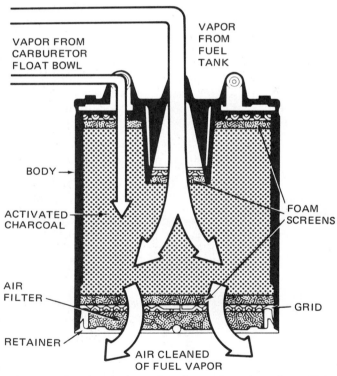

Fig. 6-7. Sectional view of a charcoal canister for a V-8 engine. The arrows show the flow of vapor from the carburetor float bowl and fuel tank down through the charcoal particles. This occurs after the engine has been turned off. (*Oldsmobile Division of General Motors Corporation*)

Fig. 6-6. Charcoal canister.

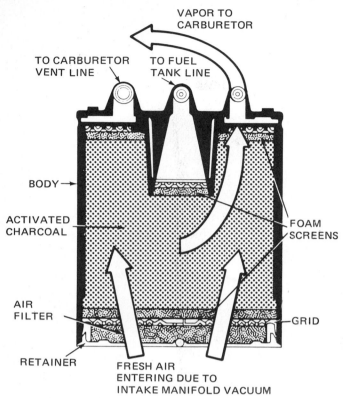

VAPOR TO
CARBURETOR

TO CARBURETOR
VENT LINE

TO FUEL
TANK LINE

BODY

ACTIVATED
CHARCOAL

FOAM
SCREENS

AIR
FILTER

RETAINER

GRID

FRESH AIR
ENTERING DUE TO
INTAKE MANIFOLD VACUUM

Fig. 6-8. Sectional view of a charcoal canister for a V-8 engine. The arrows show the flow of purging air through the canister after the engine has been started. (*Oldsmobile Division of General Motors Corporation*)

On some cars, the purge line from the canister is connected to the air cleaner, as shown in Fig. 6-11. The system operates in the manner already described.

⊘ **6-5 Separating Vapor from Liquid** The fuel tank must have a means of separating the gasoline vapor from the liquid gasoline. Otherwise, liquid gasoline could flow to the canister and then out into the atmosphere. One system uses a standpipe assembly as shown in Figs. 6-12 and 6-13. Figure 6-14 is a

VAPOR TO PCV VALVE
VACUUM SIGNAL
COVER
DIAPHRAGM
SPRING RETAINER
SPRING
RESTRICTION
BODY COVER
FILTER
RESTRICTION
FILTER
CHARCOAL
BODY
FILTER
GRID
FILTER
RETAINER
AIR UNDER VACUUM

VAPOR FROM
FUEL TANK

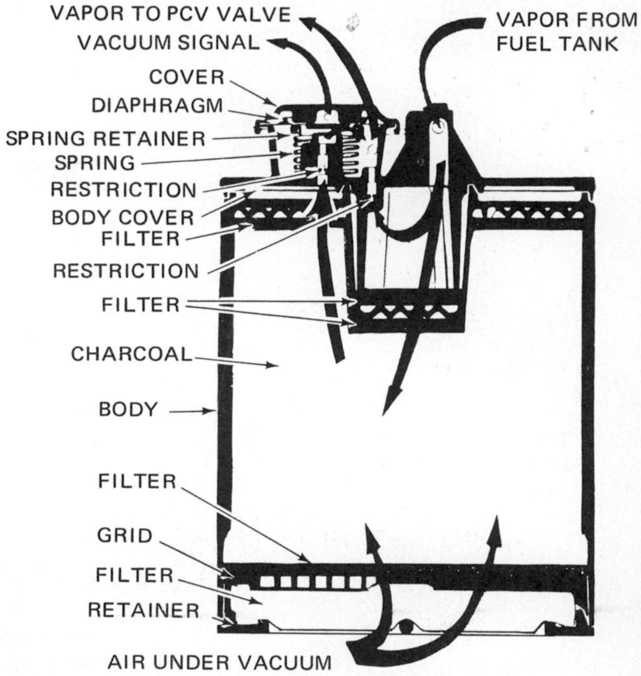

Fig. 6-9. Sectional view of a charcoal canister for a six-cylinder engine. (*Oldsmobile Division of General Motors Corporation*)

cutaway view of a standpipe assembly. It contains a series of pipes with openings at the top. Three of these pipes are connected to the center and the two sides of the fuel tank (Figs. 6-13 and 6-15). With this system, at least one of the vents is always above the fuel level, regardless of the tilt of the car. Thus, air and fuel vapor can always pass up into the standpipe and through the vent line to the canister.

Figure 6-11 shows a variation of the standpipe system. Here, a vapor-liquid separator is positioned above the fuel tank. Three vapor vent lines connect the separator to the corners of the fuel tank. A still different vapor-liquid separating arrangement is shown in Fig. 6-16. In this system, a liquid check valve is used. It is connected by tubes to the two ends of the fuel tank. Figure 6-17 is a sectional view

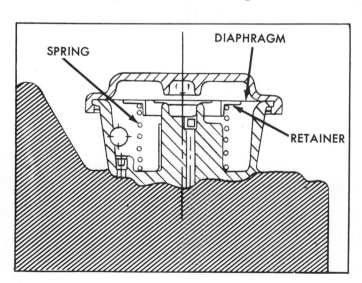

SPRING

DIAPHRAGM

RETAINER

Fig. 6-10. Sectional view of a purge valve for a canister used with a six-cylinder engine. (*Chevrolet Motor Division of General Motors Corporation*)

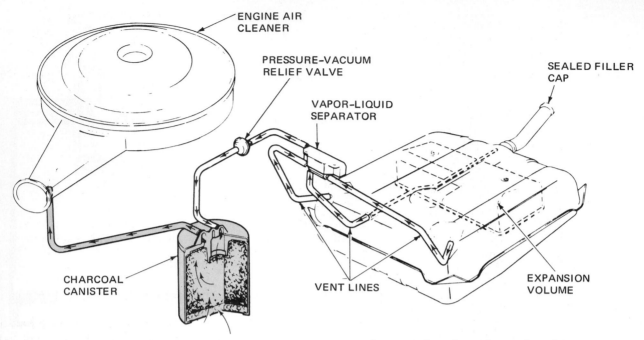

Fig. 6-11. Vapor-recovery system. In this system, the purge line from the canister is connected to the air-cleaner snorkel. (*Buick Motor Division of General Motors Corporation*)

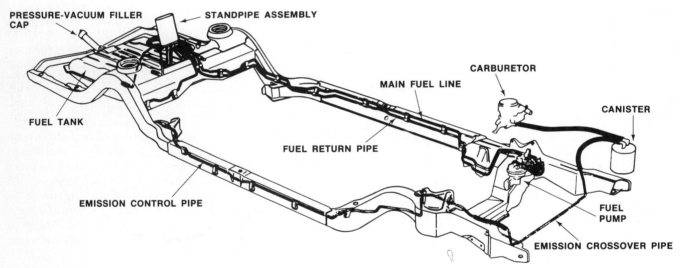

Fig. 6-12. Vapor-recovery system using a standpipe assembly.

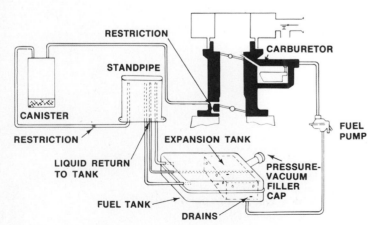

Fig. 6-13. Schematic view of a vapor-recovery system.

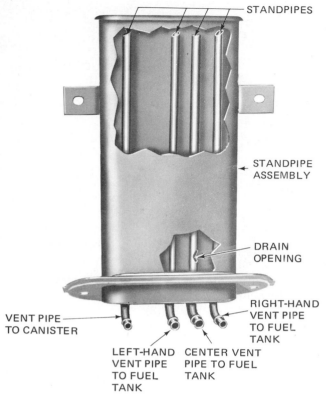

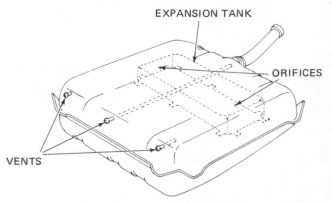

Fig. 6-15. Fuel tank used with a vapor-recovery system. The two side vents are short, but the center vent goes all the way to the rear of the tank. Note the expansion tank, which is inside the fuel tank. (*Pontiac Motor Division of General Motors Corporation*)

Fig. 6-14. Cutaway view of a standpipe assembly. (*Oldsmobile Division of General Motors Corporation*)

of the check valve. If liquid gasoline enters the valve, the float rises and forces the needle upward. This closes off the vent line to the charcoal canister, and thereby prevents liquid gasoline from flowing to the canister. In some models, the liquid check valve

is mounted on the fuel tank (Fig. 6-18). It works in the same manner.

Another type of vapor separator is shown in Fig. 6-19. It is filled with filter material that will pass vapor but not liquid gasoline. The vapor separator is mounted at the top center of the tank. This minimizes the chance of liquid gasoline getting directly to the separator.

Some systems use a domed fuel tank (Fig. 6-20). The dome forms the high point of the tank, and the emission-control pipe is connected at this point.

⊘ **6-6 Sealed Fuel Tank** Early fuel tanks had a vent pipe or a vent in the fuel-tank cap. This allowed the tank to breathe, as previously noted. It also allowed the escape of gasoline vapor from the tank. Modern

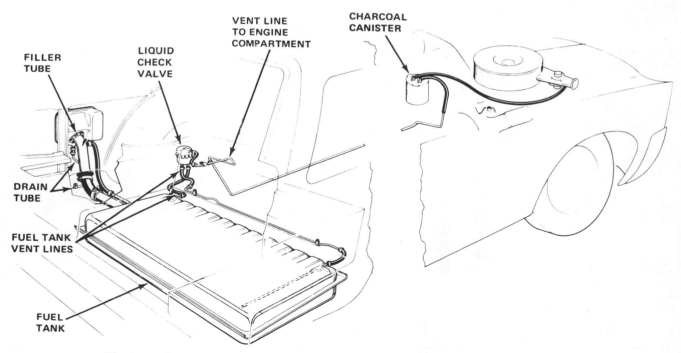

Fig. 6-16. Vapor-recovery system using a liquid check valve. (*American Motors Corporation*)

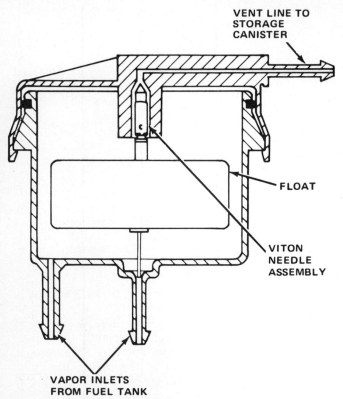

Fig. 6-17. Sectional view of a liquid check valve. (American Motors Corporation)

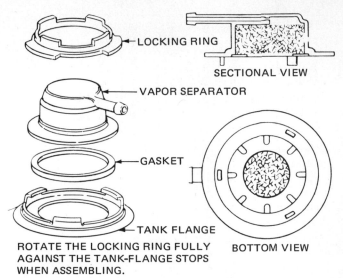

ROTATE THE LOCKING RING FULLY AGAINST THE TANK-FLANGE STOPS WHEN ASSEMBLING.

Fig. 6-19. Vapor separator using filter material. (Ford Motor Company)

automobiles, with vapor recovery systems, use a sealed fuel tank with a special cap. Figure 6-21 is a cutaway view of the cap. It has two valves, a vacuum valve and a pressure valve. The pressure valve opens if too much pressure develops in the tank. The vacuum valve opens to admit air as fuel is withdrawn, so that a vacuum does not develop in the tank. Either vacuum or pressure in the tank could damage it.

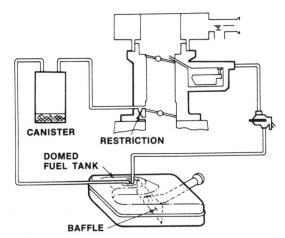

Fig. 6-20. Vapor-recovery system using a domed fuel tank. (Pontiac Motor Division of General Motors Corporation)

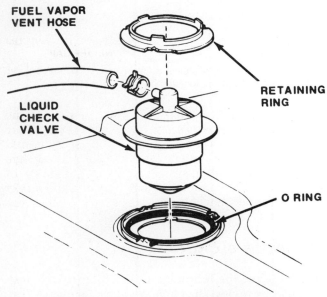

Fig. 6-18. On some cars, the liquid check valve is mounted on top of the fuel tank. (American Motors Corporation)

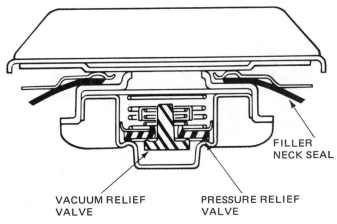

Fig. 6-21. Cutaway view of a fuel-tank cap for the tank used with a vapor-recovery system. (Ford Motor Company)

⊘ **6-7 Expansion Tank** You probably noticed, in Figs. 6-11, 6-13, and 6-15, that some fuel tanks have expansion tanks. The expansion tank is needed when there is a rise in fuel temperature after the fuel tank has been filled. As the fuel temperature goes up, the fuel expands. The expansion tank holds the overflow of fuel.

⊘ **6-8 Carburetor Insulator** Some carburetors use insulators (Fig. 6-22) to reduce the heat flow from the engine to the carburetor. The insulator is placed between the carburetor and the intake manifold. It forms a heat barrier between them. This reduces fuel evaporation from the float bowl after the engine has been turned off. Another arrangement uses an aluminum heat-dissipating plate which sticks out, as shown in Fig. 6-23.

⊘ **6-9 Vapor Storage in Crankcase** Some Chrysler Corporation cars and some foreign cars make use of the crankcase to store gasoline vapors (Fig. 6-24). When the engine is stopped, gasoline vapors from the vapor separator at the fuel tank flow to the crankcase air cleaner. From there, they flow down into the crankcase. At the same time, fuel vapors

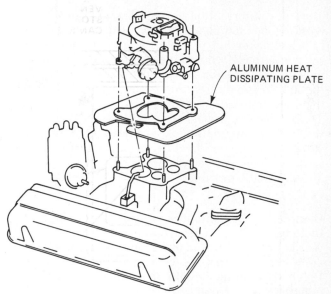

Fig. 6-23. Insulator and aluminum heat-dissipating plate between the carburetor and intake manifold, to reduce heat flow to the carburetor.

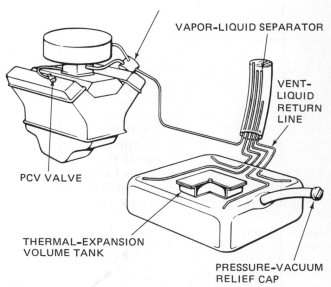

Fig. 6-24. Vapor-recovery system using the crankcase for fuel-vapor storage. (*Chrysler Corporation*)

from the carburetor float bowl flow down into the crankcase. The vapors are two to four times as heavy as air. Thus, they sink to the bottom of the crankcase. Then, when the engine is started, the positive crankcase ventilating system clears the crankcase of the vapors. The vapors are carried up into the intake manifold and then into the engine, where they are burned.

CHAPTER 6 CHECKUP

NOTE: Since the following is a chapter review test, you should review the chapter before taking the test.

You have made real progress in your study of automotive emission controls. Soon, you will be able

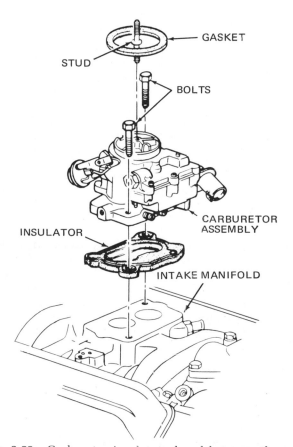

Fig. 6-22. Carburetor insulator placed between the carburetor and the intake manifold. The insulator blocks the travel of heat to the carburetor. It thus reduces evaporation of fuel from the float bowl. (*Chevrolet Motor Division of General Motors Corporation*)

to use the information you are learning in the shop, working on actual automotive smog devices. The following checkup will help you check yourself, to see how well you understand the information needed in your shop work. Turn back into the chapter and do some rereading if you are not sure about the answer to any question.

Where you are asked to write something down, write it in your notebook. By now, your notebook should have a good deal of valuable information in it. If you have not been keeping a notebook, this is a good time to start one.

Completing the Sentences The sentences below are incomplete. After each sentence there are several words or phrases, but only one of them correctly completes the sentence. Write each sentence in your notebook, ending it with the word or phrase that completes it correctly.

1. When the engine stops, some gasoline evaporates from the float bowl because of: (a) the open PCV valve, (b) engine heat, (c) high humidity, (d) the closed choke valve.
2. In the vapor-recovery system, the canister is filled with: (a) pleated paper, (b) air, (c) activated charcoal, (d) a catalyst.
3. Fresh air passing through the canister after the engine starts is called: (a) purge air, (b) stale air, (c) fresh air, (d) hot air.
4. When vapor in the pump prevents normal delivery of fuel, the condition is known as: (a) evaporative control, (b) vapor recovery, (c) fuel return, (d) vapor lock.
5. The vapor-return line is connected to the fuel pump and to the: (a) carburetor, (b) fuel tank, (c) fuel filter, (d) charcoal canister.
6. When the engine is off, vapor from the fuel tank and carburetor flows into the: (a) carburetor, (b) fuel tank, (c) fuel filter, (d) charcoal canister.
7. A purge valve is used on the canister for: (a) V-8 engines, (b) all engines, (c) rotary engines, (d) six-cylinder engines.
8. To separate gasoline vapor from liquid gasoline, evaporative control systems include a: (a) vapor-liquid separator, (b) sealed tank cap, (c) fuel pump, (d) fuel filter.
9. The two valves in the cap for a sealed fuel tank are the: (a) PCV valve and check valve, (b) vacuum valve and PCV valve, (c) pressure valve and check valve, (d) pressure valve and vacuum valve.
10. The purpose of the carburetor insulator is to prevent the carburetor from being affected by: (a) engine heat, (b) intake-manifold vacuum, (c) the expansion tank, (d) exhaust pollutants.

Correcting Lists The purpose of this exercise is to help you spot an unrelated item in a list. For example, check through the list "head, oil pump, water pump, main-bearing caps, differential housing, clutch housing." The only part that is not attached to

the cylinder block is the differential housing. Therefore, that item does not belong in the list. In each of the following lists, there is one unrelated item. Write each list in your notebook, but do not write the item that does not belong.

1. Parts in the evaporative control system include the fuel tank, charcoal canister, carburetor, and fuel filter.
2. Names used for the vapor-recovery system include ECS (evaporation control system), PCV (positive crankcase ventilation), EEC (evaporation emission control), and VVR (vehicle vapor recovery).
3. Lines connected to the charcoal canister include the fuel-tank vent line, fuel-bowl vent line, fuel line, and canister purge line.
4. Parts of a charcoal canister for a six-cylinder engine include a purge valve, activated charcoal, canister body, air filter, and standpipe assembly.
5. Lines connected to the fuel pump include the fuel-pump inlet line, fuel-pump outlet line, fuel-return line, and emission-control pipe.

Questions Write each of the following questions, and then the answer, in your notebook. If you have trouble recalling the answer to a question, turn back to the pages that cover the material and study them again.

1. What is the purpose of the evaporative control system?
2. Explain how a fuel tank breathes.
3. How does the charcoal canister work?
4. Trace the flow of fuel vapor from the fuel tank into the intake manifold.
5. How does a crankcase storage system work?
6. Why is a vapor-liquid separator necessary?
7. What helps control fuel-pump vapor lock?
8. Explain how the canister is purged.
9. How does the standpipe assembly work?
10. What is the purpose of the expansion tank in the fuel tank?

Definitions In the following, you are asked for the definitions of some words and phrases. Write them in your notebook. The act of writing the definitions does two things: It tests your knowledge, and it helps fix the information more firmly in your mind. Turn back into the chapter if you are not sure of a definition, or look it up in the glossary at the back of the book.

1. What is a vapor-recovery system?
2. Define "charcoal canister."
3. Define "adsorb."
4. What is vapor lock?
5. Define "purge."
6. What is a vapor-return pipe?
7. What is an emission-control pipe?
8. What is a fuel pipe?
9. Define "purge valve."
10. What is a carburetor insulator?

SUGGESTIONS FOR FURTHER STUDY

One of the best ways to learn more about evaporative control systems is to inspect several different makes of late-model cars. These vehicles will be equipped with evaporative control systems.

Look under the hood, and determine if the system is a canister or crankcase storage system. Locate and identify the canister, and trace the lines connected to it. Remove and inspect the fuel-tank cap. If possible, raise the car on a shop hoist, and identify and trace the lines running under the car from the engine compartment to the fuel tank. You will find the illustrations in this chapter, and in the manufacturer's service manual, helpful in identifying the lines and connections.

In your school automotive shop, you may be able to handle and study various parts of evaporative control systems. Your school shop may also have a display of cutaway and disassembled canisters, valves, and other parts. Studying these parts and displays will help you understand the construction and operation of evaporative control systems and their components.

PART THREE

CONTROLLING EXHAUST EMISSIONS

Part Three of *Automotive Emission Control* discusses the fourth source of automotive emissions—the tail pipe. That is, it discusses the pollutants that come from the exhaust system of the vehicle. As explained previously, three of the exhaust pollutants for which state and federal emission levels have been set are unburned gasoline (HC), carbon monoxide (CO), and nitrogen oxides (NO_x). In addition, there are sulfur oxides and lead (if the engine burns gasoline with lead in it). Part Three of the book explains the various engineering steps that have been taken, and the control devices that are installed on automotive vehicles, to reduce the pollutants in the exhaust. That is, we discuss the total program for cleaning up the exhaust gas:

1. Controlling the air-fuel mixture
2. Controlling combustion
3. Treating the exhaust gases

Part Three contains three chapters.

chapter 7

CONTROLLING THE AIR-FUEL MIXTURE

This chapter discusses the methods and devices used to control the air-fuel mixture as it passes through the carburetor and intake manifold on its way to the engine cylinders. Basically, this control comes from modifications that have been made to the carburetor so it delivers a leaner air-fuel mixture and produces a quicker choke action. In addition, devices have been added to shorten the time when the carburetor is delivering a cold air-fuel mixture to the engine. The emission of HC and CO is highest during the first few minutes of operation, after a cold engine is started. The chapter also discusses carburetor fundamentals. This establishes the need for, and the effects of, the various modifications and devices.

⊘ 7-1 Operating Modes Producing High Pollution

Two special operating modes that produce high amounts of pollutants in the exhaust have been studied intensively. These are choke operation immediately after starting a cold engine, and ignition-distributor vacuum advance during operation in low gear. As we shall explain later, a cold engine needs a very rich air-fuel mixture—that is, a mixture with a high proportion of fuel. Gasoline is slow to vaporize when cold. Therefore, extra amounts of gasoline must be added to the air-fuel mixture, to ensure that enough will evaporate to form a combustible mixture. This means that, during the cold-operating mode, the amounts of HC and CO in the exhaust gas are high.

Devices have been added to engines and fuel systems to shorten the cold-mixture time. That is, they shorten the time when the fuel system is delivering cold air-fuel mixture to the engine.

During operation in lower gears with a partly open throttle, the ignition-distributor vacuum-advance mechanism operates. This can produce another type of pollutant in excessive amounts—nitrogen oxides or NO_x. NO_x forms as a result of high temperature. The longer the high temperature exists, the more NO_x forms. Recall from our discussion of the ignition system (⊘ 2-14) that the vacuum-advance mechanism advances the spark at part throttle, to give the air-fuel mixture a longer time to burn. If, meantime, the engine is running rather slowly (as it would be when accelerating in lower gears), the mixture has a still longer time to burn. This allows the high temperatures more time to convert the nitrogen and oxygen in the air into nitrogen oxides. For this reason, devices have been added that prevent vacuum advance in the lower gears.

We look into these modifications and devices in later sections.

⊘ 7-2 Leaner Air-Fuel Mixture

If the air-fuel mixture is too lean, it will not ignite. That is, if there is not enough gasoline vapor in the air-fuel mixture, the mixture will not ignite and burn. Or, if the mixture does ignite, it will burn poorly. Even so, engineers have altered the design of carburetors in recent years so they supply a leaner mixture. It is about as lean as it can be and still burn without causing operating difficulties. The electronic ignition systems (and especially the high-energy system) described in ⊘ 2-15 to 2-18 supply a stronger and longer-lasting spark that helps ignite leaner mixtures.

The purpose of leaning out the mixture is to reduce the amounts of HC and CO in the exhaust gases. At one time, carburetors could be adjusted to vary the mixture richness. Automotive technicians tended to set the carburetors on the rich side, since this produced a smooth-running engine. It also produced more HC and CO in the exhaust. However, modern carburetors are not adjustable (except for limited adjustments to idle mixture and idle speed).[1] The mixture-richness factor is built into the carburetor, for all settings except idle.

Carburetors have chokes (⊘ 7-30) which increase the richness of the fuel mixture temporarily,

---

[1] Carburetors do have other adjustments, but these adjustments do not primarily affect the mixture richness.

to start a cold engine. Chokes have been refined on modern cars so they function quickly. This reduces the time when the engine receives a rich mixture and, thus, gives off large amounts of HC and CO in the exhaust gases.

⊘ 7-3 Carburetor Fundamentals

Let us look, for a moment, at the carburetor. This will help you understand the various devices that have been added or altered to control the mixture richness more exactly. Carburetors mix fuel with air to produce a combustible mixture. Carburetors must provide a rich mixture (with a high percentage of fuel) for starting, accelerating, and high-speed performance. The mixture must be leaner (less rich) for intermediate speeds with a warm engine. The carburetor has several systems that provide mixtures of varying richness. They include the:

1. Float system
2. Idle system
3. Main metering system
4. Power system
5. Accelerator-pump system
6. Choke system

We shall describe each of these. First, however, we should review the actions that cause the carburetor to mix fuel with air and turn this into a combustible mixture.

⊘ 7-4 Vaporization

When a liquid changes to a vapor, it is said to vaporize, or evaporate. Water placed in an open pan will evaporate. The shallower the pan, the faster the water evaporates. For example, a glass full of water takes a long time to evaporate. But if the same amount of water is put into a shallow pan, it evaporates much more rapidly (Fig. 7-1).

⊘ 7-5 Atomization

If a liquid is sprayed into air, it evaporates very quickly. Spraying the liquid turns it into many tiny drops or droplets. Each droplet is exposed to air on all sides, so it evaporates rapidly. The carburetor sprays liquid gasoline into the air passing through it on its way to the engine. The liquid gasoline turns to vapor, or vaporizes, almost instantly under most conditions.

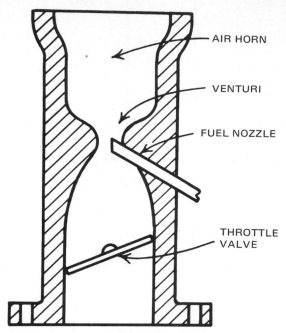

Fig. 7-2. Simple carburetor consisting of an air horn, a fuel nozzle, and a throttle valve.

⊘ 7-6 The Basic Carburetor

We could make a simple carburetor from a round cylinder with a constricted section, a fuel nozzle, and a round disk, or valve (Fig. 7-2). The round cylinder is called the *air horn;* the constricted section, the *venturi;* and the valve, the *throttle valve.* The throttle valve can be tilted more or less to open or close the air horn (Fig. 7-3). When it is in the horizontal position, it shuts off, or *throttles,* the airflow through the air horn. When the throttle is turned away from this position, air can flow through the air horn. As it flows through, it picks up a charge of gasoline.

Fig. 7-3. Throttle valve in the air horn of a carburetor. When the throttle is closed, as shown, little air can pass through. But when the throttle is opened, as shown dashed, there is little throttling effect.

Fig. 7-1. Water evaporates from the shallow pan faster than from the glass. The greater the area exposed to the air, the faster the evaporation.

⊘ **7-7 Venturi Effect** As air flows through the constriction, or venturi, a partial vacuum develops in the venturi. This vacuum causes the fuel nozzle to deliver a spray of gasoline to the air passing through. The venturi effect can be demonstrated with the setup shown in Fig. 7-4. Here, three dishes of mercury are connected by tubes to an air horn with a venturi. The greater the vacuum, the higher the mercury is pushed up in the tube by atmospheric pressure. Note that the greatest vacuum is right at the venturi.

The venturi produces another effect. The faster the air flows through it, the greater the vacuum. And the greater the vacuum in the carburetor venturi, the more gasoline is sprayed into the air. This is important, because it provides a fairly consistent ratio of fuel to air through a wide range of air speeds. And airspeed is directly related to engine speed. That is, as the throttle is opened wide, more air flows through, picking up more fuel. This increased amount of air-fuel mixture, flowing to the engine, causes the engine to pick up speed and produce more power.

⊘ **7-8 Fuel-Nozzle Action** The fuel nozzle is located in the center of the venturi, just where the maximum vacuum occurs. The other end of the fuel nozzle is in a fuel reservoir (the float bowl), as shown in Fig. 7-5. Atmospheric pressure pushes on the fuel through a vent in the float-bowl cover, as shown. When there is a vacuum at the upper end of the fuel nozzle, fuel is pushed up the fuel nozzle and out into the passing airstream. It enters the airstream as tiny droplets, and quickly turns to vapor. The more air flowing through, the greater the vacuum and the more fuel is delivered.

⊘ **7-9 Air Cleaner** A great deal of air passes through an engine when it is operating. As already mentioned, the fuel is mixed with air in the carbu-

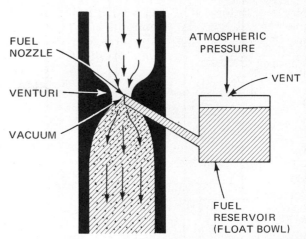

Fig. 7-5. The venturi, or constriction, causes a vacuum to develop in the airstream just below the constriction. Then atmospheric pressure pushes fuel up and out the fuel nozzle.

retor. The mixture passes into the engine cylinders, where it is ignited and burns. During normal engine operation, the carburetor supplies a mixture ratio of about 15:1. That is about 15 lb [6.804 kg] of air for 1 lb [0.454 kg] of gasoline. Put another way, 1 gal [3.785 liters] of gasoline requires as much as 1,200 ft³ [33.98 m³] of air for normal combustion in the engine. As much as 100,000 ft³ [2831.7 m³] of air may pass through the engine every 1,000 car miles [1,609.3 km].

This is a great volume of air, and it is likely to contain large quantities of floating dust and grit. This dirt and grit could cause serious damage to the engine parts if it entered the cylinders. Therefore, an air cleaner is used to filter such particles out of the air entering the carburetor. The air cleaner is mounted on the atmospheric side of the carburetor air horn. It consists of a large drum. The upper part of the drum contains a ring of nonflammable filter material such as fine-mesh threads or ribbon, special filter paper, cellulose fiber, or polyurethane. The air must pass through the filter material, which filters out the dust particles. Figures 7-6 and 7-7 show air cleaners.

Air cleaners on modern automobiles have thermostatic devices that are part of a heated-air system. This is a system that helps vaporize the fuel in the air-fuel mixture during the cold-engine operating mode (⊘ 7-34).

⊘ **7-10 Throttle-Valve Action** The throttle valve can be tilted in the air horn to allow more or less air to flow through (Fig. 7-3). When it is tilted to allow more air to flow, larger amounts of air-fuel mixture are delivered to the engine. The engine develops more power and tends to run faster. But if the throttle valve is tilted to throttle off most of the air, then only small amounts of air-fuel mixture are delivered. The engine produces less power and tends to slow down. The throttle valve is linked to an accelerator

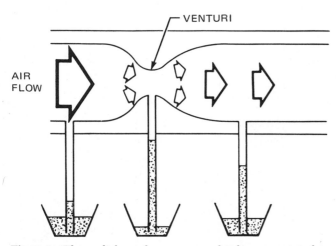

Fig. 7-4. Three dishes of mercury and tubes connected to an air horn. Differences in vacuum are shown by the distances the mercury rises in the tubes. The venturi has the highest vacuum.

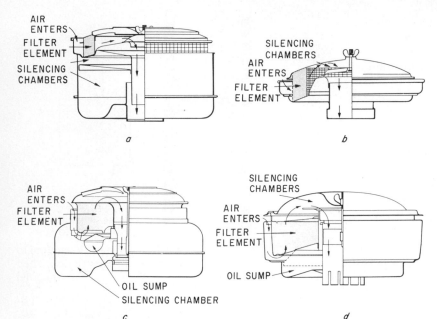

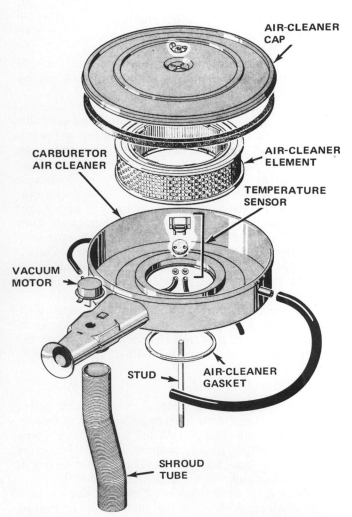

Fig. 7-6. Air cleaners. (a) and (b) are the dry type; (c) and (d) are the oil-bath type.

pedal in the driver's compartment. This permits the driver to position the throttle valve to suit operating requirements (Fig. 7-8).

⊘ **7-11 Air-Fuel-Ratio Requirements** As already noted, the fuel system must vary the air-fuel ratio to suit different operating requirements. The mixture must be rich (have a high proportion of fuel) for starting. It must be leaner (have a lower proportion of fuel) for part-throttle, medium-speed operation. Figure 7-9 is a graph showing typical air-fuel ratios as related to various car speeds. Ratios, and the speeds at which they are obtained, vary with different cars. In the example shown, a rich mixture of about 9:1 (9 lb [4.082 kg] of air to 1 lb [0.454 kg] of fuel) is supplied for starting. Then, during idle, the mixture leans out to about 12:1. At medium speeds, the mixture further leans out to about 15:1. But at higher speeds, with a wide-open throttle, the mix-

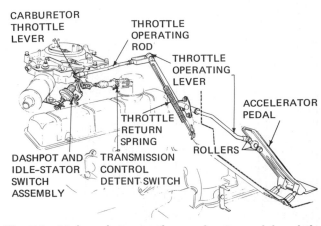

Fig. 7-8. Linkage between the accelerator pedal and the carburetor throttle lever. (*Buick Motor Division of General Motors Corporation*)

Fig. 7-7. Disassembled view of a carburetor air cleaner for a V-8 engine. (*American Motors Corporation*)

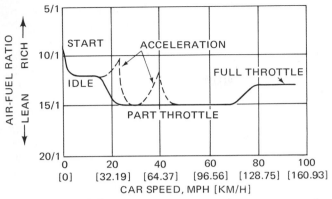

Fig. 7-9. Graph of air-fuel ratios for different car speeds. The graph is typical. Car speeds at which the various ratios are obtained may vary with different cars. Also, there may be some variation in the ratios.

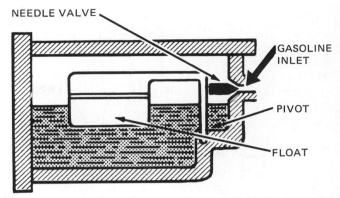

Fig. 7-10. Simplified drawing of a carburetor float system.

ture is enriched to about 13:1. Opening the throttle for acceleration at any speed causes a momentary enrichment of the mixture. This results from special carburetor systems which we shall discuss later. Two examples are shown in Fig. 7-9 (at about 20 mph [32.18 km/h] and about 30 mph [48.27 km/h]).

You might think that the engine itself demands varying air-fuel ratios for different operating conditions. This is not quite true. For example, the mixture must be very rich for starting because fuel vaporizes very poorly under starting conditions. The engine and carburetor are cold, the airspeed is low, and much of the fuel does not vaporize. Thus, an extra amount of fuel must be delivered by the carburetor so that enough will vaporize for starting. Likewise, sudden opening of the throttle for acceleration allows a sudden inrush of air. Extra fuel must enter at the same time (that is, the mixture must be enriched). This is because only part of the fuel vaporizes and mixes with the ingoing air to provide the proper proportions of air and fuel in the engine.

The following sections describe the various systems in carburetors that supply the air-fuel mixture required for different operating conditions.

⊘ **7-12 Float System** The float system includes the float bowl and a float-and-needle-valve arrangement. The float and the needle valve maintain a constant level of fuel in the float bowl. If the level is too high, then too much fuel feeds from the fuel nozzle. If it is too low, too little fuel feeds. In either event, poor engine performance results. Figure 7-10 is a simplified drawing of the float system. If fuel enters the float bowl faster than it is withdrawn, the fuel level rises. This causes the float to move up and push the needle valve into the valve seat. This, in turn, shuts off the fuel inlet so that no fuel can enter. Then, if the fuel level drops, the float moves down and releases the needle so that the fuel inlet is opened. Now fuel can enter. In actual operation, the fuel is kept at an almost constant level. The float tends to hold the needle valve partly closed so that the incoming fuel just balances the fuel being withdrawn.

Figure 7-11 shows an actual carburetor with a dual float assembly, partly cut away so that the two floats can be seen. The carburetor has a float bowl that partly surrounds the carburetor air horn. The two floats are attached by a U-shaped lever and operate a single needle valve. Some carburetors have an auxiliary fuel valve and inlet (Fig. 7-12). During heavy-load or high-speed operation, fuel may be withdrawn from the float bowl faster than it can enter through the main fuel inlet. If this happens, the fuel level drops. The end of the float lever presses against the auxiliary valve, pushing it upward. This opens the auxiliary fuel inlet so additional fuel can enter.

⊘ **7-13 Float-Bowl Vents** The float bowl of a carburetor is vented into the carburetor air horn at a point above the choke valve. (See the upper left in Fig. 7-11, and the upper left in Fig. 6-3.) The vent makes up for the effect of a clogged air cleaner. Suppose the air cleaner becomes clogged with dirt. The airflow through it is then restricted. As a result,

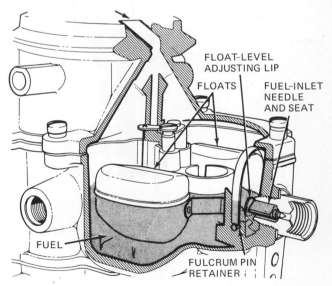

Fig. 7-11. Carburetor partly cut away to show the float system. (*Chrysler Corporation*)

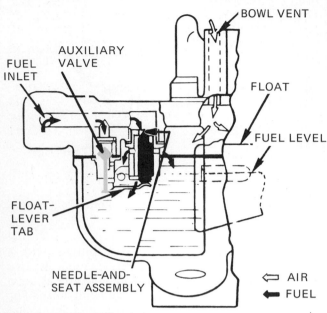

Fig. 7-12. Float system using auxiliary fuel valve and inlet. (*American Motors Corporation*)

a partial vacuum develops in the carburetor air horn. Therefore, a somewhat greater vacuum is applied to the fuel nozzle (since this vacuum is added to the venturi vacuum). This would tend to increase the fuel flow. However, the partial vacuum resulting from the clogged air cleaner is also applied to the float bowl (through the vent). Therefore, the only driving force that pushes fuel from the fuel nozzle is the air pressure in the air cleaner. This is less than atmospheric pressure. Thus, the vent has compensated for the effect of the clogged air cleaner. If the float bowl were vented to the atmosphere, then atmospheric pressure would be the driving force. This would produce a greater fuel flow from the fuel nozzle, and the mixture would be too rich.

The float bowl has another vent, shown to the upper right in Fig. 6-3. This vent is connected by a tube to the charcoal canister which is part of the fuel-vapor recovery system (⊘ 6-2). In the carburetor in Fig. 6-3, the float bowl has a pressure-relief valve. The valve opens when the vapor pressure increases in the float bowl. This allows the fuel vapor to flow to the charcoal canister. In other carburetors, the vent to the charcoal canister has a

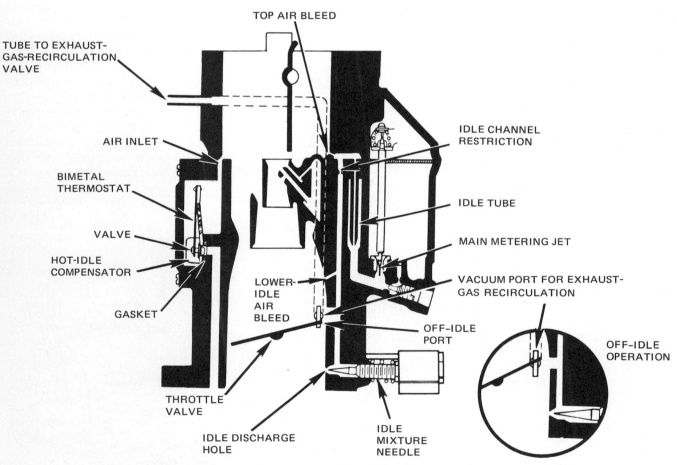

Fig. 7-13. Idle system. Note the passage to the exhaust-gas recirculation system. This passage allows some exhaust gas to feed into the air-fuel mixture when the throttle valve opens past the vacuum port. (*Chevrolet Motor Division of General Motors Corporation*)

valve operated by the accelerator-pump lever. The valve is opened when the engine is idling or when it has been turned off.

⊘ **7-14 Hot-Idle Compensator Valve** The internal vent could be a problem during idling or low-speed operation, especially during hot weather. Gasoline vapor from the float bowl can pass through the internal vent in sufficient amounts to upset the air-fuel ratio. That is, the gasoline vapor adds to the normal air-fuel mixture, and the mixture becomes too rich. To take care of this, some carburetors have a hot-idle compensator valve, shown to the left in Fig. 7-13. This valve is operated by a thermostatic blade. When the temperature reaches a preset value, the blade bends enough to open the valve port. Now additional air can flow through the auxiliary air passage. This additional air bypasses the idle system. It leans out the mixture enough to make up for the added gasoline vapor coming from the float bowl.

⊘ **7-15 Idle System** When the throttle is closed or only slightly opened, only a small amount of air can pass through the air horn. The airspeed is low, and very little vacuum develops in the venturi. This means that the fuel nozzle does not feed fuel. Thus, the carburetor must have another system to supply fuel when the throttle is closed or slightly opened.

This system, called the *idle system*, is shown in operation in Fig. 7-14. It includes passages through which air and fuel can flow. The air passage is called the *air bleed*. With the throttle closed as shown, there is a high vacuum below the throttle valve from the intake manifold. Atmospheric pressure pushes air and fuel through the passages as shown. They mix and flow past the tapered point of the idle air-fuel-mixture adjustment screw. The mixture has a high proportion of fuel (is very rich). It leans out somewhat as it mixes with the small amount of air that gets past the closed throttle valve. But the final mixture is still rich enough (see Fig. 7-9) for good

idling. The richness can be adjusted by turning the idle air-fuel-mixture adjustment screw in or out. This permits less or more air-fuel mixture to flow past the screw.

CAUTION: In late-model cars, the idle air-fuel-mixture adjustment screw is fixed or has a locking cap. It is illegal to adjust the idle mixture beyond specific limits. The mixture has been set according to federal standards and must not be tampered with.

Figure 7-15 shows a cutaway view of a carburetor with the idle system in operation.

⊘ **7-16 Idle-Enrichment System** This system is used on some cars equipped with automatic transmissions. Its purpose is to reduce cold-engine stalling during off-idle operation. The system uses an idle-enrichment valve (upper right in Fig. 7-16). This valve includes a diaphragm that is connected by a vacuum line, through a thermal valve, to the intake manifold. The thermal valve is in contact with the engine coolant. When the engine is cold, the thermal valve is open; it passes intake-manifold vacuum to the idle-enrichment valve. This vacuum then causes the valve to pull closed. Now less air can pass through the idle air-bleed system. It comes only from the air bleed to the left in Fig. 7-16. Air is shut off from the enrichment air bleed at the right. As a result the vacuum acting at the idle and idle-transfer ports is increased, causing the idle system to discharge more fuel. This enriches the air-fuel mixture. As soon as the engine coolant begins to warm up, the thermal valve closes, shutting off the vacuum to the idle-enrichment valve. Now, the diaphragm relaxes, and the idle-enrichment air-bleed circuit is opened. Additional air can feed through, so the idle and off-idle air-fuel mixture is leaned out.

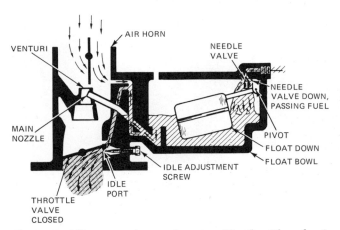

Fig. 7-14. Idle system in a carburetor. The throttle valve is closed so that only a small amount of air can get past it. All fuel is being fed past the idle adjustment screw. Arrows show the flow of air and fuel.

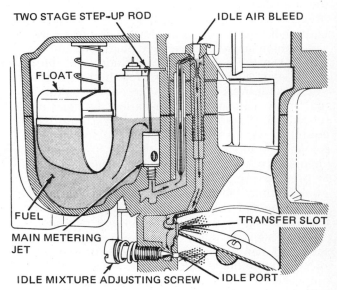

Fig. 7-15. Idle system in a carburetor. The carburetor has been cut away to show the internal arrangement. (*Chrysler Corporation*)

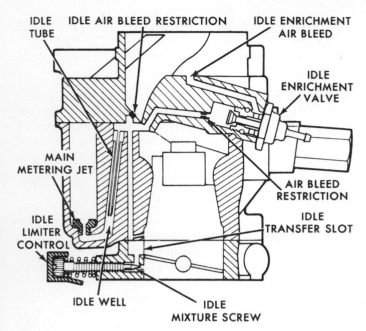

IDLE TUBE
IDLE AIR BLEED RESTRICTION
IDLE ENRICHMENT AIR BLEED
IDLE ENRICHMENT VALVE
MAIN METERING JET
AIR BLEED RESTRICTION
IDLE LIMITER CONTROL
IDLE TRANSFER SLOT
IDLE WELL
IDLE MIXTURE SCREW

Fig. 7-16. Idle-enrichment system for a carburetor in a car equipped with an automatic transmission. (*Chrysler Corporation*)

In a second system, cars have a similar thermal valve and idle-enrichment valve. But there is an additional solenoid valve that is operated by an electric timer. This timer actuates the solenoid valve about 35 seconds (s) after the engine is started. The solenoid valve then shuts the thermal valve. The thermal valve then shuts off the vacuum from the idle-enrichment valve; it relaxes and allows the enrichment air bleed to pass air into the idle mixture, leaning it out. The thermal valve prevents additional cycles of idle-system enrichment after the engine has warmed up. But while the engine is cold, each restart cycles another 35 s of enrichment.

⊘ **7-17 Antidieseling Solenoid** This is also called the *idle-stop solenoid* (Fig. 7-17). Its purpose is to prevent run-on, or "dieseling," of the engine after the ignition is turned off. Carburetors in modern cars are set on the lean side, as we have noted, to reduce HC and CO in the exhaust gases. In addition, the idle speed is set somewhat higher for the same reason. These conditions can cause the engine to diesel— that is, to continue to run—after the ignition is turned off. To prevent this, some carburetors are equipped with a throttle-positioning solenoid. The solenoid provides a movable throttle stop. When the engine is running, the solenoid plunger is extended to prevent complete closing of the throttle valve. That is, the carburetor throttle linkage comes up against the end of the solenoid plunger. This allows normal idling of the engine. (As you can see, the solenoid takes the place of the idle-speed adjustment screw. It can be adjusted for the proper idling speed.) When the engine is turned off, the solenoid plunger is retracted. Now, the throttle can close completely, to shut off the flow of air and air-fuel mixture to the engine. This prevents engine dieseling after the ignition is turned off.

Without this complete closing of the throttle, enough air-fuel mixture could continue to flow to the engine to allow the engine to run. Ignition would be by hot spots in the engine—either hot spots on the spark plugs or hot carbon particles on the surfaces of the combustion chambers or valves.

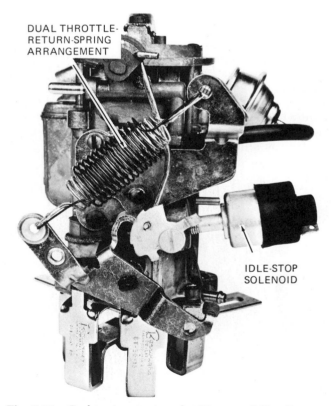

DUAL THROTTLE-RETURN-SPRING ARRANGEMENT

IDLE-STOP SOLENOID

Fig. 7-17. Carburetor equipped with an antidieseling solenoid. (*Buick Motor Division of General Motors Corporation*)

Check Your Progress

Progress Quiz 7-1   Once again we pause to give you a chance to check up on yourself—to find out how well you understand the material you are studying. If a question gives you trouble, check back into the pages you have just read to refresh your memory.

Completing the Sentences   The sentences below are incomplete. After each sentence there are several words or phrases, but only one of them correctly completes the sentence. Write each sentence in your notebook, ending it with the word or phrase that completes it correctly.

1. The two modes of engine operation that produce high exhaust pollution are: (*a*) idle and cruise, (*b*) accelerate and decelerate, (*c*) cold-engine operation and vacuum advance during low-gear operation, (*d*) hot-engine operation and vacuum advance during high-gear operation.
2. The purpose of leaning the air-fuel mixture is to reduce the exhaust emission of: (*a*) H_2O and CO_2 (*b*) HC and CO, (*c*) NO_x and SO_x, (*d*) CO and CO_2.
3. The system in the carburetor which increases the richness of the air-fuel mixture temporarily for cold-engine starting is the: (*a*) choke system, (*b*) idle system, (*c*) power system, (*d*) float system.
4. During normal medium-speed operation of the engine, the carburetor supplies an air-fuel-mixture ratio of about: (*a*) 18:1, (*b*) 15:1, (*c*) 12:1, (*d*) 8:1.
5. Internal venting of the carburetor makes up for the effect of a: (*a*) hot day, (*b*) clogged fuel filter, (*c*) cold day, (*d*) clogged air filter.
6. To reduce cold-engine stalling during off-idle operation, some cars equipped with automatic transmissions use: (*a*) an antidieseling solenoid, (*b*) a main metering system, (*c*) an accelerator-pump system, (*d*) an idle-enrichment system.
7. To prevent engine run-on, or dieseling, after the ignition is turned off, many cars are equipped with: (*a*) an ignition switch, (*b*) electronic ignition, (*c*) a starting-motor solenoid, (*d*) an antidieseling solenoid.
8. Part-throttle operation in lower gears with vacuum advance produces excessive amounts of: (*a*) NO_x, (*b*) HC, (*c*) CO, (*d*) CO_2.
9. One end of the fuel nozzle is in the float bowl, and the other end is in the center of the: (*a*) air cleaner, (*b*) venturi, (*c*) air horn, (*d*) intake manifold.
10. Carburetor air-fuel mixtures are measured in: (*a*) pounds [kilograms], (*b*) gallons [liters], (*c*) feet [meters], (*d*) pounds per square inch [kilograms per square centimeter].

Questions   Write each of the following questions, and then the answer, in your notebook. If you have trouble recalling the answer to a question, turn back to the pages that cover the material and study them again.

1. What is the job of the carburetor?
2. How are exhaust emissions reduced by leaning the air-fuel ratio?
3. What are the six systems in an automobile carburetor?
4. What causes the fuel nozzle to discharge fuel?
5. How does the throttle valve regulate engine speed?
6. When does an engine require the richest mixture?
7. What is the job of the float system?
8. What vents open into the carburetor float bowl?
9. Why do some cars need an idle-enrichment system?
10. How does the antidieseling solenoid work?

⊘ **7-18 Low-Speed Operation**   When the throttle is opened slightly (Fig. 7-18), the edge of the throttle valve moves past the low-speed port in the side of the air horn. This port is a vertical slot or a series of small holes, one above the other. Additional fuel is thus fed into the intake manifold through the low-speed port. This fuel mixes with the additional air moving past the slightly opened throttle valve. It provides sufficient mixture richness for part-throttle, low-speed operation.

Some air bleeds around the throttle plate, through the low-speed port, when the edge of the throttle is only partway past this port. This air improves the atomization of the fuel coming from the low-speed port.

⊘ **7-19 Main Metering System**   Suppose the throttle valve is opened enough so that its edge moves well past the low-speed port. Now there is little difference in vacuum between the upper and lower parts of the air horn. Thus, little air-fuel mixture discharges from the low-speed port. However, under this condition, enough air moves through the air horn to produce a vacuum in the venturi. As a result, the fuel nozzle centered in the venturi (called the

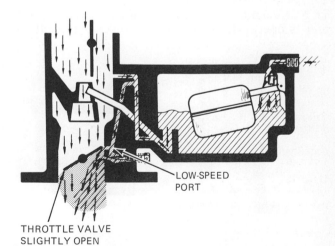

Fig. 7-18.   Low-speed operation. The throttle valve is slightly open, and fuel is being fed through the low-speed port as well as through the idle port. The dark color is fuel; the light color is air.

main nozzle or the *high-speed nozzle*) begins to discharge fuel (as explained in ⊘ 7-8). The main nozzle supplies the fuel during operation with the throttle partly to fully opened. Figure 7-19 shows this action. The system from the float bowl to the main nozzle is called the *main metering system*.

The wider the throttle is opened, and the faster the air flows through the air horn, the greater the vacuum in the venturi. This means that additional fuel is discharged from the main nozzle (because of the greater vacuum). As a result, a nearly constant air-fuel ratio is maintained by the main metering system from part- to wide-open throttle.

⊘ **7-20 Power System**   For high-speed, full-power, wide-open-throttle operation, the air-fuel mixture must be enriched (see Fig. 7-9). Additional devices are incorporated in the carburetor to provide this enriched mixture during high-speed, full-power operation. They are operated mechanically or by intake-manifold vacuum.

⊘ **7-21 Mechanically Operated Power System**   This system includes a metering-rod jet (a carefully calibrated orifice, or opening) and a metering rod with two or more steps of different diameters (Fig. 7-20). The metering rod is attached to the throttle linkage (Fig. 7-21). When the throttle is opened, the metering rod is lifted. But when the throttle is partly closed, the larger diameter of the metering rod is in the metering-rod jet. This partly restricts fuel flow to the main nozzle. However, enough fuel does flow for normal part-throttle operation. When the throttle is opened wide, the rod is lifted enough to cause the smaller diameter, or step, to move up into the metering-rod jet. Now the jet is less restricted, and more fuel can flow. The main nozzle is therefore supplied with more fuel, and the resulting air-fuel mixture is richer.

⊘ **7-22 Vacuum-Operated Power System**   This system is operated by intake-manifold vacuum. It in-

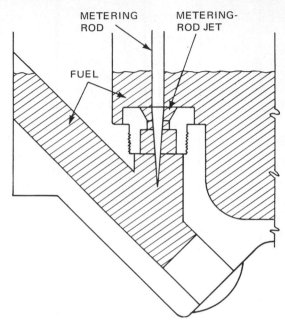

Fig. 7-20. Metering rod and metering-rod jet, for better performance at full throttle.

cludes a vacuum piston, or a diaphragm, linked to a valve or a metering rod similar to the one shown in Fig. 7-20. One design is shown in Fig. 7-22. During part-throttle operation, the piston is held in the lower position by intake-manifold vacuum. However, when the throttle is opened wide, manifold vacuum is reduced. This allows the spring under the vacuum piston to push the piston upward. This motion raises the metering rod so that the smaller diameter of the rod clears the jet. Now more fuel can flow, to handle the full-power requirements of the engine.

A carburetor using a spring-loaded diaphragm to control the position of the metering rod is shown in Fig. 7-23. The action is similar to that in the car-

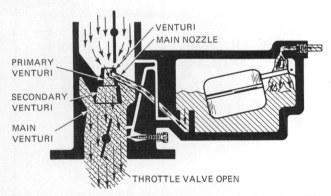

Fig. 7-19. Main metering system in a carburetor. The throttle valve is open, and fuel is being fed through the high-speed, or main, nozzle. The dark color is fuel; the light color is air.

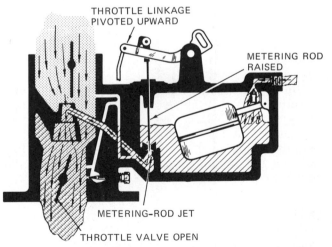

Fig. 7-21. Mechanically operated power system. When the throttle is open, as shown, the metering rod is raised so the smaller diameter of the rod clears the jet. This allows additional fuel to flow.

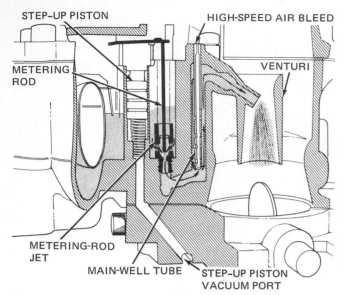

STEP-UP PISTON   HIGH-SPEED AIR BLEED

METERING ROD   VENTURI

METERING-ROD JET

MAIN-WELL TUBE   STEP-UP PISTON VACUUM PORT

Fig. 7-22. Sectional view of a carburetor using a power or step-up piston, actuated by intake-manifold vacuum, to control the position of the metering rod. (*Chrysler Corporation*)

buretor with the spring-loaded piston. When the throttle is opened so that intake-manifold vacuum is reduced, the spring raises the diaphragm. This allows the metering rod to be lifted so that its smaller diameter clears the jet, allowing more fuel to flow.

⊘ **7-23 Combination Power Systems** In some carburetors, a combination full-power system is used. It is operated both mechanically and by vacuum from the intake manifold. In one such carburetor, a me-

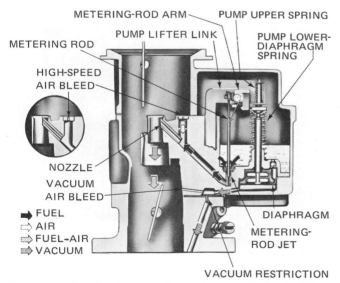

METERING-ROD ARM   PUMP UPPER SPRING

PUMP LIFTER LINK

METERING ROD

PUMP LOWER-DIAPHRAGM SPRING

HIGH-SPEED AIR BLEED

NOZZLE

VACUUM AIR BLEED

➡ FUEL
⇨ AIR
⇨ FUEL-AIR
⇨ VACUUM

DIAPHRAGM

METERING-ROD JET

VACUUM RESTRICTION

Fig. 7-23. Sectional view of a carburetor using a spring-loaded diaphragm, actuated by intake-manifold vacuum, to control the position of the metering rod. (*Ford Motor Company*)

tering rod is linked to a vacuum diaphragm as well as to the throttle linkage (Fig. 7-23). Thus, movement of the throttle to "full open" lifts the metering rod to enrich the mixture. Or, loss of intake-manifold vacuum (as during a hard pull up a hill or during acceleration) causes the vacuum-diaphragm spring to raise the metering rod for an enriched mixture.

⊘ **7-24 Factory-Adjustable Part Throttle (APT)** Some late-model carburetors have an additional metering rod and fixed metering-rod jet (shown to the left in Fig. 7-24). They provide more accurate adjustment of the part-throttle fuel flow. The metering rod is *adjusted at the factory* by turning the adjusting screw (upper left). If it is turned to lift the metering rod, more fuel can flow to the main metering rods and jets. If it is turned to lower the metering rod, less fuel can flow. The purpose of this additional APT metering rod and jet is to fine-tune the carburetor. That is, adjusting the metering rod at the factory makes up for slight difference in the power system resulting from manufacturing tolerances.

CAUTION: The position of the APT metering rod is extremely critical. It should never be adjusted in the field, unless the special instructions and tools supplied by the manufacturer are available. Even a slight adjustment, if done incorrectly, can throw the carburetor completely out of balance.

⊘ **7-25 Altitude Compensation** Note that the carburetor in Fig. 7-24 has an *aneroid* surrounding the APT metering rod. An aneroid is a sealed bellows which is sensitive to changes in atmospheric pressure. As the pressure goes up, the aneroid is squeezed so it shortens. As the pressure is reduced, the aneroid expands. These actions raise or lower the metering rod as atmospheric pressure changes. Thus, suppose the car is driven up a mountain, so that the atmospheric pressure is reduced. Without any compensating device, the air-fuel mixture would become enriched. This would happen because less air would enter the carburetor (the air pressure is lower). Also, the air that does enter is thinner, containing less oxygen. To compensate for this, the aneroid expands as a result of the reduced air pressure. This action moves the APT metering rod down so less fuel flows. As a result, the proper air-fuel ratio is maintained.

⊘ **7-26 Throttle-Position Solenoid** Many carburetors used on cars with catalytic converters (⊘ 9-2) have a throttle-position solenoid. This device prevents rapid closing of the throttle when the driver suddenly lets up on the accelerator pedal after high-speed driving. Without such a control, the sudden closing of the throttle can cause the carburetor to release a very rich mixture for a few moments. Here is why that would happen: The engine is still turning rapidly when the throttle is closed. This creates a high vacuum in the intake manifold. With

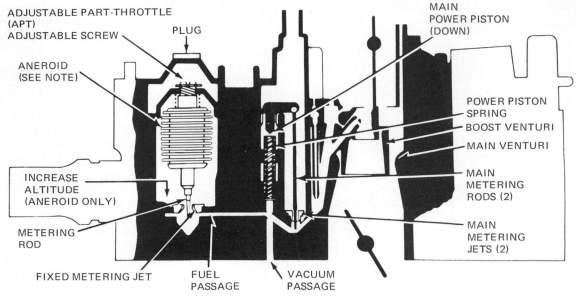

ADJUSTABLE PART-THROTTLE (APT) ADJUSTABLE SCREW
PLUG
ANEROID (SEE NOTE)
MAIN POWER PISTON (DOWN)
POWER PISTON SPRING
BOOST VENTURI
MAIN VENTURI
MAIN METERING RODS (2)
INCREASE ALTITUDE (ANEROID ONLY)
MAIN METERING JETS (2)
METERING ROD
FIXED METERING JET
FUEL PASSAGE
VACUUM PASSAGE

NOTE: ANEROID REPLACED BY FILLER BLOCK ON SOME MODELS

Fig. 7-24. Sectional view of a carburetor, showing the main metering system and the factory-adjustable part-throttle metering rod with aneroid. (*Chevrolet Motor Division of General Motors Corporation*)

the throttle closed, only a small amount of air enters the intake manifold. But for a second or two after the throttle closes, the fuel continues to flow from the main metering system. The combination results in a mixture so rich that only part of it would burn. As a result, the catalytic converter would be suddenly hit with an extremely rich mixture containing a great deal of HC (unburned gasoline). The converter would then begin converting this HC into harmless water and CO_2. But there would be so much of it that the converter might overheat and be ruined. The converter will handle normal amounts of HC and CO, but overloading can ruin it.

The throttle-position solenoid is connected to the battery through an engine-speed sensor. The speed sensor receives ignition pulses from the electronic ignition system. When the speed sensor senses that the engine speed exceeds 2,000 rpm, it connects the throttle-position solenoid to the battery. The solenoid extends a plunger that positions a throttle stop. Now, if the throttle is released, it does not close completely. This prevents the sudden flow of enriched air-fuel mixture into the engine. After the engine speed drops below 2,000 rpm, the engine-speed sensor disconnects the throttle-position solenoid from the battery. The solenoid withdraws its plunger, and the throttle can close completely.

⊘ **7-27 Throttle-Return Checks** Many carburetors use a throttle-return check (Fig. 7-25) to prevent fast throttle closing when the driver's foot is lifted from the accelerator pedal. Two things happen if the throttle closes suddenly. First, the airflow is cut off, but fuel continues to dribble from the main nozzle for a few moments. This is due to the inertia of the fuel moving up to the nozzle from the float bowl.

This momentarily enriches the air-fuel mixture. The mixture can become so rich that it does not burn, or it burns poorly. As a result, the exhaust gas contains a high concentration of the atmospheric pollutants HC and CO. Second, the engine hesitates, or stumbles, until the air-fuel mixture settles down to a combustible ratio.

Fig. 7-25. Throttle-return check on a carburetor. (*Carter Carburetor Division of AFC Industries*)

THROTTLE-RETURN CHECK (DASHPOT)

108   Automotive Emission Control

The throttle-return check prevents these conditions because it slows down the closing of the throttle. The type shown in Fig. 7-25 contains a spring-loaded diaphragm. The diaphragm traps air behind it when the throttle is opened and the shaft and adjustment screw on the check move outward. Then, when the throttle is released, the contact arm on the throttle lever moves against the check adjustment screw. Since the air trapped behind the spring-loaded diaphragm can escape only slowly through a small opening, the throttle moves to the closed position slowly.

Another type of throttle-return check is shown in Fig. 7-26. In this unit, called a *dashpot*, the mechanism is controlled by a small electromagnet. It causes the dashpot to check, or slow, the throttle return at some times, but not at others. A speed-governor device on the transmission determines when the dashpot should work. Above a certain speed (the governed speed of the transmission), the electromagnet is not operating, and the check ball is not seated. The air passage behind the dashpot diaphragm is open, and the dashpot offers no resistance to throttle closing. However, at lower speeds, the electromagnet is energized, and the check ball is seated. This restricts the airflow, retarding dashpot diaphragm movement and, thus, throttle closing.

⊘ **7-28 Air-Fuel Ratios with Different Systems** Figure 7-27 shows the air-fuel ratios with the different carburetor systems in operation. This is a typical curve only. Actual air-fuel ratios may vary for different carburetors and operating conditions. Note that the idle system supplies a very rich mixture to start with, but the mixture leans out as engine speed increases. From about 25 to 40 mph [40.24 to 64.37 km/h], the throttle is only partly opened; both the idle and the main metering system are supplying air-fuel mixture. Then, in the curve shown, the main metering system takes over at about 40 mph [64.37 km/h] and continues by itself to about 60 mph [96.56 km/h]. Note that the air-fuel ratio increases somewhat as speed increases (that is, the mixture becomes leaner). Somewhere around 60 mph [96.56 km/h], the power system comes into operation. (The power system will also operate if the throttle is opened wide at a lower speed.) Now, the mixture richness goes up as the speed increases.

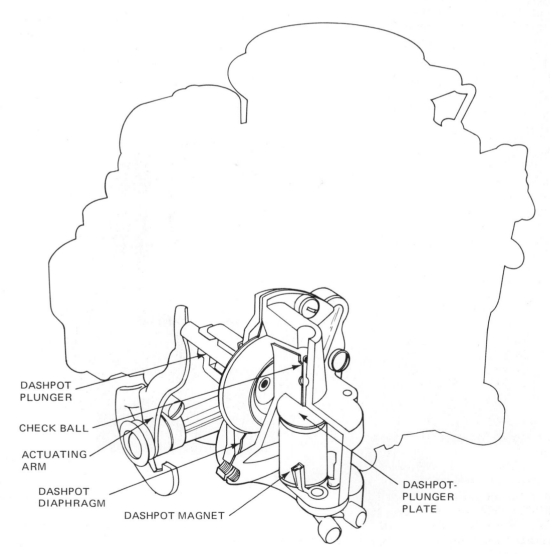

DASHPOT
PLUNGER

CHECK BALL

ACTUATING
ARM

DASHPOT
DIAPHRAGM

DASHPOT MAGNET

DASHPOT-
PLUNGER
PLATE

Fig. 7-26. Details of a dashpot controlled by an electromagnet. (*Chrysler Corporation*)

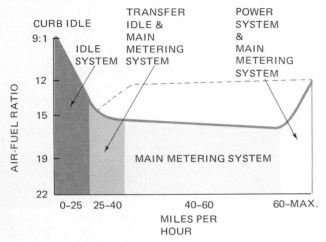

TYPICAL FLOW CURVE SHOWING
SYSTEMS OPERATION VS. MPH

Fig. 7-27. Air-fuel ratios with different carburetor systems operating at various speeds. (*Chevrolet Motor Division of General Motors Corporation*)

⊘ **7-29 Accelerator-Pump System** For acceleration, the carburetor must deliver additional fuel (see ⊘ 7-11). Rapid opening of the throttle allows a sudden inrush of air. Thus, there is a sudden demand for additional fuel. Carburetors have accelerator-pump systems to provide this extra fuel. Figure 7-28 shows one type. It includes a pump plunger which is forced downward by a pump lever that is linked to the throttle. When the throttle is opened, the pump lever pushes the pump plunger down. This forces fuel to flow through the accelerator-pump system and out the pump jet (Fig. 7-29). This fuel enters the air passing through the carburetor to supply the additional fuel needed.

However, when the throttle is opened quickly, fuel may not discharge for a long enough time to prevent stumble. To overcome this problem, most carburetors use a calibrated spring above the plunger cap to prolong the discharge. Note, in Fig. 7-30, that the pump plunger and the pump and seal are attached through a spring. This spring applies pressure to the pump, so the accelerator-pump system immediately begins discharging fuel through the jet. The spring maintains this pressure all the time that the throttle is held open, until the pump plunger is all the way down (Fig. 7-29). This arrangement allows the accelerator-pump system to discharge fuel for several seconds, or until the full-power system can take over. It therefore permits smooth acceleration.

Figure 7-30 is a cutaway view of a carburetor using a plunger-type accelerator-pump system. Figure 7-31 shows a type of accelerator pump that uses a diaphragm instead of a plunger. When the throttle is opened, the pump lower diaphragm spring lifts the diaphragm. This forces additional fuel from the chamber above the diaphragm, through the accelerator-pump system, and out the pump jet.

An accelerator-pump system for a dual carburetor is shown in Fig. 7-32. This carburetor has two barrels; there is a discharge nozzle for each. The fuel flow from the accelerator pump is split between the two barrels. Regardless of the number of barrels, most carburetors use only one accelerator pump.

⊘ **7-30 Choke System** When the engine is being started, the carburetor must deliver a very rich mixture to the intake manifold. With the engine and carburetor cold, only part of the fuel vaporizes. Extra fuel must be delivered, so that enough of it

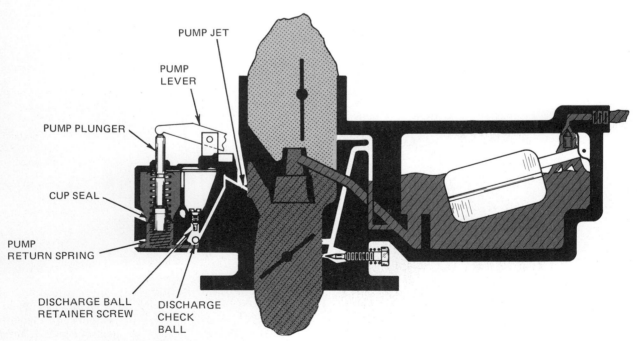

Fig. 7-28. Accelerator-pump system in a carburetor of the type using a pump plunger.

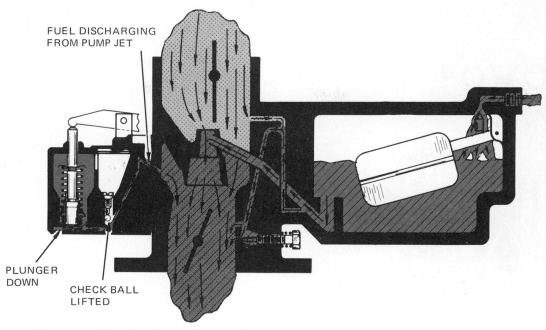

FUEL DISCHARGING
FROM PUMP JET

PLUNGER
DOWN

CHECK BALL
LIFTED

Fig. 7-29. When the throttle is opened, the pump lever pushes the pump plunger down. This forces fuel to flow through the accelerator-pump system and out the jet.

evaporates to make a combustible mixture. Otherwise, the engine might not start.

During cranking, the airspeed through the carburetor air horn is very low. Vacuum from the venturi action and vacuum below the throttle are insufficient to produce adequate fuel flow for starting. To produce enough fuel flow during cranking, the carburetor has a choke (Fig. 7-33). The choke consists of a valve, in the top of the air horn, controlled mechanically or by an automatic device. When the choke valve is closed, only a small amount of air can get past it (the valve "chokes off" the air flow). Then, when the engine is cranked, a fairly high vacuum develops in the air horn. This vacuum

causes the main nozzle to discharge a heavy stream of fuel. The quantity delivered is sufficient to produce the correct air-fuel mixture for starting the engine.

As soon as the engine starts, its speed increases from a cranking speed of 250 to 300 rpm (revolutions per minute) to over 600 rpm (idle speed). Now more air and a somewhat leaner mixture are required. One method of getting more air into the engine as soon as it starts is to mount the choke valve off center on its shaft in the air horn. Then a spring is

ACCELERATOR PUMP

PLUNGER
SPRING

DISCHARGE CHECK
BALL

INTAKE CHECK BALL

Fig. 7-30. Accelerator-pump system using a piston-type pump. (*Chrysler Corporation*)

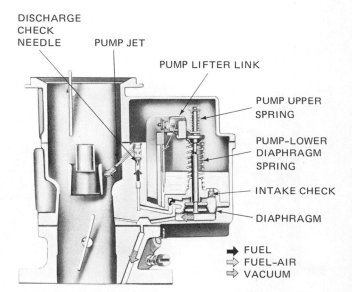

DISCHARGE
CHECK
NEEDLE   PUMP JET

PUMP LIFTER LINK

PUMP UPPER
SPRING

PUMP-LOWER
DIAPHRAGM
SPRING

INTAKE CHECK

DIAPHRAGM

➡ FUEL
⇨ FUEL-AIR
⇨ VACUUM

Fig. 7-31. Accelerator-pump system of the type using a spring-loaded diaphragm. Opening of the throttle allows the lower diaphragm spring to lift the diaphragm. This forces fuel through the accelerator-pump system and out the jet. (*Ford Motor Company*)

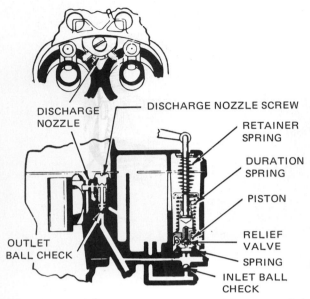

Fig. 7-32. Accelerator-pump system and location of the discharge nozzles in a dual carburetor.

added to the choke linkage. The additional air the engine requires causes the valve to partly open against the spring pressure. Another arrangement includes a small spring-loaded section in the valve. This section opens to admit the additional air.

⊘ 7-31 Automatic Chokes Mechanically controlled chokes are operated by a pullrod on the dash. The pullrod is linked to the choke valve. When it is pulled out, the choke valve is closed. The driver must remember to push the control rod in to the dechoked position as soon as the engine begins to warm up. If this is not done, the carburetor continues to supply a very rich mixture to the engine. This excessive richness causes poor engine performance, high levels of exhaust emissions, fouled spark plugs, poor fuel economy, and many other problems.

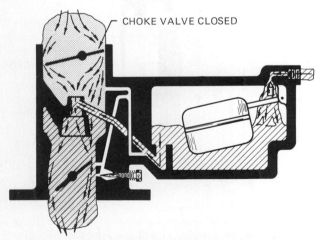

CHOKE VALVE CLOSED

Fig. 7-33. With the choke valve closed, intake-manifold vacuum is introduced into the carburetor air horn. This causes the main nozzle to discharge fuel.

To prevent such troubles, most cars now have an automatic choke. Most automatic chokes operate on exhaust-manifold temperature and intake-manifold vacuum. Figure 7-34 shows an automatic choke on a carburetor. It includes a thermostatic spring and a vacuum piston, both linked to the choke valve. The thermostatic spring is made up of two different metal strips, welded together and formed into a spiral. Owing to a difference in the expansion rates of the two metals, the thermostatic spring winds up or unwinds with changing temperature. When the engine is cold, the spring is wound up enough to close the choke valve and spring-load it in the closed position. When the engine is cranked, a rich mixture is delivered to the intake manifold. As the engine starts, air movement through the air horn causes the choke valve to open slightly (working against the thermostatic-spring tension). In addition, the vacuum piston is pulled outward by intake-manifold vacuum. This produces some further opening of the choke valve.

The choke valve is in position to let the carburetor supply the richer mixture needed for cold-engine idling. When the throttle is opened, the mixture must be enriched. The accelerator pump provides some extra fuel, but still more fuel is needed when the engine is cold. This additional fuel is secured by the action of the vacuum piston. When the throttle is opened, intake-manifold vacuum is lost. The vacuum piston releases and is pulled inward by the thermostatic-spring tension. The choke valve therefore moves toward its closed position, causing the mixture to be enriched. During the first few moments of operation, the choke valve is controlled by the vacuum piston.

However, the thermostatic spring begins to take over as the engine warms up. The thermostatic spring is in a housing that is connected to the exhaust manifold through a small tube. Heat passes through this tube and enters the thermostatic-spring housing. Soon, the thermostat begins to warm up. As it warms up, the spring unwinds. This causes the choke valve to move toward its open position. When operating temperature is reached, the thermostatic spring has unwound enough to fully open the choke valve. No further choking takes place.

Another method of speeding up the unchoking action is shown in Fig. 7-40. Here, the hot air flowing to the thermostatic coil comes from the air cleaner. It flows through a heater coil placed in the path of the exhaust gas. The air is quickly heated by the hot exhaust gas. It then passes through the case enclosing the bimetallic thermostatic coil. The thermostatic coil is therefore quickly heated; it reacts rapidly to open the choke valve. The hot air flows into the intake manifold. Figure 7-40 also shows part of the heated-air, or Thermac, system which is discussed in detail in ⊘ 7-34.

⊘ 7-32 Modulated-Choke System This system works in the same way as the choke system described in ⊘ 7-31 and illustrated in Fig. 7-34. That is,

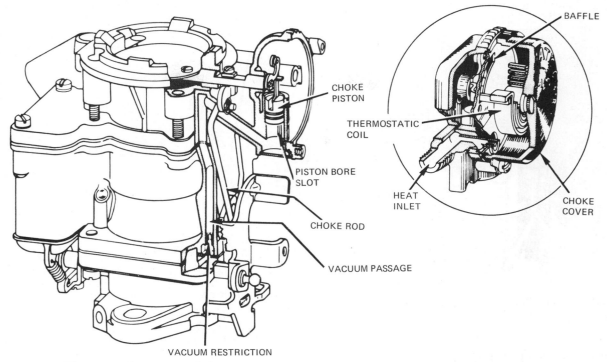

Fig. 7-34. Automatic-choke system on a carburetor. (*American Motors Corporation*)

a thermostatic spring and a vacuum piston control the closing and opening of the choke valve. However, there is an added mechanism which modifies, or modulates, this action. The additional mechanism is shown in Fig. 7-41. A disassembed view is shown in Fig. 7-42. This additional mechanism, called the *choke modulator,* works in this manner. When the engine is cold, the thermostatic spring has wound up to close the choke valve. When the engine is started, manifold vacuum pulls the modulator diaphragm down. This pulls down on the modulator arm so the other end of the arm is moved upward. The upward-moving end of the arm contacts a tang on the end of the choke-valve shaft, causing the choke valve to open slightly. This first stage of the modulator action is called the *initial choke-valve clearance.*

As the engine begins to warm up, the thermostatic spring begins to unwind and open the choke. At the same time, the modulator piston spring pulls down on the modulator arm to force some additional opening of the choke valve. This provides more accurate control of the choke valve, and thus reduces HC and CO in the exhaust gases during engine warm-up.

When the engine is stopped and cools, the thermostatic spring again winds up. This closes the choke valve and spring-loads it in the closed position.

Figure 7-34 shows a carburetor partly cut away so that the construction of the automatic choke can be seen. The vacuum passage to the vacuum piston is shown, but the heat tube to the exhaust manifold is not. The heat tube sends heat from the exhaust manifold to the thermostatic-spring housing.

In many engines, the thermostat is located in a

well in the exhaust gas crossover passage of the intake manifold. There, it can quickly react to the manifold heat as the engine starts (see Figs. 7-35 and 7-39). The thermostat is connected by a link to the carburetor. Some carburetors using this arangement have vacuum pistons. Others have vacuum diaphragms. Both work with the thermostat, as previously noted, to control the choke-valve position during warm-up.

Some carburetors use heat from the engine coolant to operate the thermostat. That is, the thermostat housing has a passage through which the

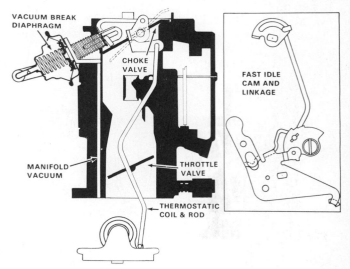

Fig. 7-35. Choke system with the thermostat located in a well in the exhaust-gas crossover passage of the intake manifold. Note the vacuum-break diaphragm. (*Chevrolet Motor Division of General Motors Corporation*)

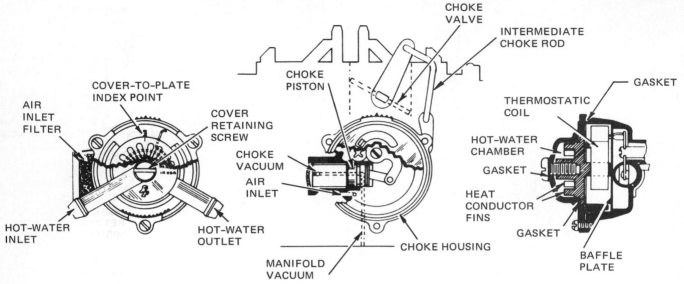

Fig. 7-36. Water-heated choke in cutaway views. (*Buick Motor Division of General Motors Corporation*)

coolant flows (Fig. 7-36). The action is similar to that in the automatic chokes previously discussed.

Instead of a vacuum piston, many automatic chokes now use a vacuum-operated diaphragm (Fig. 7-35). The operation is again quite similar. However, the diaphragm provides more force to break the choke valve loose if it gets stuck. The linkage from the diaphragm to the choke-valve lever rides freely in a slot in the lever. During certain phases of warm-up operation, the changing vacuum causes the linkage to ride to the end of the slot in the choke lever and move the choke valve. For example, when the throttle is opened during cold-engine operation, loss of intake-manifold vacuum causes the diaphragm to move. This movement carries the choke-valve lever around so that the choke valve is moved toward the closed position. This action provides a richer mixture for good acceleration.

Many late-model cars have electric automatic chokes. This type of choke includes an electric heat-

ing element (Fig. 7-37). The purpose of this heater is to assure faster choke opening. This helps reduce emissions from the engine. Emissions (HC and CO) are relatively high during the early stages of engine warm-up. At low temperatures, the electric heater adds to the heat coming from the exhaust gas. This reduces choke-opening time to as short as $1\frac{1}{2}$ min (minutes). Figure 7-38 shows the arrangement for a choke mounted in a well in the intake manifold. Figure 7-39 shows the choke and heating element removed from the well.

⊘ 7-33 Manifold Heat Control During initial warm-up of the engine, just after starting, vaporiza-

Fig. 7-37. Cutaway view of an electric-assist choke. At low temperature, the ceramic heater turns on, adding heat to the choke so it opens more quickly. (*Ford Motor Company*)

Fig. 7-38. Arrangement for an electric-assist choke mounted in a well in the exhaust-gas crossover passage of the intake manifold. (*Chrysler Corporation*)

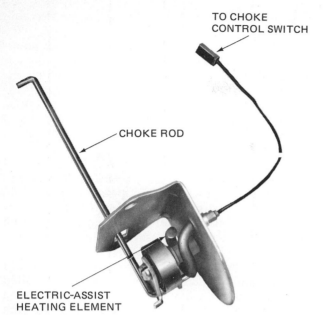

Fig. 7-39. Choke assembly removed from the well in the intake manifold to show the electric-assist heating element. (*Chrysler Corporation*)

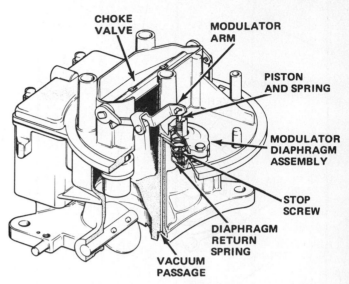

Fig. 7-41. Choke-modulator system on a carburetor which has been partly cut away to show vacuum passage to the modulator piston. (*American Motors Corporation*)

tion of the fuel is poor. To improve fuel vaporization and therefore cold-engine operation, a device is provided to heat the intake manifold when it is cold. This device, called the *manifold heat-control valve,* is built into the exhaust and intake manifolds. Two arrangements are used, one for in-line engines and another for V-8 engines.

1. *IN-LINE ENGINES* In these engines, the exhaust manifold is located under the intake manifold. At a central point, there is an opening from the exhaust manifold into a chamber, or oven, surrounding the intake manifold (Fig. 7-43). A butterfly valve is placed in this opening (see Fig. 7-44). When the valve is turned one way, the opening is closed off. The position of the valve is controlled by a thermostat. When the engine is cold, the thermostatic spring winds up and moves the valve to the closed position (left in Fig. 7-43). Now, when the engine is started, the hot exhaust gases pass through the opening and circulate through the oven around the intake manifold (Fig. 7-43). Heat from the exhaust gases quickly warms the intake manifold and helps the fuel to vaporize. Thus, cold-engine operation is improved. As the engine warms up, the thermostatic spring unwinds, and the valve moves to the open position (right in Fig. 7-43). Now, the exhaust gases pass di-

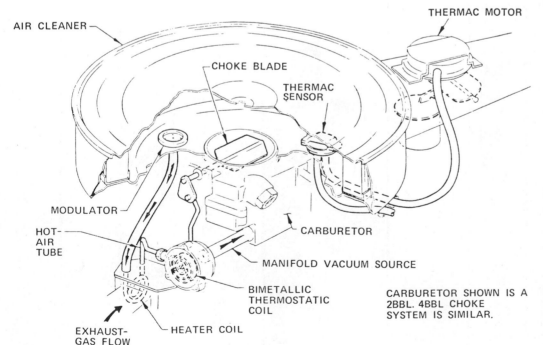

Fig. 7-40. Hot-air choke system. The air flowing to the thermostat is heated as it passes through the heater-coil tube positioned in the exhaust-gas flow. Part of the Thermac, or heated-air, system is also shown. (*Pontiac Motor Division of General Motors Corporation*)

CARBURETOR SHOWN IS A 2BBL. 4BBL CHOKE SYSTEM IS SIMILAR.

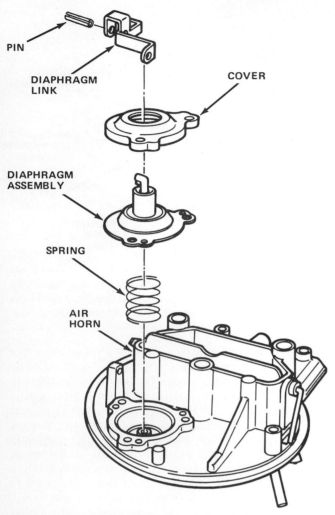

PIN

DIAPHRAGM LINK

COVER

DIAPHRAGM ASSEMBLY

SPRING

AIR HORN

Fig. 7-42. Disassembled view of the choke modulator. (*American Motors Corporation*)

rectly into the exhaust pipe. They no longer circulate in the oven around the intake manifold.

2. *V-8 ENGINES* In V-8 engines, the intake manifold is placed between the two banks of cylinders. It has a special passage (Fig. 7-45) through which exhaust gases can move. One of the exhaust manifolds has a thermostatically controlled valve that closes when the engine is cold. This causes exhaust gases to pass from that exhaust manifold through the special passage in the intake manifold. The exhaust gases then enter the other exhaust manifold. Heat from the exhaust gases thus heats the air-fuel mixture in the intake manifold for improved cold-engine operation. As the engine warms up, the thermostatically controlled valve opens. Then, the exhaust gases from both exhaust manifolds pass directly into the exhaust pipes.

3. *EARLY-FUEL-EVAPORATION (EFE) SYSTEM* Many late-model cars have a vacuum-controlled manifold heat-control valve (Fig. 7-46). That is, a vacuum motor (instead of a thermostat) controls the position of the heat-control valve. The system is called an *early-fuel-evaporation* (EFE) system because of its quick action. The heat-control valve is called the *EFE valve*. The vacuum to operate the vacuum motor comes from the intake manifold through a thermal vacuum switch. You can see the locations of the EFE valve and vacuum motor on a V-8 engine in Fig. 7-46. The EFE valve does the same job as the thermostatically operated heat-control valve for in-line and V-8 engines. However, the EFE valve does the job much faster. This reduces the time during which heat is going into the intake manifold. It thus improves engine operation during warm-up.

When the engine is off, the heat-control valve is in the open position shown to the right in Fig. 7-43

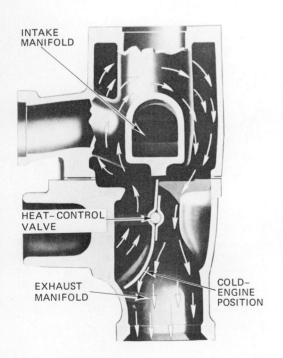

INTAKE MANIFOLD

HEAT–CONTROL VALVE

EXHAUST MANIFOLD

COLD–ENGINE POSITION

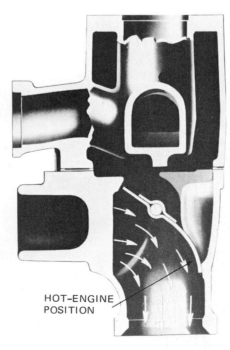

HOT-ENGINE POSITION

Fig. 7-43. Two extreme positions (in the exhaust manifold) of the manifold heat-control valve, which controls the flow of exhaust gases through the intake-manifold jacket. (*Chevrolet Motor Division of General Motors Corporation*)

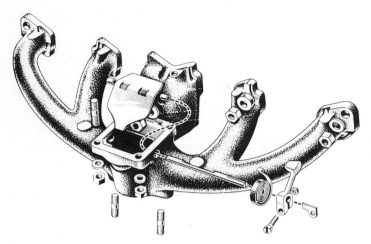

Fig. 7-44. Exhaust manifold for a six-cylinder, in-line engine, with heat-control valve and parts disassembled.

(for in-line engines). In V-8 engines, the EFE valve is open. However, when the engine is started and intake-manifold vacuum develops, the vacuum passes through the thermal vacuum switch to the vacuum motor. The vacuum motor then operates to close the EFE valve, as shown to the left in Fig. 7-43 (for in-line engines). This sends exhaust gases up through the oven around the intake manifold. In V-8 engines, closing of the EFE valve shuts off one exhaust manifold from the exhaust pipe. In either case, heat from the exhaust gases passes into the ingoing air-fuel mixture to improve fuel vaporization and cold-engine operation.

As the engine begins to warm up, the thermal vacuum switch shuts off the vacuum to the vacuum motor. Now, the motor relaxes to allow the heat-control valve in in-line engines to assume the hot-engine position (to the right in Fig. 7-43). In V-8 engines, the EFE valve opens to permit normal movement of the exhaust gases from the exhaust manifold to the exhaust pipe.

NOTE: With the introduction of thermostatic air cleaners (heated-air systems, ⊘ 7-34), some engines do not use a heat-control valve. To do so might add too much heat to the incoming air-fuel mixture. This would reduce the amount of air-fuel mixture entering, and thus reduce engine power.

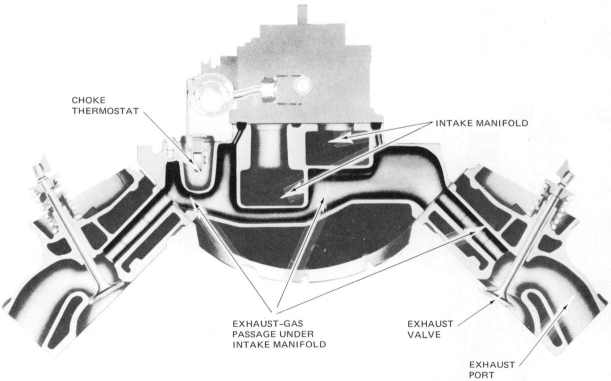

Fig. 7-45. Exhaust-gas passage under the intake manifold in a V-8 engine. Note the well in which the carburetor choke thermostat is located. (*Buick Motor Division of General Motors Corporation*)

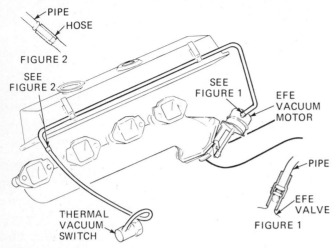

Fig. 7-46. Location of the EFE vacuum motor and thermal vacuum switch in an early-fuel-evaporation (EFE) system. (*Cadillac Motor Car Division of General Motors Corporation*)

⊘ 7-34 Thermostatically Controlled Air Cleaner

The thermostatically controlled air cleaner is part of a controlled-combustion system used on late-model cars. It is one component of the emission-control equipment discussed in detail in this and following chapters. To reduce engine emissions, carburetors are adjusted to give leaner mixtures at idle and part throttle. (That is, the amount of gasoline in the air-fuel mixture is reduced.) These leaner mixtures assure more complete burning of the gasoline. This means there is less HC coming out the tail pipe.

However, these leaner mixtures can reduce engine performance when the engine is cold. To correct this, a thermostatically controlled air cleaner is used. This system is called the *heated-air system* (HAS) by General Motors (Fig. 7-47). It sends heated

air to the carburetor during cold weather, when the engine is cold. This improves engine performance after a cold start and during engine warm-up. Thus, leaner mixtures can be used without affecting cold-engine performance.

A partly disassembled view of a heated-air system for a six-cylinder engine is shown in Fig. 7-48. A partly disassembled view of a heated-air system for a V-8 engine is shown in Fig. 7-49.

One air cleaner of this type is shown in Fig. 7-50. It contains a sensing spring which reacts to the temperature of the air entering the carburetor through the air cleaner. This spring controls an air-bleed valve (see Fig. 7-51). When the entering air is cold, the sensing spring holds the bleed valve closed. Now, intake-manifold vacuum is applied to the vacuum chamber. The diaphragm is pushed upward by atmospheric pressure, and the diaphragm spring is compressed. In this position, linkage from the diaphragm raises the control-damper assembly. This blocks off the snorkel tube. All air now has to enter from the hot-air pipe (view B in Fig. 7-51). This pipe is connected to the heat stove on the exhaust manifold. Therefore, as soon as the engine starts and the exhaust manifold begins to warm up, hot air is delivered to the carburetor and engine. This improves cold and warm-up operation.

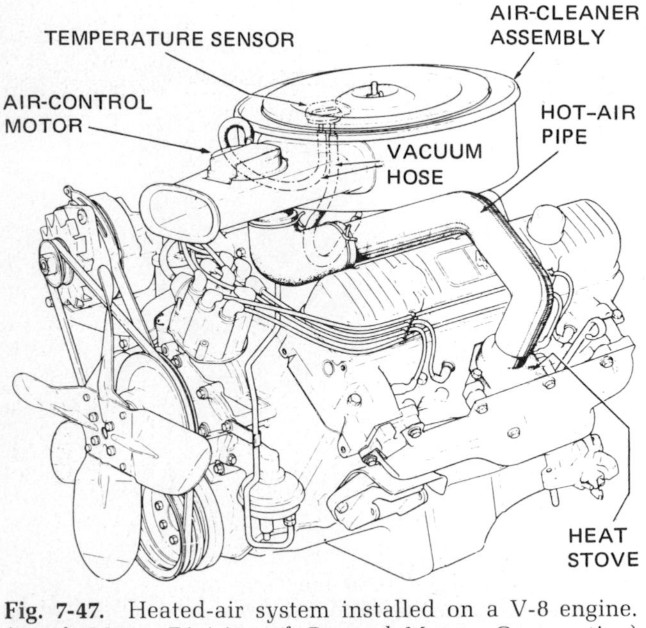

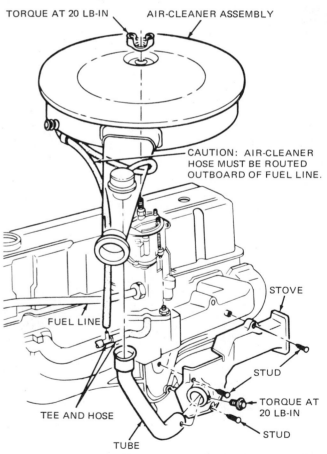

Fig. 7-48. Air cleaner, heat stove, and tube for a six-cylinder engine. (*Chevrolet Motor Division of General Motors Corporation*)

Fig. 7-47. Heated-air system installed on a V-8 engine. (*Buick Motor Division of General Motors Corporation*)

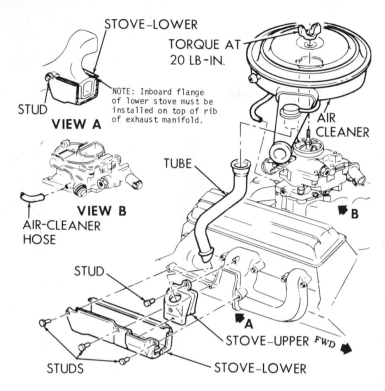

Fig. 7-49. Air cleaner, heat stove, and tube for a V-8 engine. (*Chevrolet Motor Division of General Motors Corporation*)

As the engine begins to warm up, the underhood temperature increases. If the underhood temperature goes above 128°F [53.3°C] (in the application shown), the conditions are as shown in view *C* in Fig. 7-51. That is, the temperature-sensing spring has bent enough to open the air-bleed valve. This reduces the vacuum above the diaphragm so that the diaphragm spring pushes the control damper all the way down. Now, all air entering the carburetor comes from under the hood, and none comes from the hot-air pipe.

If the temperature under the hood stays somewhere between 85 and 128°F [29.4 and 53.3°C], conditions are as shown in view *D* in Fig. 7-51. That is, the temperature-sensing spring holds the air-bleed valve partly open. Some vacuum therefore gets to the vacuum chamber above the diaphragm. This

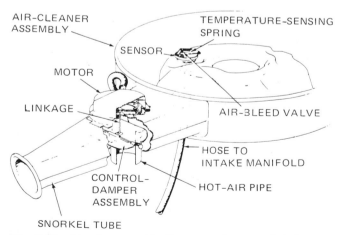

Fig. 7-50. Air cleaner with thermostatic control. (*Chevrolet Motor Division of General Motors Corporation*)

vacuum holds the control damper partly open, as shown. In this position, some air enters from the hood; and some air comes up, through the hot-air pipe, from the heat stove around the exhaust manifold.

A similar thermostatically controlled air cleaner is shown in Figs. 7-52 and 7-53. This design, however, has a thermostatic bulb that acts directly on the valve plate. When the engine is cold, the thermostatic bulb positions the valve plate as shown in Fig. 7-53. All ingoing air must come from the hot-air duct, which is connected to a shroud around the exhaust manifold. As the engine warms up, the hotter air from the shroud causes the thermostatic bulb to start moving the valve plate. Thus, some air begins to enter from the engine compartment. With further increases in temperature, the valve plate moves further, so that more engine-compartment air enters. When the engine compartment becomes hot, most or all of the ingoing air comes from the engine compartment.

The design shown in Fig. 7-52 includes a vacuum motor. This motor operates if a partial vacuum develops in the air cleaner. During cold-engine acceleration, not enough air may be getting through the heated-air system from the stove around the exhaust manifold. That is, a partial vacuum may develop in the air cleaner. If this happens, the partial vacuum opens the valve in the vacuum motor. Now, extra air is admitted to the air cleaner to satisfy the demands of the engine during cold-engine acceleration.

Some heavy-duty applications, such as trucks, use a similar thermostatically controlled air cleaner to improve engine horsepower and performance during hot weather (Fig. 7-55). The air valve is closed during initial running and in cool weather, when the

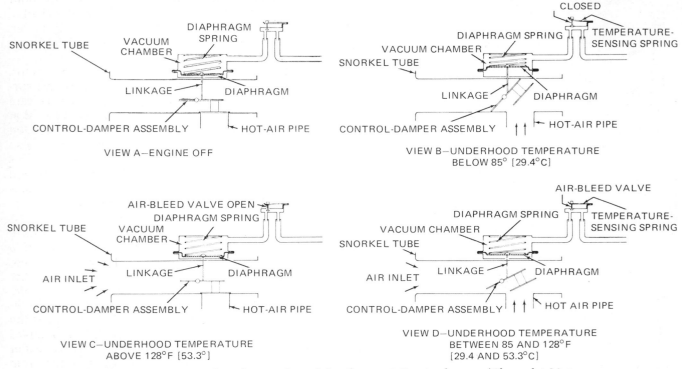

Fig. 7-51. Four modes of operation of the thermostatic air cleaner. (*Chevrolet Motor Division of General Motors Corporation*)

under-hood temperature is low. However, when the air temperature entering the air cleaner rises above 83°F [28.3°C], the thermostatic element begins to open the valve. Now, cooler outside air, being more dense, causes the engine to develop more horsepower. By the time the temperature entering the air cleaner has reached 102°F [38.9°C], the air valve is wide open. Then, all the air going into the air cleaner is outside air.

⊘ **7-35 Anti-Icing** When fuel is sprayed into the air passing through the air horn, it evaporates, or turns to vapor. As it evaporates, the fuel takes heat from the surrounding air and metal parts. This same

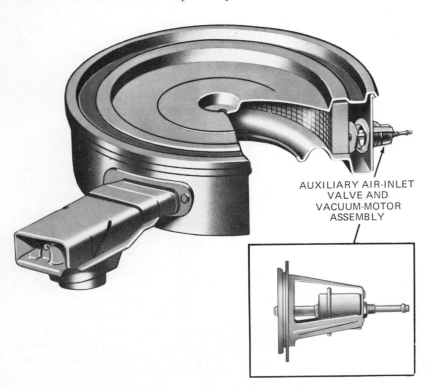

AUXILIARY AIR-INLET VALVE AND VACUUM-MOTOR ASSEMBLY

Fig. 7-52. Air cleaner with auxiliary air-inlet valve and vacuum motor. (*Ford Motor Company*)

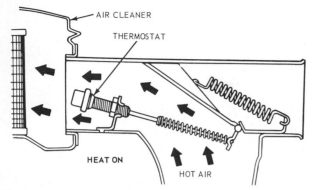

Fig. 7-53. Operation of the thermostatic air cleaner when the engine is cold and heated air is being taken from the heat stove around the exhaust manifold. (*Ford Motor Company*)

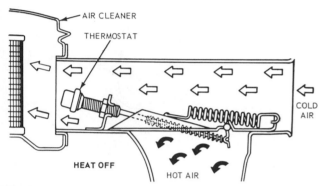

Fig. 7-54. Operation of the thermostatic air cleaner when the engine is warm and air is being taken from under the hood. (*Ford Motor Company*)

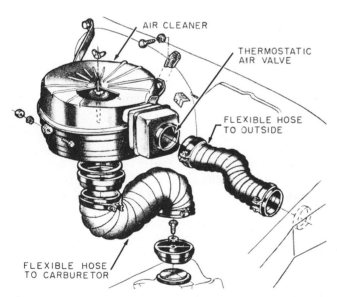

Fig. 7-55. Air cleaner with a thermostatic air valve. The thermostatic air valve has an opening (not shown) in its underside, through which air flows from under the hood during cold conditions. Under hot conditions, the valve closes this opening and opens the passage through the flexible hose to the outside. (*Chevrolet Motor Division of General Motors Corporation*)

action makes your hand feel cold when you pour alcohol on it. If you blow on your hand, the alcohol evaporates faster, and your hand feels still colder. The faster the evaporation takes heat from your hand, the colder your hand feels.

Now, let us see how this affects the carburetor. Spraying and evaporation of the fuel "rob" the surrounding air and carburetor of heat. Under certain conditions, the carburetor becomes so cold that moisture in the air condenses and actually freezes on the metal parts. If conditions are right, the ice can build up sufficiently to cause the engine to stall. This is most apt to occur during the warm-up period following the first startup of the day. It happens mostly with air temperatures in the range of 40 to 60°F [4.4 to 15.6°C] and fairly humid air.

To prevent such icing, many carburetors have special anti-icing systems. One arrangement for a V-8 engine is shown in Fig. 7-56. During the warm-up period, the manifold heat-control valve sends hot exhaust gases from one exhaust manifold to the other (see ⊘ 7-33). Part of this hot exhaust gas circulates around the carburetor idle ports and near the throttle-valve shaft. This adds enough heat to guard against ice formation. Another system has water passages in the carburetor. The water comes from the engine cooling system. A small amount of the cooling water passes through a special water manifold in the carburetor throttle body. This adds enough heat to the carburetor to prevent icing.

⊘ **7-36 Fast Idle** When the engine is cold, some throttle opening must be maintained. This causes the engine to idle faster than it would when warm. Otherwise, the slow idle and cold engine might cause the engine to stall. With fast idle, enough air-fuel mixture gets through, and airspeeds are great enough, to produce adequate vaporization and a sufficiently rich mixture. Fast idle is obtained by a fast-idle cam linked to the choke valve (Fig. 7-57).

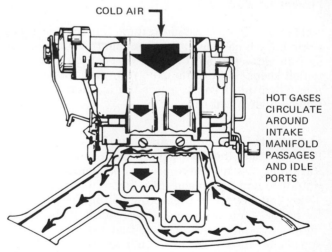

Fig. 7-56 Heating passages in the intake manifold and carburetor idle ports. Hot exhaust gases heat these areas as soon as the engine starts. (*Cadillac Motor Car Division of General Motors Corporation*)

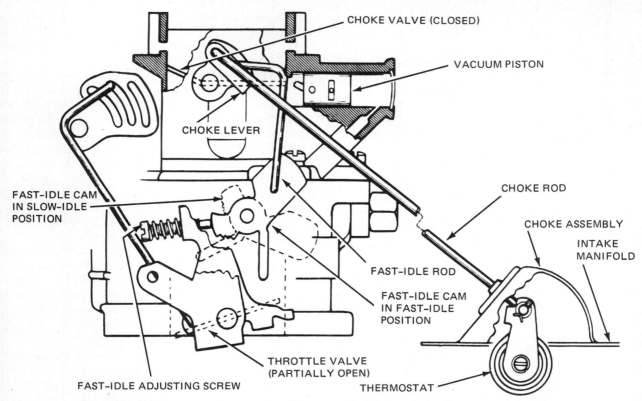

Fig. 7-57. Vacuum and thermostatically operated choke with the thermostat located in the intake manifold. Note the two positions of the fast-idle cam. (*Chrysler Corporation*)

When the engine is cold, the automatic choke holds the choke valve closed. In this position the linkage has revolved the fast-idle cam so that the adjusting screw rests on the high point of the cam. The adjusting screw prevents the throttle valve from moving to the fully closed position. That is, the throttle valve is held partly open for fast idle. As the engine warms up, the choke valve opens. This rotates the fast-idle cam so that the high point moves from under the adjusting screw. The throttle valve closes for normal hot-engine slow idle.

NOTE: In ⊘ 7-17 we described the antidieseling solenoid, which provides a movable throttle stop. In ⊘ 7-26 we described the throttle-position solenoid, which keeps the throttle from returning instantly to idle when the driver releases the accelerator pedal after a high-speed run.

⊘ 7-37 Air-Bleed and Antisiphon Passages In all the systems of the carburetor except some accelerator-pump systems, there are small openings to permit air to enter, or bleed into, the system (Fig. 7-22). This produces some premixing of the air and fuel, for better atomization and vaporization. It also helps maintain a more uniform air-fuel ratio. At higher speeds, a larger amount of fuel tends to discharge from the main nozzle. But, at the same time, the faster fuel movement through the high-speed system causes more air to bleed into the system. Thus, the air-bleed holes tend to equalize the air-fuel ratio.

Air-bleed passages are also sometimes called *antisiphon* passages. They act as air vents to prevent the siphoning of fuel from the float bowl at intermediate engine speeds.

If air-bleed passages become plugged, they may cause the float bowl to be emptied after the engine shuts off. When the engine is shut off, the intake manifold cools down; a slight vacuum forms as a result. With open air bleeds, air can move through the bleeds to satisfy the vacuum. But if the air bleeds are plugged, then the vacuum causes the float bowl to empty through the idle system.

⊘ 7-38 Summary Now, let's review the carburetor design changes and special devices used in today's engines to control the air-fuel mixture and thus minimize atmospheric pollution. As you will recall, one change is to adjust carburetor calibrations to produce a leaner mixture. Another is to refine choke operation so the choke opens more quickly. To assist in this speedy choke opening, many chokes have the thermostatic spring in a well in the exhaust gas crossover passage of the intake manifold. There, it can more quickly sense engine exhaust heat. In addition, many chokes have an electric assist to speed the choke opening. Also, some chokes include a heater tube placed in the exhaust-gas flow path. The air going to the choke thermostatic spring passes through this tube. Heat reaches the thermostatic spring more quickly, and it starts to open the choke valve sooner.

Several devices are used to improve idling with the leaner mixture. The idle-enrichment system, used on cars with automatic transmissions, reduces cold-engine stalling during off-idle operation. The antidieseling solenoid is used to prevent engine run-on, or dieseling, after the ignition is turned off. The higher idle speed required in engines because of the leaner idle mixture can allow dieseling. But the antidieseling solenoid prevents this by allowing the throttle to close completely when the ignition is turned off.

Some carburetors have a factory-adjustable part-throttle metering rod. This allows the carburetor to be fine-tuned for operation at part-throttle, so the mixture will be lean and will not tend to change from the specified ratio.

The throttle-position solenoid, used on cars equipped with catalytic converters, prevents sudden closing of the throttle when the driver releases the pedal after a high-speed run. If the throttle closed suddenly, the catalytic converter would receive a momentary surge of unburned HC and CO. This could so overheat the converter as to damage or destroy it. The throttle-position solenoid prevents this. The throttle-return check is another device used to slow throttle closing. It is used on cars with automatic transmissions to prevent a sudden surge of overrich air-fuel mixture and poor engine performance.

The warm-up operating mode has a number of devices to prevent an overly rich mixture from entering the engine for extended periods. The choke acts fast, as already noted. In addition, the heat-control valve in some cars is now controlled by a vacuum motor instead of a thermostatic spring. The vacuum motor gets its controlling vacuum from the intake manifold, through a thermal switch that senses coolant temperature. All cars now use the heated-air system, in which the air-flow into the carburetor air cleaner comes from a heat stove on the exhaust manifold. Some cars using the heated-air system do not use the manifold heat-control valve.

In summary, the emissions of HC and CO from an engine are reduced significantly by improved control of the air-fuel mixture.

CHAPTER 7 CHECKUP

NOTE: Since the following is a chapter review test, you should review the chapter before taking the test.

You have now finished the first of the three chapters on controlling exhaust emissions. By now you should have a good understanding of how exhaust pollutants are formed, and the carburetor changes that are necessary to keep them to a minimum. In the next two chapters, you will study how to control exhaust emissions by controlling combustion and by treating the exhaust gases. So, as you can see, you are making good progress in your study of automotive emission control. Work through the following checkup to see how well you understand the chapter you have been studying.

Completing the Sentences The sentences below are incomplete. After each sentence there are several words or phrases, but only one of them correctly completes the sentence. Write each sentence in your notebook, ending it with the word or phrase that completes it correctly.

1. The wider the throttle is opened and the faster the air flows through the air horn, the greater the: (a) manifold vacuum, (b) venturi vacuum, (c) choke action, (d) compression ratio.
2. A factory-adjustable part throttle allows the carburetor to be calibrated to compensate for: (a) improper air-fuel-mixture adjustment, (b) manufacturing tolerances, (c) high idle speed, (d) fast choke action.
3. A carburetor which is sensitive to changes in atmospheric pressure has: (a) an antidieseling solenoid, (b) a dashpot, (c) an early-fuel-evaporation system, (d) altitude compensation.
4. Cars with catalytic converters may use a throttle-position solenoid to prevent: (a) engine dieseling, (b) excessive idle speed, (c) sudden closing of the throttle, (d) vapor buildup in the float bowl.
5. The catalytic converter changes the HC in the exhaust gas into: (a) water and CO_2, (b) HC and CO, (c) CO and NO_x, (d) liquid gasoline.
6. The throttle-return check, or dashpot, reduces exhaust emissions by: (a) slowing the closing of the throttle, (b) lowering the idle speed, (c) increasing the idle speed, (d) retarding the vacuum advance.
7. From about 40 to 60 mph [64 to 97 km/h], fuel for engine operation is metered by the: (a) idle system, (b) power system, (c) main metering system, (d) choke system.
8. An early-fuel-evaporation system uses a vacuum-controlled: (a) automatic choke, (b) throttle valve, (c) air cleaner, (d) manifold heat-control valve.
9. To open the choke more quickly, some carburetors use: (a) a thermostatic spring, (b) an electric-assist choke, (c) a vacuum-break diaphragm, (d) a manifold heat-control valve.
10. The device that sends heated air to the carburetor during cold weather when the engine is cold is the (a) manifold heat-control valve, (b) early-fuel-evaporation system, (c) automatic choke, (d) thermostatically controlled air cleaner.

Correcting Lists The purpose of this exercise is to enable you to spot unrelated items in a list. For example, look through the list "distributor, coil, spark plugs, fuel pump, ignition switch." You can see that "fuel pump" does not belong, because it is the only item that is not part of the ignition system. Each of the lists below contains one item that does not belong. Write each list in your notebook, but do not write the unrelated item. Check your work with the answers at the back of the book.

1. Fuel systems in the carburetor include the float system, main metering system, power system, ignition system, and idle system.
2. Parts of a simple carburetor include the air horn, air cleaner, venturi, and throttle valve.
3. Devices added to the carburetor to help reduce exhaust emissions include the manifold heat-control valve, throttle-position solenoid, throttle-return check, and dashpot.
4. Devices added to the engine to help reduce exhaust emissions during initial warm-up of a cold engine include the thermostatically controlled air cleaner, early-fuel evaporation system, electric-assist choke, and factory-adjustable part throttle.

Definitions In the following, you are asked for the definitions of some words and phrases. Write them in your notebook. The act of writing the definitions does two things: It tests your knowledge, and it helps fix the information more firmly in your mind. Turn back into the chapter if you are not sure of an answer, or look up the definition in the glossary at the back of the book.

1. What is a rich air-fuel mixture?
2. What is a combustible mixture?
3. Define "vaporization."
4. What is the venturi effect?
5. What is a fuel nozzle?
6. Define "air bleed."
7. What is engine run-on?
8. Define "metering rod."
9. What is a throttle-return check?
10. What is a dual carburetor?

SUGGESTIONS FOR FURTHER STUDY

After studying this chapter, you know how important the carburetor is in reducing exhaust emissions. By controlling the air-fuel mixture more accurately than in past years, the carburetor and its devices keep the engine running on a lean mixture, without periods of very rich operation.

One of the best ways to understand a late-model carburetor is to take one apart by following the step-by-step instructions in the manufacturer's service manual. Identify the parts, and trace each fuel system in the carburetor. Assemble the carburetor, making each check and adjustment called for in the service manual.

Examine several different makes and models of new cars. With the air cleaner off, examine the carburetor carefully. Locate and identify as many of the add-on carburetor devices as you can. Note whether the engine has a thermostatically controlled air cleaner. Then, check for a heat-control valve on the exhaust manifold. If you locate one, determine whether it is vacuum controlled. If it is, the engine is equipped with an early-fuel evaporation system. By checking several late-model cars, you can learn to identify the devices that help the carburetor reduce exhaust emissions by controlling the air-fuel mixture.

chapter 8

CONTROLLING COMBUSTION

In this chapter, we describe ways of controlling the combustion process to reduce the formation of atmospheric pollutants. As mentioned in ⊘ 3-8 and 3-10, three pollutants come from the combustion chamber. HC and CO result from incomplete combustion of the air-fuel mixture. NO$_x$ is formed as a result of the high combustion temperatures. Reducing the combustion temperature, and reducing the time when peak temperatures are maintained, will reduce the amount of NO$_x$. In Chap. 7 we discussed various carburetor changes that have helped to reduce exhaust-gas emissions. These include leaning out the air-fuel mixture, shortening the choking time, and shortening the warm-up period. Shortening the warm-up period reduces the length of time when partly vaporized fuel enters the engine intake manifold. These changes relate to the air-fuel mixture before combustion. Now let us look at what can be done to control the combustion process.

⊘ **8-1 The Combustion Process** The combustion process seems simple at first glance. A mixture of air and gasoline vapor is compressed in the combustion chamber. A spark ignites it. It burns and produces the high pressure that pushes the piston down. However, the process is actually complicated. Here are some of the factors involved:

1. QUENCH The layers of air-fuel mixture next to the relatively cool metal surfaces of the combustion chamber do not burn. These metal surfaces include the head of the piston, and the cylinder head with its intake and exhaust valves (Fig. 3-8). They are kept comparatively cool by the engine cooling system. The layers of air-fuel mixture next to these metal surfaces are chilled below the combustion temperature.

Combustion starts at the spark between the spark-plug electrodes. It spreads out from this point, almost like a balloon being blown up (Fig. 8-1). As the flame front approaches the layers of air-fuel mixture next to the cool metal surfaces, the metal takes heat away from these layers as fast as the hot flame adds heat. As a result, the layers of air-fuel mixture never get hot enough to combust, or burn. The flame is quenched before it can get to the cool layers.

Quench is used in the wedge-shaped combustion chamber to reduce the possibility of detonation, or spark knock. In the wedge chamber (Fig. 8-2), the flame starts at the spark plug and moves out in all directions. It arrives last at the quench area. The compressed air-fuel mixture within the quench area

is called the *end gas*. During combustion, the end gas is subjected to increasing pressure and temperature. It is this increasing temperature and pressure that tends to detonate the end gas. If the end gas explodes before the flame front reaches it, spark knock, or detonation, results (Fig. 8-3). However, with a quench area (Fig. 8-2), the end gas loses heat as fast as the approaching flame front adds it. So it never burns. Detonation is therefore prevented.

The layers of unburned air-fuel mixture are swept out of the combustion chamber during the exhaust stroke. Some of this air-fuel mixture has

Fig. 8-1. A balloon being blown up demonstrates flame propagation, or travel, through the combustion chamber.

125

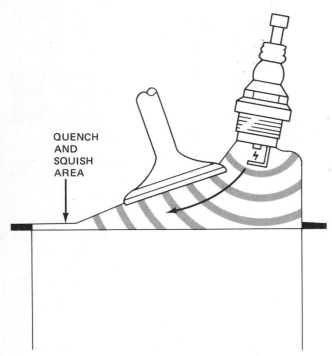

Fig. 8-2. Flame front approaching the quench area in a wedge-type combustion chamber.

QUENCH AND SQUISH AREA

actually started to burn. That is, it contains some CO.

There are two methods of reducing the effects of quenching. One is to use stratified charge or fuel injection. The other is to reduce the surface area that bounds the combustion chamber. We shall come back to these later.

2. TEMPERATURE If the combustion temperature is high enough, some of the air-fuel mixture lying next to the cool metal parts will burn. However, this high temperature increases the amount of NO_x that is formed during the combustion process. We discuss control of NO_x in a later section.

3. TIME The longer the high combustion temperatures are maintained, the more time NO_x has to form. During part-throttle operation, the ignition system advances the spark (⊘ 2-14). The reasoning behind this spark advance at part throttle is as follows. During part throttle, there is a vacuum in the intake manifold. This means that less air-fuel mixture gets into the engine cylinders on the intake strokes. With less air-fuel mixture, the compression pressure is lower at the end of the compression stroke. At lower pressure, the mixture does not burn as fast. Therefore, advancing the spark gives the mixture enough time to burn and develop pressure before the piston goes over TDC.

Advancing the spark, and thus giving the air-fuel mixture a longer time to burn, also gives the NO_x more time to form. At road speeds, this is not so important, because the combustion time is very short at high engine speeds. However, on engines with manual transmissions, when accelerating from a standing start or in low gear, the combustion time is significantly longer. Therefore, devices have been added to modern engines to prevent vacuum advance in lower gears.

The previous paragraph states that the combustion time is longer *on cars with manual transmissions.* This is because the manual transmission has no slippage. Therefore, engine speed increases relatively slowly as the car is accelerated in the lower gears. But with an automatic transmission, the torque converter does permit slippage. Thus, the engine speed picks up very rapidly on acceleration. With an automatic transmission, therefore, the combustion time is very short, and vacuum advance does not greatly increase the formation of NO_x.

We describe mechanisms that prevent vacuum advance under the given conditions in a later section.

4. Carbon Carbon buildup in the combustion chamber increases the HC in the exhaust gas. The

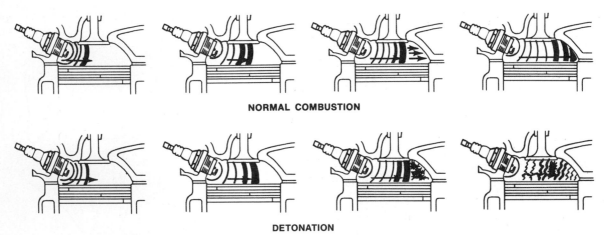

NORMAL COMBUSTION

DETONATION

Fig. 8-3. Normal combustion without detonation is shown in the top row. The fuel charge burns smoothly from beginning to end, providing an even, powerful thrust to the piston. Detonation is shown in the bottom row. The last part of the fuel explodes, or burns, almost all at once, to produce detonation, or spark knock. (*General Motors Corporation*)

carbon has pores that fill up during the compression and combustion strokes. Then, during the exhaust stroke, when the pressure drops, the HC escapes from the carbon pores and exits with the exhaust gas. In a normally running engine, carbon buildup is not usually a serious problem. But if the air-fuel mixture is running rich owing to some carburetor problem, or if oil is working up into the combustion chamber, considerable carbon will form. The rich mixture leaves carbon on the spark plug, valve heads, piston head, and cylinder head. The oil burns and leaves a residue of carbon. The oil can come from worn cylinder walls, rings, pistons, or valve guides. Also, a spark plug that runs too cold can collect carbon, because the plug is not hot enough to burn it off. This carbon acts as a momentary reservoir for HC, as previously explained, and can cause the plug to misfire. The high voltage can leak across the carbon instead of jumping the spark-plug gap and igniting the compressed mixture.

⊘ 8-2 Reducing Combustion-Chamber Surface Area

The surface of the combustion chamber is kept relatively cool by the engine cooling system. This relatively cool area quenches the flame progressing through the air-fuel mixture. This keeps the layers of air-fuel mixture next to the metal from burning. If this surface area is reduced, then less quenching results, and there is less HC and CO in the exhaust gases. Actually, what we are discussing here is the surface-to-volume ratio (the S/V ratio in Fig. 8-4). This is the ratio between the surface area S and the volume V of the combustion chamber. A sphere has the lowest possible S/V ratio. The wedge combustion chamber (Fig. 8-2) has a relatively high S/V ratio. The hemispheric combustion chamber has a low S/V ratio and a low surface area. There is less surface to chill the air-fuel mixture and quench the flame. Therefore, the hemispheric combustion chamber produces less unburned HC in the exhaust gases.

⊘ 8-3 Stratified Charge

In a stratified-charge engine, the air-fuel mixture is not uniform when it enters the combustion chamber and is compressed. There are strata, or layers, that are relatively lean; other strata, or layers, are relatively rich. The purpose of stratified charging is to concentrate the richest air-fuel mixture around the spark plug. The leanest part of the air-fuel charge is next to the combustion-chamber surfaces. The relatively rich mixture is ignited first. As the flame approaches the metal surfaces, it is quenched, as already explained. However, the layers that do not burn have less HC in them, so the exhaust gases are relatively clean of unburned HC.

With stratified charging, a leaner air-fuel mixture, on the average, can be used. The HC is more completely burned because less of it is in the quenched layers.

One way to achieve stratified charging is to give the air-fuel mixture a swirling motion as it enters the cylinder. Careful placement of the intake valve and valve port can help achieve this. Much research has been devoted to the problem, and to date two systems have been put into production—the so-called Honda system (⊘ 8-4) and fuel injection (⊘ 8-5).

⊘ 8-4 Honda System

In the Honda system, a separate small precombustion chamber is used. This precombustion chamber has the spark plug and its own intake valve. Figure 8-5 is an outline view of the engine showing the valves, spark plug, and piston for one cylinder. Figure 8-6 shows how the arrangement works. In operation, the carburetor delivers a very lean mixture to the main combustion chamber, and a very rich mixture to the precombustion chamber. Ignition takes place in the precombustion chamber. The rich mixture, under the high pressure of combustion, streams out into the main combustion chamber, as shown in 3 and 4 of Fig. 8-6. There, it mixes with the lean mixture, and combustion continues. This ensures good burning of the fuel, so that the pollutants carbon monoxide, HC, and nitrogen oxide are kept to a low level. Figure 8-6 shows the sequence of actions.

⊘ 8-5 Fuel Injection

In the fuel-injection system, the carburetor is replaced with a high-pressure fuel pump and nozzles. They inject, or spray, the fuel into the combustion chambers or into the intake manifold. The design that injects the fuel directly

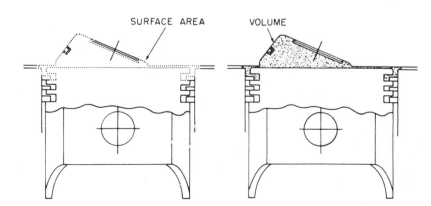

Fig. 8-4. The ratio of the surface area to the volume of the combustion chamber, or S/V. This ratio has an effect on the amount of unburned hydrocarbons in the exhaust gas.

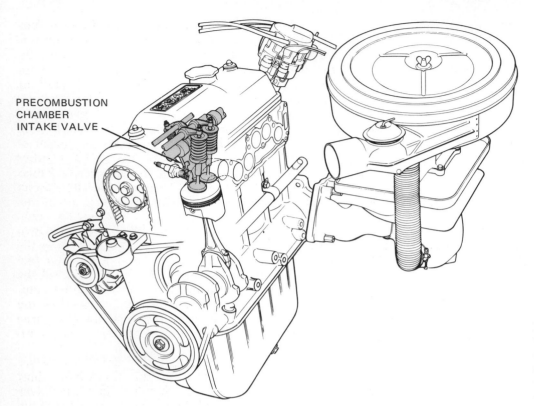

PRECOMBUSTION
CHAMBER
INTAKE VALVE

Fig. 8-5. Outline view of the Honda four-cylinder engine, showing the essential working parts of one cylinder. (*Honda Motor Company, Ltd.*)

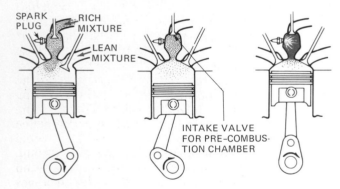

(1) INTAKE STROKE   (2) COMPRESSION STROKE   (3) IGNITION

SPARK
PLUG   RICH
            MIXTURE

            LEAN
            MIXTURE

INTAKE VALVE
FOR PRE-COMBUS-
TION CHAMBER

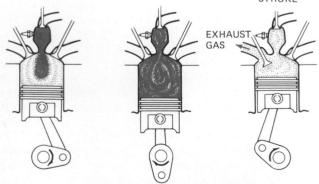

(4) POWER STROKE   (5) BOTTOM DEAD CENTER   (6) EXHAUST
                                                  STROKE

EXHAUST
GAS

Fig. 8-6. Sequence of actions in the Honda system. (*Honda Motor Company, Ltd.*)

into the combustion chambers (Fig. 8-7) is not used at present in any spark-ignition engine. It is, however, used in diesel engines. The system shown in Fig. 8-8, in which the fuel is injected into the intake manifold, is used in a number of cars.

⊘ **8-6 Diesel-Engine Fuel Injection** In the diesel engine, air alone enters the engine cylinders and is compressed. The heat of compression raises the temperature of the air to 1,000°F [538°C] or more.

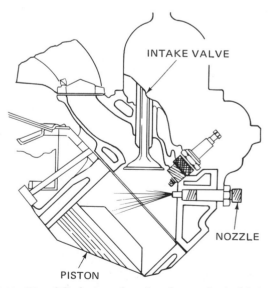

INTAKE VALVE

NOZZLE

PISTON

Fig. 8-7. Simplified view showing the method of injecting fuel directly into the combustion chamber of the engine.

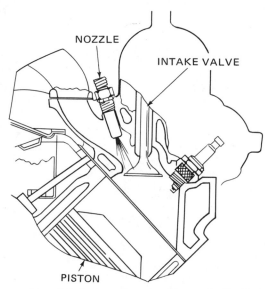

Fig. 8-8. Simplified view showing the method of injecting fuel into the intake manifold just back of the intake valve.

Then, when the fuel is injected directly into the hot compressed air, it is ignited by the heated air. Diesel engines are sometimes called compression-ignition engines for this reason. This is in contrast to the typical automotive engine, which is called a spark-ignition engine because combustion is started by an electric spark.

A typical fuel-injection system for a four-cycle diesel engine is shown in Figs. 8-9 and 8-10. The fuel must be delivered to the combustion chambers at high pressure. It must be at a higher pressure than the pressure of compressed air. The system shown uses a fuel-injection pump that is somewhat like the distributor in the ignition system of a spark-ignition engine. But instead of delivering sparks, the fuel-injection pump delivers fuel to the injection nozzles in the combustion chambers. The fuel is delivered so it arrives at the combustion chambers at the right moment. This is the moment when the piston is approaching TDC on the compression stroke.

The system includes a mechanism that controls the amount of fuel injected. This determines how much power each power stroke will deliver and, thus, engine power output. The system also includes a timing-advance mechanism. This is a form of governor that pushes the injection-pump drive shaft ahead as engine speed increases. This gets the fuel to the combustion chambers earlier, so it has ample time to burn and deliver its power to the piston. As you can see, this is like the centrifugal advance in the distributor of a spark-ignition engine.

The diesel-engine injection system is a type of stratified-charging system. The fuel is injected into the center of the combustion chamber; it begins to burn almost the instant it meets the highly compressed air. Thus, most of the combustion takes place near the center of the combustion chamber, and there is relatively little quench to prevent burning of the fuel.

⊘ **8-7 Fuel Injection for Gasoline Engines** A fuel-injection system for a gasoline engine is shown in Fig. 8-11. Note that this system does not inject the fuel directly into the engine combustion chambers. Instead, it injects the fuel into the intake manifold, opposite the intake valves. Thus, the system does not lead directly to stratified charging. However, it is claimed to give more perfect fuel distribution and more accurate metering of fuel to the cylinders.

In operation, the electric fuel pump supplies fuel at high pressure to the solenoid injection valves in the intake manifold (Fig. 8-12). At the correct instant, contact points in the distributor close. When the contact points close, they send an electric signal to the electronic control unit. The control unit then connects half the solenoid injection valves to the battery. In a four-cylinder engine, this would be two of the valves; in a six-cylinder engine, three of the valves. The solenoid injection valves are not actuated individually. Instead, half are actuated at any one time. This is shown in Fig. 8-13, in which three of the valves are spraying fuel into the intake manifold.

The fuel enters just opposite the intake valves (Fig. 8-11). Figure 8-14 is the injection timing chart for a six-cylinder engine. Note that the intake valves open at varying crankshaft degrees after injection. For example, look at the top line, which is for cylinder No. 1. Injection takes place at 300° of crankshaft rotation. Then, almost 60° later (near 360°), the intake valve opens and the intake stroke starts. For cylinder No. 5, next in the firing order, injection takes place at the same point—at 300° of crankshaft rotation. But the intake valve for this cylinder opens near 480°. The intake valve for No. 3 opens 120° later, about 300° after fuel injection. During these varying intervals between fuel injection and intake-valve opening, the fuel is, in effect, stored in the intake manifold opposite the intake valves. Having only two groups of injection valves simplifies the system. No appreciable loss of engine performance results from this storage of the fuel. The whole action takes place in a small fraction of a second. At highway speed, for example, the time between injection and opening of the intake valve averages only about 0.01 second.

⊘ **8-8 Decreasing Combustion Temperatures** We have already noted that increasing the combustion temperature increases the formation of NO_x. So it is desirable, from the standpoint of pollution control, to reduce combustion temperatures. One method is to reduce compression ratios. This reduces the top combustion temperatures and, thus, the amount of NO_x that is formed. In recent years, engine compression ratios have been reduced for this reason. This has also reduced engine performance and fuel economy. However, that seems to be the penalty to be paid for reduced NO_x in our atmosphere.

Other NO_x reduction methods are also used. One of these reduces NO_x formation during normal

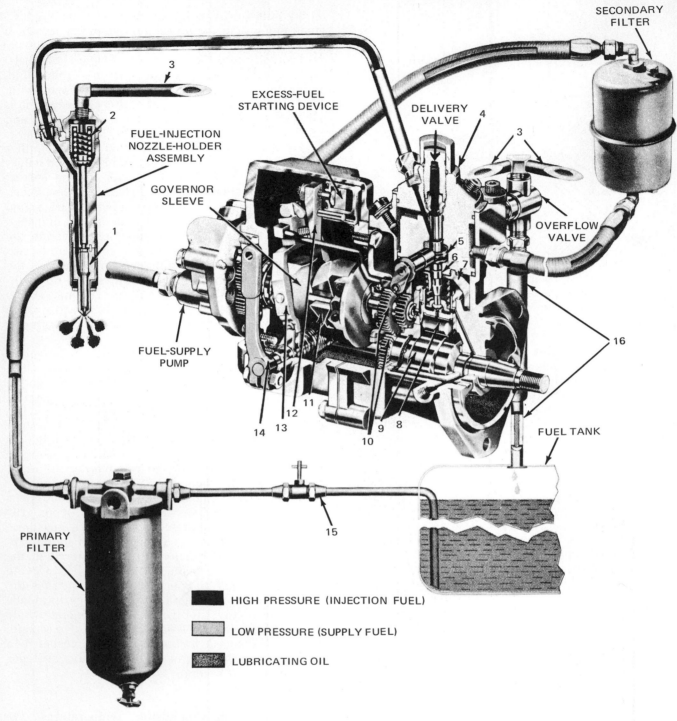

Fig. 8-9. Diesel-engine fuel-injection system. (*Chevrolet Motor Division of General Motors Corporation*)

SECONDARY FILTER

EXCESS-FUEL STARTING DEVICE

DELIVERY VALVE

FUEL-INJECTION NOZZLE-HOLDER ASSEMBLY

GOVERNOR SLEEVE

OVERFLOW VALVE

FUEL-SUPPLY PUMP

FUEL TANK

FUEL TANK

PRIMARY FILTER

HIGH PRESSURE (INJECTION FUEL)

LOW PRESSURE (SUPPLY FUEL)

LUBRICATING OIL

1. Nozzle valve and body
2. Nozzle valve spring
3. Leak-off lines
4. Hydraulic head assembly
5. Fuel-metering sleeve
6. Pump plunger
7. Face gear
8. Tappet and roller
9. Cam
10. Governor gears
11. Governor weights
12. Governor stop plate
13. Fulcrum lever
14. Stop lever
15. Shutoff
16. Fuel-return line

Fig. 8-10. Diesel engine with the high-pressure-pump type of fuel-injection system. (*Waukesha Motor Company*)

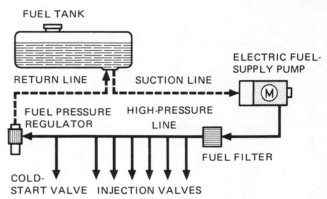

Fig. 8-12. Schematic diagram of the fuel system. (*Robert Bosch GmbH*)

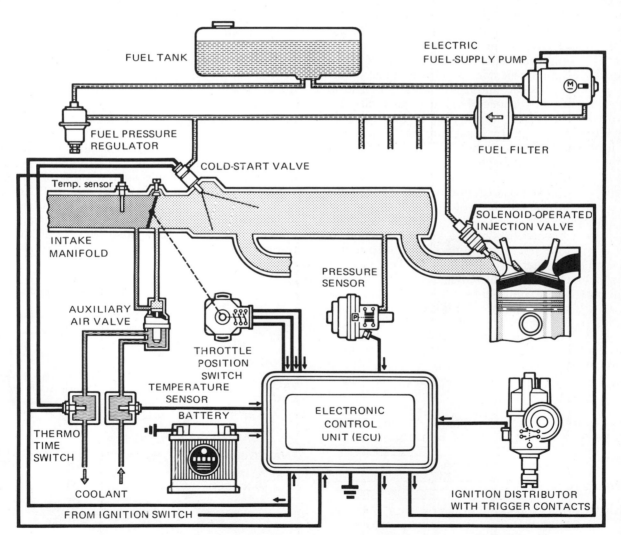

Fig. 8-11. Schematic diagram of an electronic gasoline-injection system. (*Robert Bosch GmbH*)

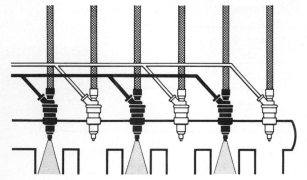

Fig. 8-13. Injection-valve grouping. (*Robert Bosch GmbH*)

running of the engine by sending some of the exhaust gases back through the engine. This is the exhaust-gas recirculation, or EGR, system. Another system reduces NO_x formation during acceleration in lower gears and during part-throttle, high-vacuum conditions. We look at these various systems now.

⊘ 8-9 Exhaust-Gas Recirculation If a small part of the exhaust gas is sent back through the engine, it reduces the combustion temperature and lowers the formation of NO_x. The amount sent through the engine should vary according to operating conditions. The simplest system is shown in Fig. 8-15. There, a special passage connects the exhaust manifold with the intake manifold. This passage is opened or closed by a special exhaust-gas recirculation (EGR) valve. The upper part of this valve is sealed. It is connected by a vacuum line to a signal port in the carburetor, as shown. When there is no vacuum at work on the signal port, there is no vacuum in the EGR valve. The spring holds the valve closed. No exhaust gas recirculates. This is the situation during engine idling, when NO_x formation is near the minimum.

However, when the throttle valve is opened, it passes the signal port. This allows the intake-manifold vacuum to operate the EGR valve. The vacuum raises the diaphragm in the valve. This lifts the valve off the seat. Now exhaust gas can pass into the intake manifold. There, it mixes with the air-fuel mixture and enters the engine cylinders. The exhaust gas lowers the combustion temperature and thus reduces the formation of NO_x. Note that, at wide-open throttle, there is little vacuum in the intake manifold. Thus, the EGR valve is nearly closed. At wide-open

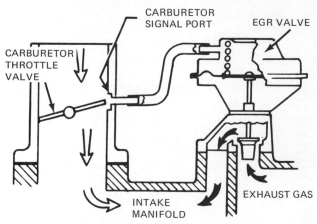

Fig. 8-15. Schematic drawing of an exhaust-gas recirculating system. (*Chevrolet Motor Division of General Motors Corporation*)

throttle there is less need for exhaust-gas recirculation.

Figure 8-16 shows the EGR valve in the fully open position. On many late-model cars, a thermal vacuum switch prevents exhaust-gas recirculation until engine temperature reaches about 100°F [37.8°C]. The thermal switch is connected into the vacuum line between the carburetor and the EGR valve. The thermal switch is mounted in the cooling-system-thermostat housing, so it senses coolant temperature. If this temperature is below 100°F [37.8°C], the thermal switch remains closed. This prevents the vacuum from reaching the EGR valve, so exhaust gas does not recirculate. This improves cold-engine performance for the first few moments of operation. After the engine warms up to where it can tolerate exhaust-gas recirculation, the thermal valve opens. Now vacuum can get to the EGR valve, so that exhaust gas can recirculate.

There are several variations of this basic system. For instance, some EGR valves have a second diaphragm. Its purpose is to produce increased ex-

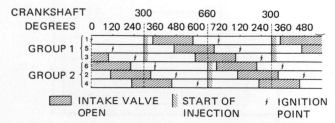

Fig. 8-14. Injection timing chart for a six-cylinder engine. (*Robert Bosch GmbH*)

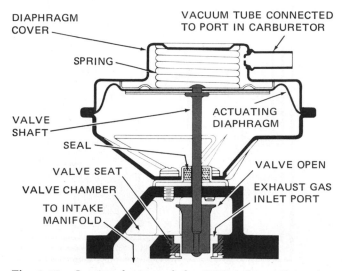

Fig. 8-16. Sectional view of the EGR valve. (*Chevrolet Motor Division of General Motors Corporation*)

haust-gas recirculation when the engine is heavily loaded, as during hard acceleration. Also, some high-performance engines use an additional modulator system to provide additional control based on car speed. One system of this type is shown in Fig. 8-17. The modulator system is enclosed in dashed lines. It includes a solenoid valve that is normally open, allowing intake-manifold vacuum to pass through it. When the engine temperature is high enough to open the thermal switch, and the throttle is partly open, intake manifold can operate the EGR valve. Exhaust-gas recirculation results. However, when the car speed reaches a certain level, the speed sensor sends a signal to the electronic amplifier. This causes the amplifier to close the solenoid valve. Now the vacuum line is closed, and exhaust-gas recirculation stops.

⊘ **8-10 Valve Overlap** One feature of the Chrysler complete emission-control systems is additional valve overlap. The complete set of systems is shown in Fig. 8-18. Additional valve overlap does the same thing as the EGR system, but in a different way. Increased valve overlap leaves more of the exhaust gas in the cylinders. That is, the intake valve opens while there is still quite a bit of exhaust gas in the cylinder. So exhaust gas mixes with the air-fuel mixture entering the cylinder. The result is that top combustion temperatures are reduced, and there is

less NO_x formation. However, increased valve overlap can cause rough idling.

⊘ **8-11 Control of Vacuum Advance: TCS System** During part-throttle operation, the distributor vacuum advance operates. This provides more time for the leaner air-fuel mixture to burn. However, this added time also allows more NO_x to develop. Thus, a variety of controls have been used to prevent vacuum advance under certain conditions. For example, Chevrolet uses a transmission-controlled spark (TCS) system on cars with manual transmissions. The TCS system prevents vacuum advance when the car is operated in reverse, neutral, and low forward gears. Under these special conditions, vacuum advance could greatly increase the formation of NO_x.

Figure 8-19 shows the Chevrolet TCS system for a six-cylinder engine in a manual-transmission car. The diagram also shows the engine temperature switch (lower left) and the idle-stop solenoid. Figure 8-20 shows the situation during starting. Turning on the ignition switch energizes the idle-stop solenoid. The plunger extends to contact the throttle lever. This prevents the throttle from closing completely, so that idle speed stays high enough. When the engine is turned off, the idle-stop solenoid allows the throttle to close completely. This prevents dieseling, or the engine running with the ignition off.

Now, refer to Fig. 8-20 again. Turning on the ignition switch completes the circuit through the vacuum-advance solenoid and temperature-switch cold terminal. At the same time, the circuit to the 20-second time relay is completed. With either of these circuits completed, the vacuum-advance solenoid is energized. Vacuum is admitted to the distributor vacuum-advance mechanism so vacuum advance is obtained.

Figure 8-21 shows the system in low-gear operation. If the engine temperature has gone up enough, the temperature-switch cold points are open. Also, after 20 seconds, the time-relay-switch points are open. Thus, the circuit to the vacuum-advance solenoid is opened by either of these conditions. The solenoid plunger moves to block vacuum to the distributor vacuum-advance mechanism. No vacuum advance results.

Figure 8-22 shows the system in high-gear operation. The transmission switch closes its points when the transmission is shifted into high. This energizes the vacuum-advance solenoid so that vacuum is admitted to the distributor vacuum-advance mechanism. Vacuum advance can then result.

Some systems have a temperature-override switch. This switch causes the system to provide vacuum advance under any condition if the engine begins to overheat. The system is shown in Fig. 8-23. If the engine becomes too hot, the hot points in the temperature-override switch close. This energizes the solenoid so that vacuum is admitted to the distributor vacuum-advance mechanism. With vacuum advance, the engine speed increases and improved cooling results.

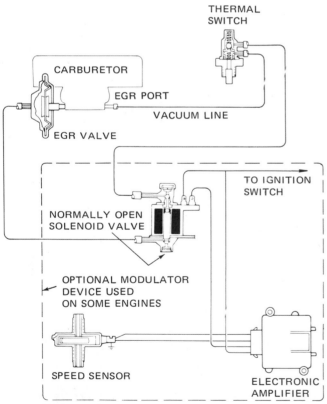

Fig. 8-17. Exhaust-gas recirculation system, showing optional modulator device for some engines. (*Ford Motor Company*)

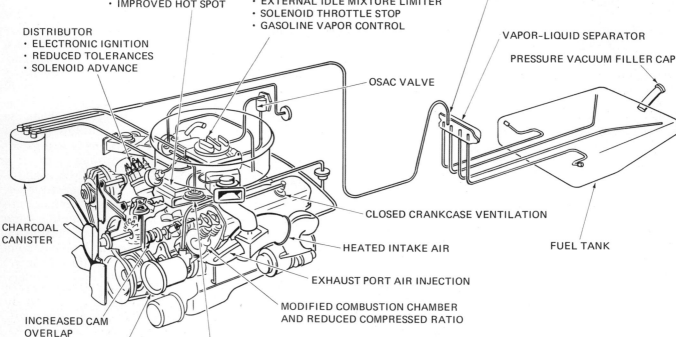

Fig. 8-18. Complete emission-control systems used on Chrysler Corporation V-8 engines. They include a vapor-recovery system, positive crankcase ventilation, exhaust-gas recirculation (plus increased valve overlap), and other features. (*Chrysler Corporation*)

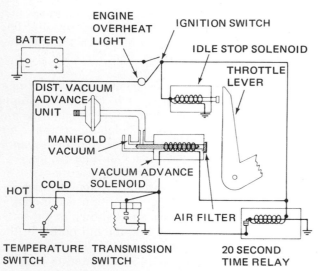

Fig. 8-19. Transmission-controlled spark (TCS) system with engine off. (*Chevrolet Motor Division of General Motors Corporation*)

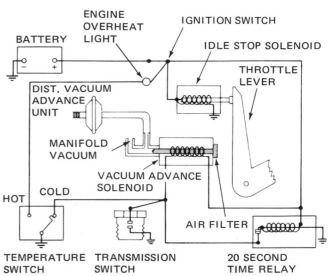

Fig. 8-20. TCS system with cold engine running. (*Chevrolet Motor Division of General Motors Corporation*)

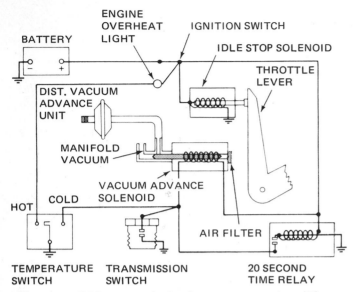

Fig. 8-21. TCS system during low-gear operation. (*Chevrolet Motor Division of General Motors Corporation*)

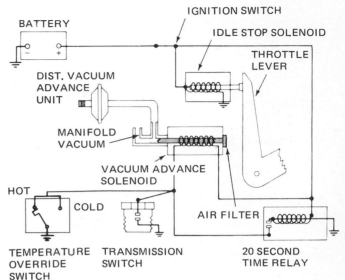

Fig. 8-23. Schematic view of the TCS system which uses a thermostatic temperature-override switch. (*Chevrolet Motor Division of General Motors Corporation*)

⊘ 8-12 Control of Vacuum Advance: TRS System

A Ford transmission-regulated spark (TRS) system is shown in Fig. 8-24. It is for both manual and automatic transmissions. The system works in about the same way as the Chevrolet TCS system described in ⊘ 8-11. The solenoid valve is normally open, allowing vacuum advance when the transmission is in high gear. In the lower gears, the transmission switch is closed. This closes the solenoid valve. With the solenoid valve closed, vacuum is shut off from the distributor vacuum-advance mechanism. Thus, there is no vacuum advance.

⊘ 8-13 Other Vacuum-Advance Control Systems

There are other vacuum-advance controls. Most are specially designed for the engines and vehicles with which they are used. Late-model cars produced by

the Chrysler Corporation use an orifice spark-advance control (OSAC). It includes a very small hole, or orifice in the device. This orifice delays any change in the application of vacuum to the distributor by about 17 s, between idle and part throttle. There is thus a delay in vacuum advance until acceleration is well under way. This is a critical time, during which vacuum advance could produce much NO_x.

Ford has a somewhat similar system called the spark-delay valve system (Fig. 8-25). This system delays vacuum advance during some vehicle-acceleration conditions. The spark-delay valve is con-

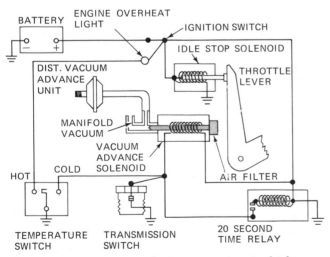

Fig. 8-22. TCS system during operation in high gear. (*Chevrolet Motor Division of General Motors Corporation*)

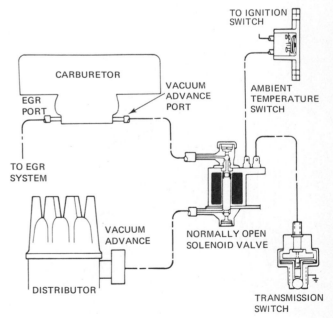

Fig. 8-24. Tranmission-regulated spark (TRS) system. (*Ford Motor Company*)

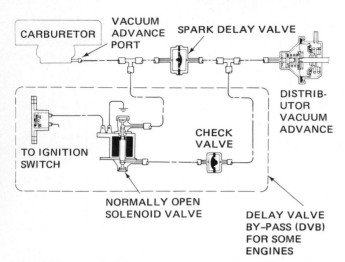

Fig. 8-25. Spark-delay valve system. (*Ford Motor Company*)

nected in series with the vacuum supply from the vacuum-advance port in the carburetor and with the distributor vacuum-advance mechanism. During mild acceleration, the spark-delay valve only allows the vacuum to pass through slowly. Because of this, the vacuum signal to the distributor can increase only gradually. During deceleration or heavy acceleration, the change in vacuum is great enough to open a check delay valve. The valve allows the vacuum to bypass the spark-delay valve. This produces vacuum advance during these critical times, for better engine performance. If engine temperatures are low, the temperature switch actuates the solenoid valve. The actuated valve then passes vacuum directly to the distributor vacuum-advance mechanism (through the check valve). This provides vacuum advance when the engine is cold.

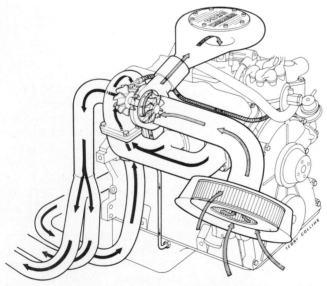

Fig. 8-26. Turbocharged version of the Ford 182-in³ [3-liter] V-6 engine. (*Ford Motor Company*)

⊘ **8-14 Superchargers and Turbochargers** The word "supercharger" tells you what this device is—a mechanism for supplying the engine with a "super" charge of air-fuel mixture. The idea is simple. A centrifugal pump (somewhat similar to the engine water pump) is located between the carburetor and the engine cylinders (Fig. 8-26). It is driven at high speed, and it compresses the air-fuel mixture from the carburetor and delivers it to the cylinders. A greater amount of air-fuel mixture therefore enters the cylinders, and the power strokes are stronger. Thus, the engine can deliver more horsepower. The supercharger can increase the pressure on the air-fuel mixture as much as 16 psi [2.235 kg/cm²] above normal air pressure. An increase in engine horsepower of up to 50 percent is possible.

The problem with the early supercharger was in the drive arrangement. It was driven by a belt, by gears, or by a chain and sprockets. These mechanical drives were put to great stress and sometimes caused trouble. Today, the supercharger is driven by the exhaust gas, and it carries the name "turbosupercharger," or simply "turbocharger." Figure 8-26 shows the arrangement. The exhaust gas, still under some pressure as it leaves the engine cylinder, is directed into a turbine. The turbine wheel is spun by the exhaust gas. The turbine wheel is on the same shaft as the compressor-pump rotor. So the pump rotor is driven to produce the high pressure on the air-fuel mixture entering the cylinders.

According to some reports, adding a turbocharger to an engine is another way to control exhaust emissions. Here's the way it works: To prevent detonation and preignition, a turbocharged engine is designed with a lower compression ratio. This causes the engine to form less NO_x during combustion. Because the turbocharger is driven by exhaust gas, there is a back pressure in the exhaust system which tends to reduce HC and NO_x emissions. This back pressure works as an exhaust-gas recirculation system. It causes some exhaust gas to remain in the cylinder and mix with the next incoming air-fuel charge. This lowers the combustion temperature, reducing NO_x formation. The hot turbine section of the turbocharger acts as a thermal reactor (see ⊘ 9-1). Any unburned HC leaving the cylinders and reaching the turbine section is harmlessly burned up while passing through.

The turbocharger is also credited with doing a better job of mixing the air and fuel, and of delivering a more even air-fuel mixture to each cylinder.

CHAPTER 8 CHECKUP

NOTE: Since the following is a chapter review test, you should review the chapter before taking the test.

You are making excellent progress in learning how exhaust emissions are controlled. By now you should have a good understanding of the basic combustion process, and of how and when exhaust pollutants are created. Once again, it is time to check how well you have absorbed the material you are studying. If you are not sure of the answer to any checkup question, turn back into the chapter and reread the pages that give you the answer.

NOTE: It is still not too late to start a notebook, in case you have not been keeping one. A notebook becomes increasingly important as you move into the shop-work part of *Automotive Emission Control.* You will want to write down and keep important details of how to check, service, and repair different automotive emission control devices.

Completing the Sentences The sentences below are incomplete. After each sentence there are several words or phrases, but only one of them correctly completes the sentence. Write each sentence in your notebook, ending it with the word or phrase that completes it correctly.

1. The process that keeps layers of air-fuel mixture that are next to combustion-chamber surfaces from burning is called: (*a*) quench, (*b*) combustion, (*c*) carbon formation, (*d*) the *S/V* ratio.
2. High combustion-chamber temperatures increase the formation, during combustion, of: (*a*) HC, (*b*) CO, (*c*) NO_x, (*d*) H_2O.
3. Carbon buildup in the combustion chamber increases the exhaust emission of: (*a*) HC, (*b*) CO, (*c*) NO_x, (*d*) H_2O.
4. A hemispheric combustion chamber produces less: (*a*) carbon monoxide, (*b*) unburned hydrocarbons, (*c*) nitrogen oxides, (*d*) water.
5. In a stratified-charge engine, the rich air-fuel mixture should be located around the: (*a*) combustion-chamber surfaces, (*b*) exhaust valve, (*c*) intake valve, (*d*) spark plug.
6. The Honda system is a method of: (*a*) fuel injection, (*b*) stratified charging, (*c*) quench, (*d*) supercharging.
7. Fuel injection for gasoline engines delivers the fuel: (*a*) directly into the combustion chambers, (*b*) into the carburetor, (*c*) into the exhaust manifold, (*d*) opposite the intake valves.
8. Exhaust-gas recirculation is maximum at: (*a*) idle, (*b*) part throttle, (*c*) wide-open throttle, (*d*) low engine temperatures.
9. Valve overlap is a method of reducing: (*a*) HC, (*b*) CO, (*c*) NO_x, (*d*) H_2O.
10. The transmission-controlled spark system allows vacuum advance only in: (*a*) high gear, (*b*) low gears, (*c*) neutral, (*d*) reverse.

Correcting Lists The purpose of this exercise is to help you spot unrelated items in a list. For example, in the list "valve, spring, lifter, retainer, spark plug," the only item that is not part of the valve mechanism is "spark plug." Therefore, this part does not belong in the list. In each of the following lists, there is one

unrelated item. Write each list in your notebook, but do not write the item that does not belong. The answers at the back of this book show you which item you should have left out.

1. Methods of controlling combustion include treating the exhaust gas, stratified charging, fuel injection, and transmission-controlled spark.
2. Factors involved in the combustion process include quench, temperature, time, carbon, and throttle-return check.
3. Characteristics of a stratified charge are lean layers next to combustion-chamber surfaces, rich layers around the spark plug, ignition of lean mixture first, leaner overall air-fuel mixture, and ignition of rich mixture first.
4. A gasoline-engine fuel-injection system includes a nozzle for each cylinder, high-pressure pump, turbocharger, and electronic control unit.
5. Devices used to control NO_x formation include exhaust-gas recirculation, valve overlap, high combustion temperature, and transmission-controlled spark.

Definitions In the following, you are asked for the definitions of several words and phrases. Write them in your notebook. The act of writing the definitions does two things: It tests your knowledge, and it helps fix the information more firmly in your mind. Turn back into the chapter if you are not sure of an answer, or look up the definition in the glossary at the back of the book.

1. Define "combustion."
2. What is quench?
3. What is carbon?
4. Define "S/V ratio."
5. What is stratified charge?
6. What is a precombustion chamber?
7. Define "fuel injection."
8. What is EGR?
9. Define "valve overlap."
10. What is TCS?

SUGGESTIONS FOR FURTHER STUDY

If you would like to learn more about diesel engines, stratified charge, fuel injection, and supercharging, you can probably find books about them in your local public or school library. In addition, your school science department or your automotive instructor may have books or manuals on them. If Honda, or some other manufacturer using one of these engines, has a dealership in your locality, you can probably find out a great deal about the system from people working in the dealership. Another place you might check would be a local trucking or bus company using diesel engines. Often these companies have old copies of pamphlets and trade magazines that you will find very interesting.

chapter 9

TREATING THE EXHAUST GASES

This chapter describes the methods used to treat exhaust gases to reduce the amounts of HC and CO that the engine emits. One of the two methods used today is the air-injection method, in which air is injected into the exhaust manifolds. The additional oxygen in the injected air becomes available to burn any HC and CO in the exhaust gases. The second method is to run the exhaust gases through a catalytic converter which converts the HC and CO into harmless H_2O (water) and carbon dioxide (CO_2).

⊘ 9-1 Treating the Exhaust Gases by Air Injection

After the exhaust gases leave the engine cylinders, they can be treated to reduce their HC, CO, and NO_x content. One method is to blow fresh air into the exhaust manifold. Such a system is called an *air-injection* system. It provides additional oxygen to burn HC and CO coming out of the cylinders. Figure 9-1 shows the details of the system.

The air-injection pump pushes air through the air lines and the air manifold into a series of air-injection tubes. These tubes are located opposite the exhaust valves. The oxygen in the air helps to burn any HC or CO in the exhaust gases in the exhaust manifold. The check valve prevents any backflow of exhaust gases to the air pump, in case of backfire. The air-bypass valve operates during engine deceleration, when intake-manifold vacuum is high. The bypass valve momentarily diverts air from the air pump to the air cleaner, instead of to the exhaust manifold. This tends to prevent backfiring in the exhaust system.

A variation of this system uses a special chamber, called a *thermal reactor* (Fig. 9-2). In the V-8 engine shown, there are two thermal reactors, one for each cylinder bank. These reactors are basically enlarged exhaust manifolds. Being larger, they hold the exhaust gas a little longer. This gives the HC and CO additional time to burn with the oxygen in the pumped air.

Note that the system in Fig. 9-2 includes an exhaust-gas recirculation system, discussed in ⊘ 8-9. Note also that the air-injection system does nothing to the NO_x in the exhaust gas. NO_x requires a different sort of treatment.

⊘ 9-2 Treating the Exhaust Gases with Catalytic Converters

A second method of treating exhaust gases is to use catalytic converters. These convert the gaseous pollutants into harmless gases. An early developmental system using catalytic converters is shown in Fig. 9-3. Note that this is a dual-exhaust system for a V-8 engine. Each exhaust line has two catalytic converters. One handles HC and CO, and the other handles NO_x.

A catalyst is a material that causes a chemical change without entering into the chemical reaction. In effect, the catalyst stands by and encourages two chemicals to react. For example, in the HC/CO catalytic converter, the catalyst encourages the HC to unit with oxygen to produce H_2O (water) and CO_2 (carbon dioxide). The catalyst in the NO_x converter splits the nitrogen from the oxygen. The NO_x becomes harmless oxygen and nitrogen.

A late-model system, engineered by General Motors, is shown in Fig. 9-4. The converter is filled with pellets of metal. They are coated with a thin layer of platinum or similar catalytic metal. The pellets form a matrix through which the exhaust gas must pass. Figure 9-5 shows one design of catalytic converter. As the exhaust gas flows through (see Fig. 9-6), the platinum or other catalyst produces the chemical reactions. Figure 9-7 illustrates another type of catalytic-converter design which has been developed.

One advantage of the system shown is that the pellets are replaceable. In other words, the converter can be recharged with fresh pellets when the catalyst has lost its efficiency.

NOTE: As of now, no NO_x catalytic converter is in use, although there are laboratory designs that work. If an efficient and inexpensive NO_x catalytic converter could be produced, it would allow compression ratios to be increased again so that higher efficiency would be restored to the engine.

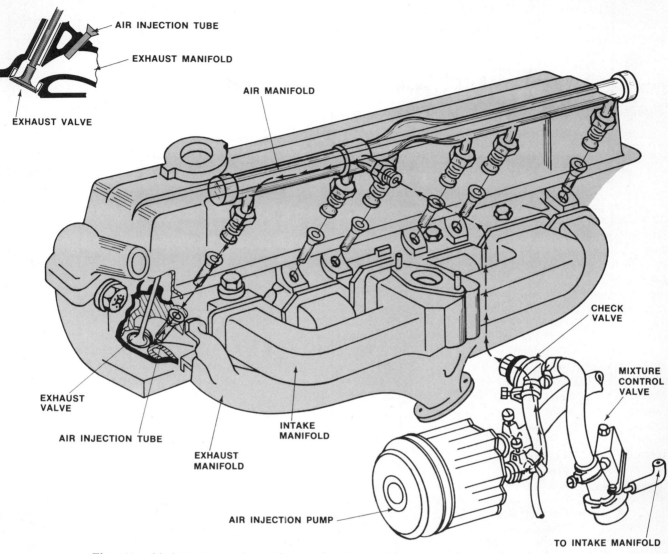

Fig. 9-1. Air-injection system. The air manifold and other parts of the system are shown detached, so they can be seen better. The cylinder head has been cut away at the front to show how the air-injection tube fits into the head.

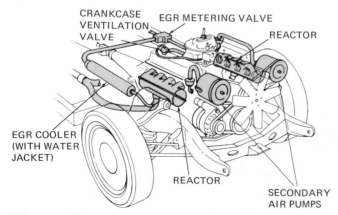

Fig. 9-2. Thermal-reactor system for exhaust-emission control.

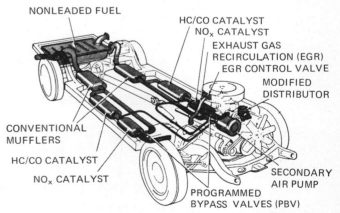

Fig. 9-3. Dual catalytic-converter system for exhaust-emission control. (*Inter-Industry Emission Control Program*)

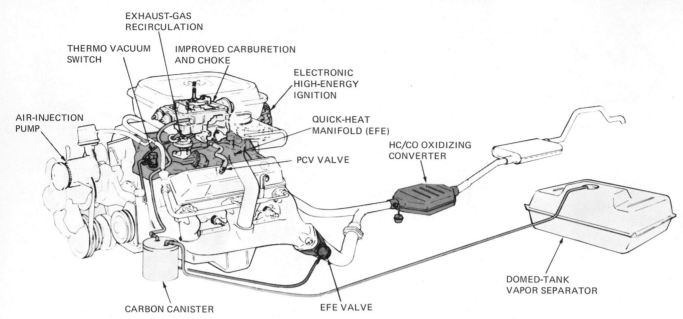

Fig. 9-4. One 1975 emission-control system using an under-the-floor catalytic converter. Note that the system uses air injection and other emission-control features described previously. (*General Motors Corporation*)

Fig. 9-5. Cutaway view of the catalytic converter shown in Fig. 9-4. (*General Motors Corporation*)

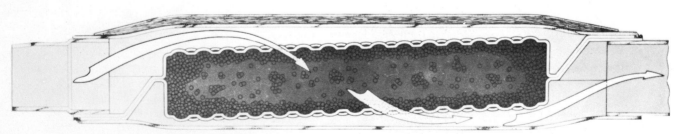

Fig. 9-6. The flow of exhaust gas through the converter is shown by the arrows. (*General Motors Corporation*)

Fig. 9-7. A second design of catalytic converter, cut away so the pellets can be seen. (*General Motors Corporation*)

⊘ **9-3 Sulfates from HC and CO Catalysts** One of the problems that has been discussed is the presence of sulfur in the fuel being burned in the engine. The catalytic converter (which is an oxidizing converter) converts the sulfur into sulfur oxide. This sulfur oxide may then be converted into sulfuric acid by the action of the sun. The danger of this latter conversion is still being debated. However, it is generally agreed that the only way to prevent the oxidizing converter from producing sulfur oxide is to remove the sulfur from the gasoline. This can be done, of course, but it would be expensive. The alternative is not to use catalytic converters.

⊘ **9-4 Lead in Gasoline** As mentioned in Chap. 1, tetraethyl lead has been added to gasoline so it will not knock in high-compression engines. That is, the lead increases the octane rating or antiknock value of gasoline. Lead in gasoline, however, can cause a serious problem with catalytic converters. The lead tends to coat the pellets and thus reduce their effectiveness. Some authorities state that a tank or two of leaded gasoline will effectively destroy the catalytic action of the converter.

To prevent this, service stations now dispense nonleaded gasoline. They have special tanks to hold the nonleaded gasoline, and special pumps to dispense it. To prevent a service station from putting leaded gasoline in a car equipped with catalytic converters, the fuel-tank filler neck has a nozzle restriction (Figs. 9-8 and 9-9). The standard pump nozzle will not fit this restriction. Therefore, the nonleaded gasoline pumps use a special nozzle that is smaller in diameter, as shown. It fits the restriction. In addition, the fuel door on the car carries the warning, "Unleaded Gasoline Only." (See Fig. 9-10.)

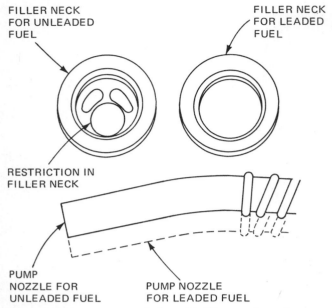

FILLER NECK FOR UNLEADED FUEL

FILLER NECK FOR LEADED FUEL

RESTRICTION IN FILLER NECK

PUMP NOZZLE FOR UNLEADED FUEL

PUMP NOZZLE FOR LEADED FUEL

Fig. 9-8. Comparison of the old filler neck and pump nozzle, for leaded gasoline, with the new filler neck (with restriction) and pump nozzle, for unleaded gasoline.

Also, cars with catalytic converters use a threaded fuel-filler cap (Fig. 9-11). This cap has a special ratchet-tightening device designed to alert the service-station attendant (who may not have seen the warning sign or noticed the nozzle restriction) that the car must have unleaded gasoline only.

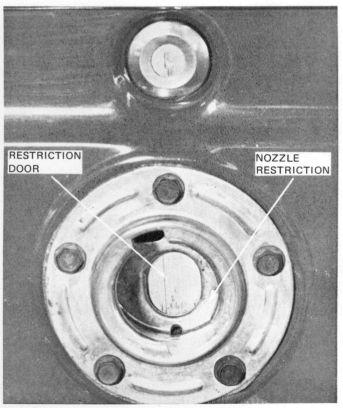

RESTRICTION DOOR

NOZZLE RESTRICTION

Fig. 9-9. Fuel-tank filler cap removed, in readiness to pump gasoline into the tank. (*Ford Motor Company*)

MAVERICK

UNLEADED GASOLINE ONLY

Fig. 9-10. The bumper carries the notice "Unleaded Gasoline Only." (*Ford Motor Company*)

⊘ **9-5 Lead as a Health Hazard** Lead is a very toxic, or poisonous, substance. Lead in human blood can cause many ills, including bone damage, crippling, brain damage, and death. For this reason, some authorities have been working to legally bar the use of tetraethyl lead in all gasoline. According to these authorities, tests have shown that in certain metropolitan areas where traffic is very heavy, with considerable starting, stopping, and idling, the concentration of lead in the air is at the danger point. People who breathe the air take in lead, and it be-

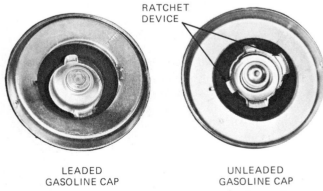

RATCHET DEVICE

LEADED GASOLINE CAP

UNLEADED GASOLINE CAP

Fig. 9-11. The fuel-tank filler cap has a ratchet-tightening device that indicates that the tank should have unleaded fuel only. (*Ford Motor Company*)

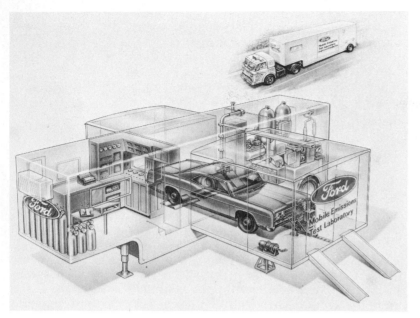

Fig. 9-12. Mobile emissions test laboratory. (*Ford Motor Company*)

comes concentrated in the human body, possibly leading to the ills mentioned above.

If lead were barred, then new refineries would have to be built which could produce high-octane gasoline that does not contain lead. This would be expensive and time-consuming. For the present, no specific actions have been taken to bring this about.

⊘ 9-6 Industry at Work to Reduce Pollution from Cars The automotive industry has been working on the reduction of air pollution from automobiles for many years. As noted earlier, many modifications have been made, and a number of antipollution devices have been added to cars. These include positive crankcase ventilation systems, exhaust-gas recirculation, air-injection systems, fuel-vapor recovery systems, nitrogen oxides control systems, and catalytic converters.

New testing instruments and procedures have been developed to monitor the effectiveness of these systems. Ford, for example, has developed a mobile emissions test laboratory (Fig. 9-12). This laboratory can be moved from one part of the country to another so that cars can be checked in different climates and under different operating conditions. For moving, the laboratory is folded up into the trailer, as shown to the upper right. When it arrives on location, the center section is expanded (center, in Fig. 9-12), so there is room for a car to be brought in and tested.

CHAPTER 9 CHECKUP

NOTE: Since the following is a chapter review test, you should review the chapter before taking the test.

You are still moving along in your study of automotive emission control. You have just completed a very important chapter on treating exhaust gases. The systems discussed are widely used, and you should have a good understanding of their operation. The following chapter checkup gives you a chance to review what you learned in the chapter. Be sure to write the answers in your notebook.

Completing the Sentences The sentences below are incomplete. After each sentence there are several words or phrases, but only one of them correctly completes the sentence. Write each sentence in your notebook, ending it with the word or phrase that completes it correctly.

1. Two methods of treating the exhaust gases are catalytic converters and: (*a*) fuel injection, (*b*) water injection, (*c*) air injection, (*d*) oil injection.
2. Air injection provides additional oxygen to burn the excess: (*a*) H_2O and CO_2, (*b*) HC and CO, (*c*) HC and NO_x, (*d*) CO and NO_x.
3. Catalytic converters convert the HC and CO into: (*a*) H_2O and CO_2, (*b*) HC and CO, (*c*) HC and NO_x, (*d*) CO and NO_x.
4. The catalytic converter used by General Motors is filled with: (*a*) lead shavings, (*b*) steel wool, (*c*) gold bars, (*d*) platinum-coated pellets.
5. Catalytic converters for HC and CO control also convert the: (*a*) sulfur in gasoline to sulfur oxides, (*b*) oil residue in gasoline to carbon, (*c*) lead in gasoline to tetraethyl lead, (*d*) nitrogen in air to nitrogen oxides.
6. Compared to the regular gasoline-pump nozzle, the nozzle for unleaded gasoline is: (*a*) larger, (*b*) the same diameter, (*c*) smaller in diameter, (*d*) longer.
7. A thermal reactor is basically: (*a*) a muffler, (*b*) a resonator, (*c*) an air pump, (*d*) an exhaust manifold.
8. The development of a catalytic converter for NO_x would allow the raising of: (*a*) engine compression ratios, (*b*) fuel octane rating, (*c*) idle speed, (*d*) highway speed limits.

Questions To make certain that you understand the operation of the air-injection system and the catalytic converter, answer the following questions. Write the answers in your notebook. If you do not know the answer to a question, reread the pages covering that question.

1. What is the difference between an air-injection system and a catalytic converter?
2. How does the air-injection system control HC and CO?
3. What is the difference between a thermal reactor and a catalytic converter?
4. What can be done with a catalytic converter that no longer works?
5. How does lead in gasoline affect our health?

Definitions In the following you are asked for the definitions of several words and phrases. Write them in your notebook. The act of writing the definitions does two things: It tests your knowledge, and it helps fix the information more firmly in your mind. Turn back into the chapter if you are not sure of an answer, or look up the definition in the glossary at the back of the book.

1. Define "air-injection system."
2. What is a thermal reactor?
3. Define "catalytic converter."
4. What are sulfates?
5. What is an oxidizing converter?
6. Define "tetraethyl lead."
7. What is nonleaded gasoline?
8. What is a toxic substance?

SUGGESTIONS FOR FURTHER STUDY

There are other books dealing with automotive fuel systems. For instance, *Automotive Fuel, Lubricating and Cooling Systems* (another book in the McGraw-Hill Automotive Technology Series) contains several chapters on fuel systems. Also, your local automotive service shop, or your school automotive shop, may have worn-out or cutaway catalytic converters or air-injection-system parts that you can examine and disassemble. In addition, you can study service bulletins, trade magazines, and car magazines that have articles about catalytic converters and air-injection systems.

PART FOUR

TUNING THE ENGINE

Part Four of this book explains how to service the fuel and ignition systems. Proper operation of both systems is vital to a pollution-free engine. Engine testing instruments and engine tuneup procedures are also covered. As you know from studying earlier chapters of this book, 60 percent of the hydrocarbon emissions, and all the CO and NO_x, come from the tail pipe. To have low exhaust emissions, the engine must be mechanically sound. That is, the engine must have good compression pressure, piston rings, and valve operation. The fuel and ignition systems must be operating properly—delivering the correct air-fuel mixture to the cylinders and igniting it at the correct time. Without this, poor fuel economy and high exhaust emissions result. Part Four of this book discusses how to service and tune the engine for maximum fuel economy and minimum exhaust emissions. Part Four contains four chapters.

⊘ **CHAPTER 10** Fuel-System Service

⊘ **CHAPTER 11** Ignition-System Service

⊘ **CHAPTER 12** Engine Trouble Diagnosis

⊘ **CHAPTER 13** Engine Tuneup and Testing Instruments

chapter 10

FUEL-SYSTEM SERVICE

This chapter describes various troubles that can develop in the fuel system. The chapter also discusses the services required on the different fuel-system components. Failure to service fuel-system troubles wastes gasoline. Exhaust emissions go up, and fuel economy goes down. We begin this chapter by reviewing fuel-system troubles.

⊘ **10-1 Analyzing Fuel-System Troubles** Fuel-system troubles usually show up in engine operation. They cause poor acceleration, hard starting, missing, loss of power, stalling, and so on. These conditions are discussed in Chap. 12, "Engine Trouble Diagnosis." Let us take a quick look at some engine troubles that might be due to the fuel system.

NOTE: Remember that the conditions we discuss here can be caused by many conditions outside the fuel system. However, in this chapter, we are concentrating on possible trouble causes in the fuel system. Chapter 12 covers complete trouble diagnosis of all engine problems.

1. ENGINE CRANKS NORMALLY BUT WILL NOT START This could be due to lack of fuel, underchoking or overchoking, or to the failure of the carburetor to deliver air-fuel mixture normally. Make sure there is gasoline in the fuel tank and in the carburetor. The engine may be flooded due to overchoking. Open the throttle wide, and try cranking. This clears the engine of excess fuel; the engine will start if the trouble was flooding. If this doesn't work, perhaps the choke is not closed so the trouble is underchoking. Remove the air cleaner to check the choke position with the engine cold.

CAUTION: Do not crank the engine with the air cleaner off. The engine could backfire up through the open carburetor and cause a fire, or burn your face.

You can check for fuel in the carburetor by pushing the throttle to the floor several times. This should cause the accelerator pump to squirt fuel into the carburetor air horn. Watch for this with the air cleaner off. (Engine not running!) If fuel squirts out, you can assume there is fuel in the float bowl. Reinstall the air cleaner. Try starting now, after having

primed the engine with the accelerator pump. If the engine starts and runs briefly, the carburetor is probably at fault. If nothing happens, then there may be some other trouble, such as a clogged fuel-tank strainer, a defective fuel pump, a stopped-up fuel-tank vent or cap, or the wrong tank cap.

2. ENGINE RUNS BUT MISSES This can be caused by many things—defective ignition, spark plugs, valve action, piston rings, leaking intake-manifold or gasket, or a disconnected or split vacuum line. In the fuel system, it could be caused by too lean or too rich a mixture. This could mean a problem in the carburetor, fuel pump, flex line, or fuel tank.

3. ENGINE LACKS POWER This complaint is best checked with a dynamometer and oscilloscope (Chap. 11). If the problem is poor acceleration, check to see if the throttle valve opens fully. On four-barrel carburetors, make sure that the secondary throttle valves are opening properly. Also make sure the accelerator-pump system is working (⊘ 10-2). If the complaint is lack of power cold, the problem could be due to a defective choke or the manifold heat-control valve stuck open. Lack of power hot could mean that the choke or manifold heat-control valve is stuck closed. Many other conditions can cause lack of power, including automatic-transmission problems, as explained in Chap. 13.

4. ENGINE STALLS COLD OR AS IT WARMS UP This could be due to a choke opening too quickly or to a manifold heat-control valve that is stuck open. It could also mean that not enough fuel is getting to or through the carburetor because of fuel-pump or carburetor troubles. There are several other possibilities in other engine components (Chap. 12).

5. DIESELING OR RUN-ON This could be due to the idle-stop solenoid not functioning to close the throttle completely when the ignition is turned off. As a result, enough air-fuel mixture continues to get through the carburetor to allow the engine to continue to run. Ignition is by hot spots in the combustion chamber (see ⊘ 12-14).

6. *EXCESSIVE FUEL CONSUMPTION* This can be due to many causes—driving habits, high speed, short runs, choke partly closed, high carburetor float level, worn jets in the carburetor, internal carburetor leaks, external fuel leaks, or stuck metering rod or accelerator pump. Engine troubles such as defective rings or valve action, excessive friction in the drive line, low tire pressure, and improperly operating automatic transmission can increase fuel consumption.

7. *AIR-FUEL-MIXTURE TEST* A rough test of mixture richness can be made without any testing instruments. Start by installing a set of new or cleaned spark plugs of the correct heat range for the engine. Operate the car for 15 to 20 min, on the road or on a dynamometer. Stop the car, and remove and examine the spark plugs. If they are coated with a black carbon deposit, the mixture is probably too rich. Black exhaust smoke also shows an excessively rich mixture. The mixture is too rich to burn fully, so the exhaust gas contains "soot" or unburned gasoline.

⊘ 10-2 Quick Carburetor Checks A number of quick checks can be made that will give you a rough idea of how the carburetor is working. More accurate analysis requires test instruments such as an exhaust-gas analyzer and an intake-manifold-vacuum gauge, as explained in Chap. 13.

1. *FLOAT-LEVEL ADJUSTMENT* With the engine warmed up and running at idle speed (so there is no danger of backfiring), remove the air cleaner. Note the condition of the high-speed nozzle. If the nozzle tip is wet or is dripping gasoline, chances are that the float level is too high. This could cause a continuous discharge of gasoline from the nozzle, even on idle.

2. *IDLE SYSTEM* If the engine does not idle smoothly after it is warmed up, the idle system could be at fault. Slowly open the throttle to about the 25-mph [40.23-km/h] engine speed. If the speed does not increase evenly and the engine runs roughly through this speed range, chances are the idle or main metering system is out of order.

3. *ACCELERATOR-PUMP SYSTEM* With the air cleaner off and the engine not running, open the throttle suddenly. See if the accelerator-pump system discharges a squirt of gasoline into the air horn. The flow should continue for a few moments after the throttle reaches the open position.

4. *MAIN METERING SYSTEM* With the engine warmed up and running at about the 2,500 rpm speed, slowly cover part of the air horn with a piece of stiff cardboard. The engine should speed up slightly, since this causes a normally operating main metering system to discharge more gasoline.

CAUTION: Do not use your hand to cover the air horn. The vacuum could pull your fingers into the air horn and injure them.

⊘ 10-3 Cautions in Fuel-System Work The following cautions should be carefully observed in fuel-system work.

1. Remember that even a trace of dirt in a carburetor or fuel pump can cause fuel-system and engine trouble. Be very careful about dirt when repairing these units. Your hands, the workbench, and the tools should be clean.

2. Gasoline vapor is very explosive. Wipe up spilled gasoline at once, and put the cloths outside to dry. Never smoke or bring an open flame near gasoline!

3. When using the solvent tank, be careful not to splash solvent in your eyes. Do not add gasoline to the solvent tank; this increases the danger of fire. Dump any gasoline from the carburetor or fuel pump into a container before cleaning the unit in solvent.

4. When air-drying parts with the air hose, handle the hose with care. Wear safety goggles, and don't point the air hose at anyone near you.

⊘ 10-4 Air-Cleaner Service Air-cleaner service recommendations vary with different automotive manufacturers. Always check the manufacturer's shop manual for specifications. Here are sample recommendations and service procedures.

1. *CHRYSLER PAPER FILTER ELEMENT (Fig. 10-1)* The paper filter element should be inspected and cleaned every 12 months, and replaced every 2 years. If the car is operated in dusty areas, or performs heavy-duty service (police, taxi, etc.), the filter element should be inspected and cleaned more often. To remove the element, disconnect the air-cleaner hose. Remove the cleaner from the carburetor. Take the element out of the cleaner.

Examine the filter element carefully. If the cleaner is partly saturated with oil, discard it. To clean the element, use a compressed-air hose as shown in Fig. 10-2, blowing from inside out. Hold the

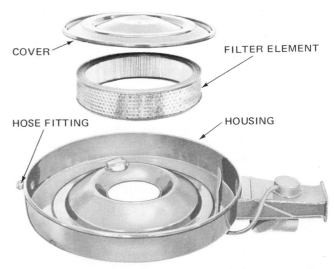

COVER

FILTER ELEMENT

HOSE FITTING

HOUSING

Fig. **10-1.** A carburetor air cleaner of the type with a paper element. (*Chrysler Corporation*)

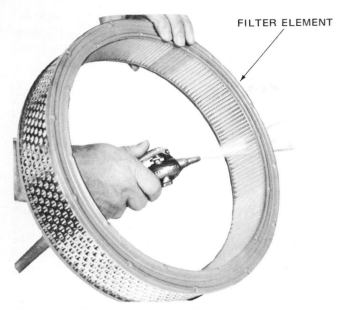

FILTER ELEMENT

Fig. 10-2. Cleaning the paper element with compressed air. Note that air is being blown from inside the element. (*Chrysler Corporation*)

nozzle of the hose at least 2 in [50.8 mm] away from the inside.

CAUTION: Do not use compressed air on the outside of the element. This embeds dust particles in the paper and damages the element.

Examine the cleaned element for punctures. Discard it if it has even pinpoint punctures. Make sure the soft plastic rings on both sides of the element are smooth. They should be able to form a good seal when the element is reinstalled.

2. CHEVROLET (TYPICAL OF GENERAL MOTORS) Two types of filter elements are used: the paper filter only, and the polywrap element (paper filter with polyurethane band). The paper element should be replaced every 24,000 mi [38,623 km] on V-8 engines, and every 12,000 mi [19,310 km] on six-cylinder engines. Figure 10-3 shows the air cleaner and related parts for a V-8 engine.

Before you replace the paper filter with the polyurethane band, the band must be cleaned and reoiled. To clean the band, wash it in kerosene or mineral spirits. Then squeeze out the excess solvent.

CAUTION: Do not use solvent containing acetone or similar compounds, or a hot degreaser. Do not wring, shake, or swing the element. Any of these will damage the element.

If the band is in good condition, dip it in light engine oil and squeeze out the excess oil. Then install the band around the outer surface of the paper element.

3. FORD Ford recommends replacement of the carburetor air-filter element every 12,000 mi [19,310 km]. They do not recommend cleaning and reusing the element.

CAUTION: Air filters which are not installed directly on the carburetor are connected to it by a flexible hose. This hose must be connected airtight to both the filter and the carburetor. The hose must have no tears or punctures that could leak unfiltered air into the carburetor.

⊘ **10-5 Thermostatically Controlled Air Cleaner** To check the system, first make sure the hoses and heat tube are tightly connected. See that there are no leaks in the system. The system can be checked with a temperature gauge. Remember that failure of the thermostatic system usually results in the damper door staying open. This means that the driver would probably not notice anything wrong in warm weather. But, in cold weather, the driver will notice hesitation, surge, and stalling. A typical checking procedure is given in Chap. 15.

⊘ **10-6 Automatic Chokes** As a rule, automatic chokes require no service once they are adjusted for the operating conditions and engine. To adjust an automatic choke (the type with adjustable cover), loosen the cover clamp screws. Turn the cover one way or the other to enrich or lean out the mixture (Fig. 10-4). Other types of chokes are adjusted by bending a linkage rod.

A thermometer is needed to check the operation of the electric automatic choke. Specifications vary, so look up the testing procedure in the shop manual for the car you are checking. A typical procedure for a carburetor-mounted choke is to tape a bulb thermometer to the choke housing, and then start the

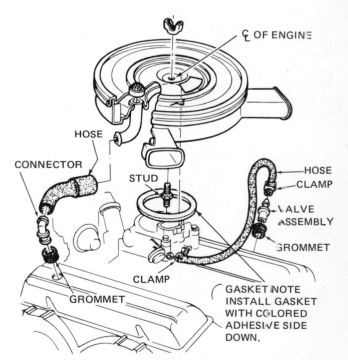

Fig. 10-3. Air cleaner and related parts for a V-8 engine. (*Chevrolet Motor Division of General Motors Corporation*)

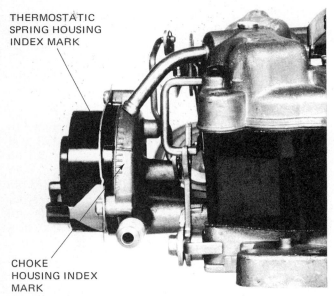

THERMOSTATIC
SPRING HOUSING
INDEX MARK

CHOKE
HOUSING INDEX
MARK

Fig. 10-4. An automatic choke of the type shown is adjusted by turning the cover. (*Ford Motor Company*)

engine. Note the temperature at which the choke opens, and the amount of time required for the choke to open.

⊘ **10-7 Fuel Tanks and Fuel Gauges** Fuel gauges (Fig. 10-5) require very little in the way of service. Defects in either the dash unit or the tank unit usually require replacement of the unit. However, on the type of gauge with vibrating thermostatic blades, dirty contact points may cause fluctuations of the needle. Points can be cleaned by pulling a strip of clean bond paper between them.

Dirt or water in the fuel may clog the fuel-tank filter (Fig. 10-5). The fuel pickup tube, which is part of the fuel gauge, has a filter on it to screen out any dirt or water in the fuel. Fuel can become contaminated by dirty gasoline-station storage tanks, or water, dirt, or rust in the vehicle fuel tank. If the in-tank fuel filter is clogged, the engine may not start or keep running. If dirt or water has clogged the

in-tank fuel filter, drain the fuel from the tank. Remove and clean out the fuel tank. If the filter is dirty or clogged, but in good condition, clean and reinstall it. Otherwise, replace the filter.

⊘ **10-8 Fuel-Pump and Filter Service** Fuel-pump pressure and capacity can be checked with special testers (Fig. 10-6). Low pump pressure causes fuel starvation and poor engine performance. High pressure causes an overrich mixture, excessive fuel consumption, and such troubles as fouled spark plugs, rings, and valves (from excessive carbon deposits). Fuel-pump testers are connected into the fuel line from the pump. They measure either the pressure that the pump can develop or the amount of fuel that the pump can deliver during a timed interval. The vacuum that the fuel pump can develop should also be checked. This is done by connecting the tester to the suction side of the pump.

Fuel filters require no service except periodic checks to make sure that they are not clogged, and replacement of the filter element or cleaning of the filter (depending on the type). On many models, the filter is part of the fuel pump (Fig. 10-7), and can be removed to replace the element. Another type is the in-line filter (Figs. 10-8 and 10-9). The filter in Fig. 10-8 is replaced by first unclamping and detaching the fuel hose from the filter. Then the filter can be unscrewed from the carburetor and replaced. In the type shown in Fig. 10-9, the fuel line is detached. Then the nut is removed so the old filter element can be slipped out and replaced.

⊘ **10-9 Fuel-Pump Troubles** Fuel-system troubles that might be caused by the fuel pump are discussed below.
1. *INSUFFICIENT FUEL DELIVERY* This could result from low pump pressure, which in turn could be due to any of the following:

a. Broken, worn-out, or cracked diaphragm
b. Improperly operating fuel-pump valves
c. Broken or damaged rocker arm
d. Clogged pump-filter screen or filter
e. Leakage of air into the sediment bowl because of a loose bowl or a worn gasket

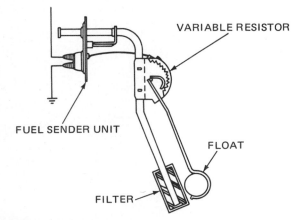

VARIABLE RESISTOR

FUEL SENDER UNIT

FLOAT

FILTER

Fig. 10-5. Fuel-tank fuel-sender unit and filter. (*Ford Motor Company*)

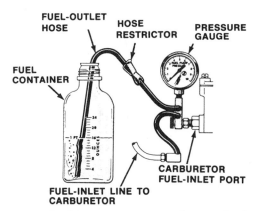

FUEL-OUTLET
HOSE

HOSE
RESTRICTOR

PRESSURE
GAUGE

FUEL
CONTAINER

FUEL-INLET LINE TO
CARBURETOR

CARBURETOR
FUEL-INLET PORT

Fig. 10-6. Fuel-pump pressure and capacity tests.

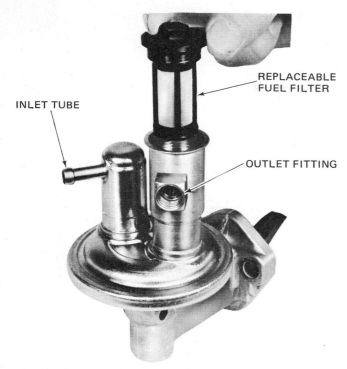

INLET TUBE

REPLACEABLE FUEL FILTER

OUTLET FITTING

Fig. 10-7. Removing the fuel filter from the fuel pump. (*Chrysler Corporation*)

These causes of insufficient fuel delivery are all conditions within the pump. In addition, there are conditions outside the pump that could prevent delivery of normal amounts of fuel. These include such things as a clogged fuel-tank-cap vent, clogged fuel line or filter, air leaks into the fuel line, and vapor lock. Of course, in the carburetor, an incorrect float level, a clogged inlet screen, or a malfunctioning inlet needle valve would prevent delivery of adequate amounts of fuel to the carburetor.

2. *EXCESSIVE PUMP PRESSURE* High pump pressure causes delivery of two much fuel to the carburetor. The excessive pressure tends to lift the needle valve off its seat. As a result, the fuel level in the float bowl is too high. This results in an overrich mixture and excessive fuel consumption. Usually, high pump pressure occurs only after a fuel pump has been removed, repaired, and replaced. If a fuel

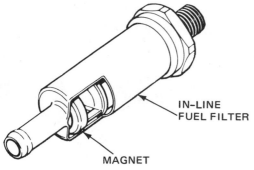

IN-LINE FUEL FILTER

MAGNET

Fig. 10-8. Cutaway view of an in-line fuel filter, showing the magnet which picks up any small metal particles in the fuel. (*Ford Motor Company*)

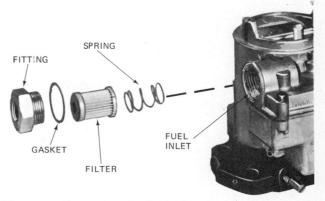

FITTING

SPRING

GASKET

FILTER

FUEL INLET

Fig. 10-9. Removing the fuel filter from the carburetor. (*Chevrolet Motor Division of General Motors Corporation*)

pump has been operating satisfactorily, its pressure should not increase enough to cause trouble. High pressure could come from installation of too strong a diaphragm spring or from incorrect reinstallation of the diaphragm. If the diaphragm is not flexed properly when the cover and housing are reattached, it will have too much tension and will produce too much pressure.

3. *FUEL-PUMP LEAKS* The fuel pump will leak fuel from any point where screws have not been properly tightened. It will leak if the gasket is damaged or incorrectly installed. If tightening the screws does not stop the leak, then the fuel pump requires replacement. Note, also, that leaks may occur at fuel-line connections which are loose or improperly coupled.

4. *FUEL-PUMP NOISES* A noisy pump is usually the result of worn or broken parts within the pump. These include a weak or broken rocker-arm spring, a worn or broken rocker-arm pin or rocker arm, and a broken diaphragm spring. In addition, a loose fuel pump or a scored rocker arm or cam on the camshaft may cause noise. Fuel-pump noise may sound something like engine-valve tappet noise. Its frequency is the same as camshaft speed. If the noise is bad enough, it can actually be "felt" by gripping the fuel pump firmly in the hand. Also, careful listening will usually show that the noise is coming from the fuel pump. Tappet noise is usually heard all along the engine or in the valve compartment of the engine.

⊘ **10-10 Fuel-Pump Removal** Before removing the fuel pump, wipe off any dirt or grease, so it will not get into the engine. Then take off the heat shield (where present), and disconnect the fuel lines. Remove the attaching nuts or bolts, and lift off the pump. If it sticks, work it gently from side to side or pry lightly under its mounting flange or attaching studs. On an engine using a pushrod to operate the fuel pump, remove the rod and examine it for wear and sticking.

⊘ **10-11 Fuel-Pump Disassembly and Assembly** Most automotive service departments do not attempt to disassemble and repair fuel pumps. Pump manufacturers have special pump-exchange programs. The old pumps can be traded in on new or factory-rebuilt units.

NOTE: Most late-model fuel pumps are assembled by crimping and cannot be disassembled. If defective, the pump must be replaced with a new assembly (Fig. 10-10).

⊘ **10-12 Fuel-Pump Installation** Make sure the fuel-line connections are clean and in good condition. Connect the fuel lines to the pump before attaching the pump to the engine. Then place a new gasket on the studs of the fuel-pump mounting or over the opening in the crankcase. The mounting surface of the engine should be clean. Insert the rocker arm of the fuel pump into the opening. Make sure that the arm goes on the proper side of the camshaft, or that it is centered over the pushrod (Fig. 10-11). If it is hard to get the holes in the fuel-pump flange to align with the holes in the block or timing cover, do this: Turn the engine over until the low side of the camshaft eccentric is under the fuel-pump rocker arm. Now the pump can be installed without forcing or prying it into place. Attach it with bolts or nuts. Check the pump operation, as explained in ⊘ 10-8.

⊘ **10-13 Fuel-line Connections** Fuel-line connections, or couplings, take various forms. When loosening a coupling of the type having two nuts, use two wrenches (Fig. 10-12) to avoid damaging the line. If available, a broad-jaw, flare-nut wrench should be used.

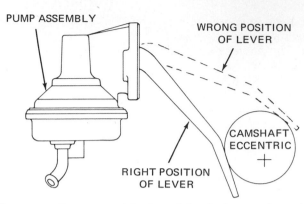

Fig. 10-11. Correct positioning of the fuel-pump lever on the camshaft eccentric. (*Chevrolet Motor Division of General Motors Corporation*)

⊘ **10-14 Carburetor Troubles** In ⊘ 10-1, we mentioned various engine troubles and possible fuel-system causes of these troubles. Remember that engine troubles can have many other causes, besides problems in the fuel system. In Chap. 12 we list and describe all engine troubles and all possible causes. Now, let us see what troubles can be related to conditions inside the carburetor itself.

1. Excessive fuel consumption can result from:
a. A high float level or a leaky float
b. A sticking or dirty float needle valve
c. Worn jets or nozzles
d. A stuck metering rod or power piston
e. An idle that is too rich or too fast
f. A stuck accelerator-pump check valve
g. A leaky carburetor

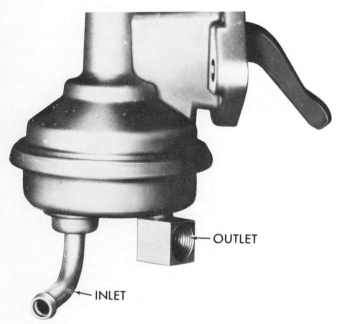

Fig. 10-10. Typical fuel pump. Note that it is assembled by crimping the cover and that it cannot be disassembled for service. (*GMC Truck and Coach Division of General Motors Corporation*)

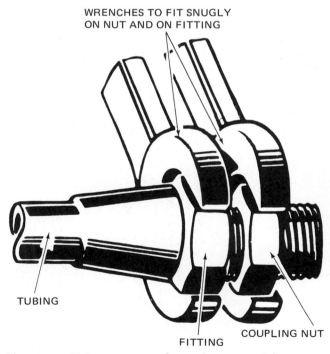

Fig. 10-12. Using two wrenches to loosen or tighten coupling nuts, to avoid twisting and damaging the line.

2. Lack of engine power, acceleration, or high-speed performance can result from:
a. The power step-up on the metering rod not clearing the jet
b. Dirt or gum clogging the fuel nozzle or jets
c. A stuck power piston or valve
d. A low float level
e. A dirty air filter
f. The choke stuck or not operating
g. Air leaks into the manifold
h. The throttle valve not fully opening
i. A rich mixture, due to causes listed in item 1, above
3. Poor idle can result from a leaky vacuum hose, stuck PCV valve, or retarded timing. Also, it could be due to an incorrectly adjusted idle mixture or speed, a clogged idle system, or any of the causes listed in item 2, above.
4. Failure of the engine to start unless primed could be due to no gasoline in the fuel tank or carburetor, the wrong tank cap (1970 cars and later), or a stopped-up tank or cap vent. The latter causes a vacuum to develop in the tank, which prevents delivery of fuel to the carburetor. Holes in the fuel pump flex line will allow air leakage which prevents fuel delivery. Other causes include clogged carburetor jets or lines, a defective choke, a clogged fuel filter, and air leaks into the manifold.
5. Hard starting with the engine warm could be due to a defective choke, a closed choke valve, or an improperly adjusted throttle-cracker linkage.
6. Slow engine warm-up could be due to a defective choke or manifold heat-control valve.
7. A smoky, black exhaust is due to a very rich mixture. Carburetor conditions that could cause this are listed in item 1 above.
8. If the engine stalls as it warms up, the problem could be a defective choke or a closed choke valve.
9. If the engine stalls after a period of high-speed driving, the problem could be a malfunctioning antipercolator.
10. If the engine backfires, the problem could be an excessively rich or lean mixture. Backfiring in the exhaust system is usually caused by an excessively rich mixture in the exhaust. This results from a

defective air-injection-system antibackfire valve. Lean mixtures usually cause a popback in the carburetor.
11. If the engine runs but misses, the most likely cause is a vacuum hose that has come off an intake-manifold fitting (causing the nearest cylinders to miss), or a leaky intake-manifold gasket. It may be that the proper amount and ratio of air-fuel mixture are not reaching the engine; this might be due to clogged or worn carburetor jets or an incorrect fuel level in the float bowl.

Some of the conditions noted above can be corrected by carburetor adjustment. Others require removal of the carburetor from the engine so that it can be disassembled, repaired, and reassembled. Following sections discuss carburetor adjustments and servicing procedures.

⊘ **10-15 Carburetor Adjustments** At one time, there were several adjustments that could be made on carburetors. In recent years, however, automotive emission control laws have been passed which limit the adjustments that can be made. The only procedure now recommended for late-model cars during tuneup is to adjust the idle speed. The idle mixture is preset at the factory, and a limiter cap is installed to prevent tampering. The adjustment procedure is spelled out in a special tuneup decal in the engine compartment. This decal (Fig. 10-13) lists the specific procedure that must be followed. Of course, if some carburetor trouble has occurred which requires disassembling the carburetor, the locking cap or caps may be removed. Then, the idle mixture must be readjusted and new limiter caps installed. The procedures follow.

Setting Idle Speed
Here is a typical procedure, as given in Fig. 10-13:

1. Disconnect the fuel-tank hose from the vapor canister.
2. Disconnect the vacuum hose to the distributor. Plug the hose leading to the carburetor.
3. Make sure distributor contact-point dwell and ignition timing are correct (covered in Chap. 11).

XZ 350-400 CU. IN. 2 BBL. CARB. GM 104-2	VEHICLE EMISSION CONTROL INFORMATION GENERAL MOTORS CORPORATION [GM]	AIR-EGR EXHAUST EMISSION CONTROL	TRANSMISSION	
			AUTOMATIC	MANUAL
MAKE IDLE SPEED AND TIMING ADJUSTMENTS WITH ENGINE AT NORMAL OPERATING TEMP., CHOKE OPEN, AIR COND. OFF, AIR CLEANER INSTALLED, AND DISTR. VACUUM LINE DISCONNECTED AND PLUGGED. RECONNECT DISTR. VACUUM LINE WHEN ADJUSTMENTS ARE COMPLETED.		DWELL	30°	30°
SET PARKING BRAKE AND BLOCK DRIVE WHEELS.		TIMING (°BTC @ RPM)	8° @ 600	0° @ 900
1. DISCONNECT FUEL TANK HOSE FROM VAPOR CANISTER.		SOLENOID SCREW (RPM)	600 (DR)	900 (N)
2. ADJUST CARBURETOR SOLENOID SCREW TO SPECIFIED RPM.		BASE IDLE SCREW (RPM)	500 (DR)	500 (N)
3. SET DWELL AND TIMING AT SPECIFIED RPM. RESET IDLE SPEED IF NECESSARY. 4. ADJUST CARBURETOR IDLE CAM SCREW TO SPECIFIED BASE IDLE RPM ON LOW STEP OF CAM		LEAN DROP IDLE MIXTURE (RPM)	650-600 (DR)	1000-900 (N)
WITH SOLENOID WIRE DISCONNECTED. RECONNECT WIRE AFTER ADJUSTMENT.		MAX. IDLE CO (% @ RPM)	0.5 @ 600 (DR)	0.5 @ 900 (N)
5. IDLE MIXTURE HAS BEEN SET AT THE FACTORY. IF IDLE MIXTURE ADJUSTMENT IS NECESSARY, SEE SERVICE MANUAL FOR PROCEDURES. IDLE MIXTURE SPECIFICATIONS ARE SHOWN AT RIGHT. 6. REMOVAL OF MIXTURE SCREW CAPS AND/OR ALTERING IDLE MIXTURE TO OTHER THAN SPECIFICATIONS MAY VIOLATE FEDERAL AND OTHER STATE LAWS. 7. RECONNECT FUEL TANK HOSE TO VAPOR CANISTER. SEE SERVICE MANUAL FOR ADDITIONAL INFORMATION		FUEL REQUIREMENTS—USE 91 OCTANE OR HIGHER.		
PRINTED IN USA	THIS VEHICLE CONFORMS TO U.S. E.P.A. REGULATIONS APPLICABLE TO 1974 MODEL YEAR NEW MOTOR VEHICLES.			PT. NO. 346258

Fig. 10-13. Tune-up decal typical of the decals found in the engine compartments of modern cars.

4. Adjust the idle speed by the means provided. In earlier models, this was a screw in the throttle linkage at the carburetor. In later models equipped with idle-speed solenoids, the adjustment screw is in the solenoid (Fig. 10-14). Regardless of the location of the adjustment screw, use a tachometer to measure engine speed (Fig. 10-15). Make the adjustment to get the specified idle speed.

5. Reconnect the distributor vacuum hose and the fuel-tank hose.

Setting Idle Mixture

This adjustment is permitted only if the carburetor has required major service. A typical procedure is:

1. With the limiter caps off, turn the mixture screws in until they lightly touch the seats. Then back them off two full turns.

2. Adjust the idle speed as already noted.

3. Connect a CO meter to the exhaust system. Adjust the idle-mixture screws to get a satisfactory idle at the specified rpm and a CO reading at or below the specified allowable maximum. The engine should be running at normal idle with an automatic transmission in D (drive) or a manual transmission in neutral.

4. After setting the idle mixture, recheck the idle speed as detailed above. If everything checks, install new limiter caps on the idle-mixture screws.

⊘ **10-16 Carburetor Removal** To remove a carburetor, first disconnect the air and vacuum lines, and take off the air cleaner. Then disconnect the throttle and choke linkages. Disconnect the hot-air tube to the choke (if present). Disconnect the fuel line and the distributor vacuum-advance line from the carburetor. Use two wrenches, as necessary, to avoid damage to the lines or couplings. Disconnect any wires from switches and other electric controls (where present). Take off the carburetor attaching nuts or bolts, and lift off the carburetor. Try to avoid jarring the carburetor. (There may be dirt in the float bowl. Rough treatment may stir up this dirt and get it into carburetor jets or fuel systems.)

After the carburetor is off, put it in a clean place where dirt and dust cannot get into its openings.

NOTE: If the carburetor is to be off the engine for any length of time, cover the exposed manifold holes

Fig. 10-15. Using a tachometer to measure engine speed while adjusting the carburetor.

with masking tape (Fig. 10-16). Do not use shop cloths, because threads and lint can drop off and get into the manifold. Protecting the manifold holes in this way prevents engine damage from loose parts dropped into the manifold. Such parts could end up in the engine combustion chambers, where they could cause serious damage.

⊘ **10-17 Carburetor Overhaul Procedures** Carburetor disassembly and reassembly procedures vary according to their design. The manufacturer's recommendations should be carefully followed. The time required to overhaul a carburetor varies from approximately $\frac{3}{4}$ to 2 hours depending on type. A few special carburetor tools may be required. The gauges needed to measure float clearance, float centering, float height, choke clearance, and so on are usually included in the carburetor overhaul kit.

Complete carburetor overhaul kits are supplied for many carburetors. These kits contain instructions and all the parts (gaskets, washers, springs, etc.) required to overhaul the carburetor and restore it to its original performing condition.

Figure 10-17 shows a widely used type of carburetor kit, called a "Jiffy Kit" by its manufacturer. The kit shown in Fig. 10-17 fits a Rochester two-barrel

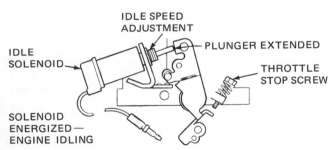

Fig. 10-14. An idle-speed solenoid shown in the engine-idling position. The engine idle speed is adjusted by turning the energized solenoid in or out of its bracket. (*Ford Motor Company*)

Fig. 10-16. If the carburetor is to be off the engine for any length of time, cover the manifold holes with masking tape to keep parts from falling into the manifold.

Fig. 10-17. Contents of a carburetor kit for a widely used two-barrel carburetor. (*Standards Motor Products, Inc.*)

carburetor. It contains all new gaskets and seals, needle and seat, accelerator-pump plunger, limiter caps for the idle-mixture screws, and a hardware package of clips, springs, and other small parts. A special disposable gauge is included for making the very important float-level and float-drop adjustments.

For easier disassembly and assembly of the carburetor, and to simplify the necessary adjustments, a detailed instruction sheet is also included. Always read and follow the instructions that come in the kit you are using. The same basic carburetor, but with some changes, may be used on different engines. Different engine applications often require different carburetor settings and specifications. They are all printed on the instruction sheet in the kit.

CAUTION: When removing and handling a carburetor, be extremely careful to avoid spilling gasoline. Remember that the carburetor float bowl has gasoline in it, so keep the carburetor upright. Gasoline is extremely flammable. Any gasoline that is spilled should be wiped up immediately. Allow the gasoline-soaked towels to dry outside the building, in a safe area.

NOTE: Disassembly and assembly procedures on carburetors vary greatly according to their design. What follows are general service procedures, used on all carburetors.

1. Disassemble the carburetor. Note carefully the position of each part as it is removed. Place the parts in small pans.
2. Thoroughly clean the carburetor castings and metal parts in carburetor cleaner. Be sure that both the inside and outside of each casting are clean.

CAUTION: Do not splash cleaner in your eyes. It can seriously harm them. Wear goggles to protect your eyes.

NOTE: Never soak the pump plunger or any fiber or rubber parts in carburetor cleaner. Wipe these parts with a clean, dry shop towel.

3. Wash the parts carefully in hot water or kerosene, as recommended by the cleaner manufacturer. Blow off all parts until they are dry. Blow out all passages in the castings with compressed air. Make sure all jets and passages are clean.

CAUTION: Use the air hose with care. To be completely safe, wear goggles while blowing out the carburetor.

NOTE: Do not use drills or wires to clean fuel passages or air bleeds. (This may enlarge the openings.) Instead, clean the openings with a chemical cleaner.

4. Check all parts for damage and wear. If damage or wear is noted, the part or assembly must be replaced. Check the float needle and seat for wear. Check the float hinge pin for wear, and the floats for dents or distortion. Shake metal floats to see if they have water or fuel in them. Power pistons that are scored or burred should be replaced. Check the throttle and choke shaft bores for wear and out-of-round.
5. Inspect the idle-mixture adjusting screws for burrs and grooves. These conditions require replacement of the screws. Inspect the pump plunger cup. If the cup is damaged, worn, or hard, it must be replaced. Inspect the pump well in the fuel bowl for wear and scoring.
6. Check the fuel filter and fuel screen (if used) for dirt and lint. Check the automatic-choke housing for exhaust deposits and corrosion. Check the choke piston for free movement.

NOTE: Deposits or corrosion in the choke housing indicate a defective choke heat tube.

7. Carefully inspect the cluster assembly. If any parts are loose or damaged, replace the cluster assembly. Inspect all gasket mating surfaces for nicks and burrs. Repair any damage to the gasket mating surfaces. Inspect any remaining carburetor parts for damage and excessive looseness. Replace any parts that are worn, damaged, or excessively loose.
8. Assemble the carburetor in the proper order. Install all the gaskets and parts contained in the overhaul kit.

NOTE: Be sure your hands, the workbench, and your tools are really clean.

CAUTION: Gasoline and other solvents used to clean carburetors are highly flammable. Use extreme care when working around these flammable liquids.

⊘ **10-18 Carburetor Installation** Use a new gasket to assure a good seal between the carburetor and the mounting pad. Put the carburetor into position on the intake manifold, and attach it with nuts or bolts. Connect the fuel line and the distributor vacuum-advance line to the carburetor, using two wrenches if necessary to avoid damage to the lines or couplings. Reconnect the wires to switches and other electric controls (where present). Make the idle-speed, idle-mixture, and other adjustments as described (⊘ 10-15). Install the air cleaner.

CHAPTER 10 CHECKUP

NOTE: Since the following is a chapter review test, you should review the chapter before taking the test.

An understanding of fuel-system service is essential for the technician servicing automotive emission controls. A problem almost anywhere in the fuel system can cause excessive emissions. In this chapter we reviewed basic fuel-system service. We also discussed how to adjust and service carburetors. Now find out how well you understand the subject by working through the checkup below.

Completing the Sentences The sentences below are incomplete. After each sentence there are several words or phrases, but only one of them correctly completes the sentence. Write each sentence in your notebook, ending it with the word or phrase that completes it correctly.

1. An engine that cranks normally but does not start could have a: (*a*) dead battery, (*b*) defective starting motor, (*c*) locked-up engine, (*d*) lack of fuel.
2. Dieseling, or run-on, of the engine after the ignition is off can be caused by: (*a*) high idle speed, (*b*) lack of fuel, (*c*) a dead battery, (*d*) a defective starting motor.
3. To check the accelerator-pump system, with the air cleaner off and the engine not running, you should: (*a*) check the float-level adjustment, (*b*) make an air-fuel-mixture test, (*c*) open the throttle and look for fuel discharge, (*d*) cover the air horn and crank the engine.
4. A clogged in-tank fuel filter may cause the engine to: (*a*) not start or keep running, (*b*) idle fast, (*c*) leak gasoline, (*d*) overheat.
5. High fuel-pump pressure may cause: (*a*) fuel starvation, (*b*) an overrich mixture, (*c*) poor engine performance, (*d*) dirt in the carburetor.
6. In carburetors on new cars, the idle mixture is: (*a*) adjusted with a screwdriver, (*b*) preset at the factory, (*c*) controlled by the accelerator pump, (*d*) not adjustable in any way.
7. Limiter caps are factory-installed on the: (*a*) idle-speed screws, (*b*) idle-stop solenoid, (*c*) idle air bleed, (*d*) idle-mixture screws.

8. Noises from the fuel pump usually require: (*a*) no service, (*b*) new timing gears, (*c*) replacing the fuel pump, (*d*) replacing the fuel filter.
9. Defective fuel pumps are usually: (*a*) adjusted, (*b*) rebuilt, (*c*) replaced, (*d*) overhauled.
10. The wrong fuel-tank cap could cause: (*a*) failure of the engine to start, (*b*) high idle speed, (*c*) failure of the engine to stop, (*d*) fuel leaks at the carburetor.

Questions Here are some questions that deal with fuel-system service. In your notebook, write each question and the answer in your own words. If you do not know an answer, turn back through the last few pages and restudy the material that gives it to you.

1. If overchoking has flooded an engine, what can you do to start the engine?
2. Why should you not crank the engine with the air cleaner off?
3. How do you make the mixture-richness test with spark plugs of the correct heat range?
4. Explain how you can quick-check the accelerator-pump system.
5. Name four cautions to observe in fuel-system work.
6. How can you clean the Chrysler paper air-filter element?
7. In the fuel system, what could cause failure to start when the engine cranks normally?
8. Name eight possible causes of excessive fuel consumption.
9. What is the only carburetor adjustment to be made on a late-model car during an engine tuneup?
10. What is the most common method of servicing a defective fuel pump?

SUGGESTIONS FOR FURTHER STUDY

There are instruction sheets in carburetor overhaul kits. These instructions tell you, step by step, how to overhaul the carburetors for which the kit was designed. They have pictures showing the various steps in the procedure. You should be able to get several instruction sheets from local shops or service stations that handle carburetor work. Also, your school shop may have copies of instruction sheets. Study them, and make a collection of them if you can. Tape them to sheets of paper, and file them in your notebook. In the shop-work part of your automotive-mechanics course, you will be working on carburetors. Studying the instruction sheets in advance will give you a head start in becoming a carburetor expert.

chapter 11

IGNITION-SYSTEM SERVICE

In this chapter we discuss the testing and servicing of the ignition system and its components. The ignition system includes the distributor, spark plugs, ignition coil, ignition condenser, switch, and wiring. Of these, only the distributor and spark plugs require periodic service. If there is difficulty with the coil, condenser, switch, or wiring, the faulty part is replaced.

⊘ **11-1 Ignition Testing Equipment** Complete testing of the ignition system and its component parts requires a variety of testing equipment. These include the oscilloscope, coil tester, condenser tester, distributor tester, contact-point-opening testers, and contact-pressure gauge. In addition, electronic ignition systems can be tested with a special tester developed for this purpose. We discuss all these testers in this chapter.

⊘ **11-2 Oscilloscope Testers** In recent years, many service facilities have adopted the oscilloscope ignition tester (Fig. 11-1) as a diagnostic device. It can quickly pinpoint troubles in the ignition system. The oscilloscope is a high-speed voltmeter that uses a televisionlike picture tube to show ignition voltages. Figure 11-1 shows an electronic engine tester which includes an oscilloscope. The oscilloscope, or "scope," is to the left center in the picture.

The oscilloscope "draws" a picture of the ignition voltages on the face of the tube. The picture shows what is happening in the ignition system. If something is wrong, the picture shows what it is.

Before we discuss oscilloscope pictures, let us quickly review the ignition system. When the ignition-coil primary circuit is opened (either by opening of the contact points or by the electronic amplifier), a very high voltage is induced in the secondary winding. It can go above 20,000 V (volts). This high voltage surges to a spark plug and produces a spark. That is, the high voltage jumps the gap between the insulated and grounded electrodes of the spark plug. It takes a high voltage to start the spark. But after the spark is established, much less voltage is needed to keep the spark going. The scope can, among other things, draw a picture of how and when this voltage goes up and then drops down.

The picture is drawn on the face of the tube by a stream of electrons. This is exactly how the picture tube works in a television set. In the scope, however, the stream of electrons draws a picture of just one thing—the ignition-system voltages feeding into the scope.

When a voltage (such as the voltage that fires a spark plug) is detected by the scope, a "spike," or vertical line, appears on the face of the tube. This is shown as the *firing line* in Fig. 11-2. The higher the spike, the higher the voltage. If the voltage spike points down, it indicates that the ignition coil or the battery is connected backward.

To see what the scope pictures mean, we shall analyze the *basic pattern* (see Fig. 11-2). The basic pattern is what the scope would show if it were drawing the voltage picture for one spark plug. To start with, the contact points have opened (or the electronic amplifier has opened the primary circuit). The high-voltage surge from the coil has arrived at the spark plug. The voltage goes up, from *A* to *B*, as shown. This is the firing line. After the spark is established, the voltage drops off considerably and holds fairly steady, from *C* to *D*. Of course, this is a very short time, measured in hundred-thousandths of a second. But the spark lasts for as long as 20° of crankshaft rotation. This is long enough to ignite the compressed air-fuel mixture in the cylinder.

After most of the magnetic energy in the coil has been converted into electricity to make the spark, the spark across the spark-plug gap dies. However, there is still some energy left in the coil, and this produces a wavy line, from *D* to *E*. This line is called the *coil-condenser oscillation line*. The waviness means that the remaining energy is pushing electricity back and forth in the ignition secondary circuit. The voltage alternates, but it is no longer high enough to produce a spark. After a very short time, the voltage dies out. Then, at *E*, the points close, sending current to the primary winding of the ignition coil. Now an alternating voltage is produced in the secondary. This is the result of the buildup of current in the coil primary winding. This is shown

Fig. 11-1. Electronic-diagnosis engine tester. This tester includes an oscilloscope (top center) and devices that check the condenser, distributor contact-point dwell, engine speed, and so on. (*Sun Electric Corporation*)

by the oscillations following E. The section from E to F is called the *dwell section*. This is the time during which the contact points are closed. During this time, the magnetic field is building up in the ignition-coil primary. Then, when the points open at F, we have the same situation as at A. The magnetic field collapses, and the whole process is repeated.

⊘ **11-3 Oscilloscope Patterns** The curves that the scope draws on the tube face are called *patterns*. The patterns can be drawn on the tube face in dif-

ferent ways. For example, the scope can be adjusted to draw a *parade* pattern, as shown in Fig. 11-3. It is called a parade pattern because the traces for the separate cylinders follow one another across the tube face, like marchers in a parade. Note that they follow from left to right across the screen, in normal firing order, with No. 1 cylinder on the left.

By adjusting the scope in a different way, the traces can be stacked one above the other, as shown

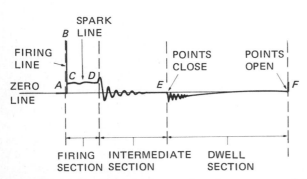

Fig. 11-2. A waveform, or trace, showing one complete spark-plug firing cycle. (*Sun Electric Corporation*)

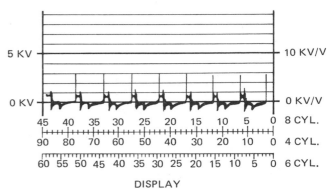

Fig. 11-3. A parade (or display) pattern of the ignition secondary voltages in an eight-cylinder engine. (*Sun Electric Corporation*)

in Fig. 11-4. This is called a *raster* pattern. It lets you compare the traces, so you can see if something is wrong in a cylinder. The pattern is read from the bottom up in the firing order, with No. 1 cylinder at the bottom.

A third way to display the traces is to superimpose them (Fig. 11-5). That is, put them one on top of another. This gives a quick comparison; it shows whether the voltage pattern for any one cylinder differs from the others. If everything is okay in the cylinders, only one curve appears on the tube face. This is because all the curves fall on top of each other.

⊘ **11-4 Using the Scope** There are several makes of oscilloscopes. Many are combined, in consoles, with other instruments for testing the separate ignition components, engine rpm, intake-manifold vacuum, and so on. Figure 11-1 shows a complete tester of this type. Scopes have pickup sensors that can be clamped onto the ignition wires. Thus, it is not necessary to disconnect and reconnect the ignition circuits. The pattern-pickup sensor is clamped onto the wire that goes from the ignition coil to the distributor-cap center terminal. This sensor senses the high-voltage surges going to all the spark plugs. The trigger-pickup sensor is clamped onto the wire that goes to the plug in No. 1 cylinder. The trigger pickup senses when the No. 1 plug fires. This is the signal to the scope to start another round of traces.

⊘ **11-5 Reading the Patterns** The patterns in Fig. 11-6 show different troubles that occur in ignition systems. The pattern for any cylinder shows what voltages are occurring in its ignition circuit. The way that the pattern varies from normal shows you where the electrical problem is. The scope can de-

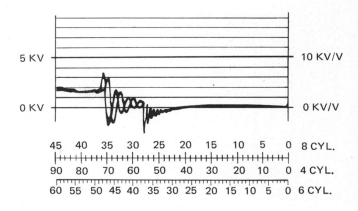

SUPERIMPOSED

Fig. 11-5. A superimposed pattern of the ignition secondary voltages in a six-cylinder engine. (*Sun Electric Corporation*)

tect wide and narrow spark-plug gaps, open spark-plug wires, shorted coils or condensers, arcing contact points, improper contact-point dwell, and other problems. Many abnormal engine conditions change the voltage needed to fire the plug. This, too, shows up on the scope. When you work in the shop, you will be instructed on how to use the oscilloscope.

⊘ **11-6 Ignition-Coil Testers** Two general types of ignition-coil testers are widely used. One type makes use of a spark gap or neon tube. The coil to be tested is connected to the spark gap, and the spark it can produce is measured. A coil known to be good is then tested, and its performance is compared with that of the coil in question. Minor variations can distort the results of this type of test, unless great care is taken in making connections, adjusting the gap, and selecting the comparison coil (it should have the same number of turns of wire, and be connected in same manner). Then, too, this type of coil tester will not always detect such defects as, say, shorted primary turns in a coil.

Most engineers now recommend the use of a scope-type coil tester (Figs. 11-7 and 11-8). This type of tester measures coil performance and gives an accurate picture of coil conditions.

⊘ **11-7 Ignition-Condenser Testers** Ignition condensers are relatively inexpensive, and most ignition technicians replace the condenser on any ignition job. Yet it is sometimes desirable to test the condenser, particularly where trouble is being traced. Four factors are important in the operation and testing of an ignition condenser. These are:

1. Grounding or shorting of the condenser, caused by a breakdown of the insulation between the two condenser plates. This condition prevents any condenser action. It can be detected with a test light.
2. Low resistance, which prevents the condenser from holding a charge, so that the condenser is said

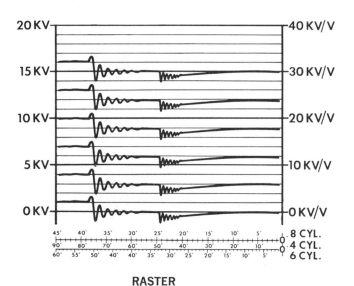

RASTER

Fig. 11-4. A stacked (or raster) pattern of the ignition secondary voltages in a six-cylinder engine. (*Sun Electric Corporation*)

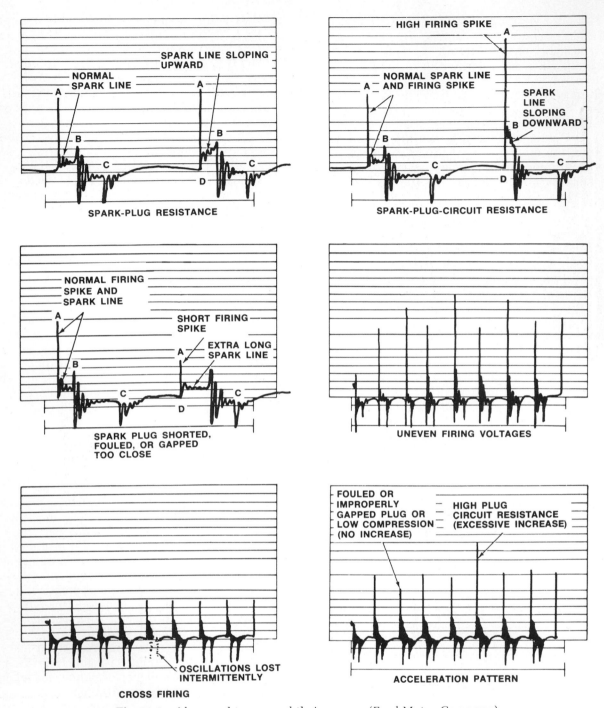

Fig. 11-6. Abnormal traces and their causes. (*Ford Motor Company*)

to be "weak." The insulation permits the charge to leak from one plate to the other. The presence of moisture weakens the insulation and is one cause of low insulation resistance. A good condenser tester usually has a means of testing for low insulation resistance.

3. High series resistance, which results from a defective condenser lead or a poor connection within the condenser. No means of testing for this condition is available except by high frequency. Condenser testers usually have a high-frequency test for checking the condenser for high series resistance.

4. Capacity, which determines the amount of charge that the condenser can take. The capacity of any condenser depends on the area of the plates and on insulating and inpregnating materials. It will not normally change in service.

Condenser testers that can check all these factors are available. Such a tester should be used whenever a condenser must be checked (Fig. 11-7).

⊘ **11-8 Distributor Testers** Distributor testers, or synchroscopes, are variable-speed devices into

Fig. 11-7. Combination coil and condenser tester. (*Sun Electric Corporation*)

which a distributor is clamped to check the centrifugal-advance mechanism (Fig. 11-9). As the distributor speed is increased, the synchroscope indicates the distributor rpm and the amount of centrifugal advance. Many such testers include vacuum-advance testers. In these, a vacuum is applied to the vacuum-advance mechanism on the distributor, so that the degree of vacuum advance and the amount of vacuum required to secure it can be checked. These testers also detect shaft eccentricity caused by worn bearings and bent shafts. Usually, the tester includes a dwell meter for measuring contact-point settings (Fig. 11-10). If it does not, then a separate meter, a feeler gauge, or a dial indicator should be used to measure point opening.

The distributor tester must include a source of vacuum if a full-vacuum-control distributor is to be tested and adjusted.

NOTE: To test electronic distributors, a special *distributor pulse amplifier* must be fitted to the tester. This takes the place of the pulse amplifier, which is left on the car.

◇ **11-9 Contact-Point-Opening Testers** The opening of the distributor contact points must be correct to ensure good ignition performance. Therefore, this adjustment is of great importance. There are three methods of testing the amount of contact-point opening. One makes use of a feeler gauge placed between the points. The breaker cam must be positioned so that the lever-arm rubbing block rests on

the high point of one cam lobe. This method, although satisfactory for new points, should not be used for worn points (Fig. 11-11). Points that have been used are likely to be rough, even though they are good for many more miles of service. To test such points, a dial indicator or a dwell meter should be used. The dwell is the number of degrees of cam rotation from the instant the contact points close until they open again (Fig. 11-10). Increasing the dwell decreases the contact-point opening. Decreasing the dwell increases the contact-point opening. Adjustment is made by loosening a locking screw and turning an eccentric. Some contacts are adjusted by loosening a locking nut and turning the contact screw.

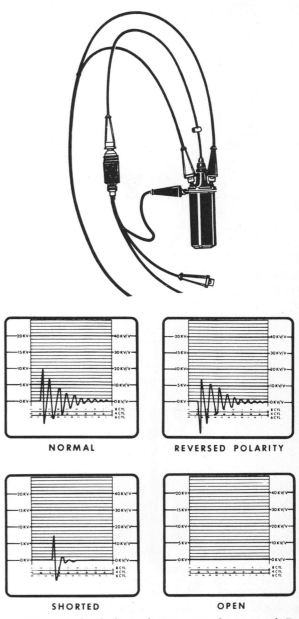

Fig. 11-8. Top, leads from the scope to the test coil. Bottom, scope patterns for various coil conditions. (*Sun Electric Corporation*)

Fig. 11-9. Ignition-distributor tester. (*Sun Electric Corporation*)

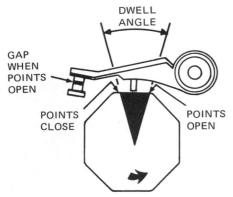

Fig. 11-10. Dwell angle. This is the number of degrees of cam rotation during which the points are closed.

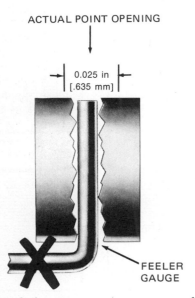

Fig. 11-11. A feeler gauge may not accurately measure the point opening of used and roughened points. The roughness of the points is exaggerated. (*Delco-Remy Division of General Motors Corporation*)

⊘ **11-10 Contact-Pressure Gauge** The contact-point pressure must be within specifications. Low contact-point pressure allows the points to bounce and burn. High pressure causes rapid wear of the points, cam, and rubbing block. A spring gauge can be used to measure the spring pressure. Adjust the pressure by bending the breaker-lever spring, or by loosening the spring attachment and sliding the spring in or out as required. Then tighten the screw, and retest the adjustment.

NOTE: The contact-point sets in many late-model distributors are preadjusted so that it is not necessary to check or adjust spring tension. Only the point opening, or dwell, requires checking on these types.

⊘ **11-11 Electronic-Ignition Testers** Electronic ignition systems require special testing procedures and equipment. Figure 11-12 shows the special electronic-ignition tester recommended by Chrysler. It is simple to use. You plug the tester into the wiring harness between the distributor connector and the control-unit connector. Then, with the ignition switch turned on, you check the ignition system with the tester. The green lights come on if everything is okay. The red lights come on to signal trouble. When you use the tester, follow the special instructions that explain the testing procedure.

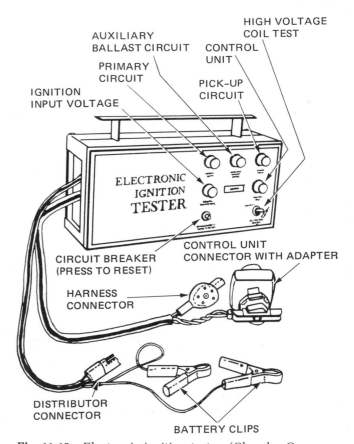

Fig. 11-12. Electronic-ignition tester. (*Chrysler Corporation*)

⊘ **11-12 Ignition Timing** There are various devices for timing the engine. As mentioned earlier, the spark must occur at the spark-plug gap as the piston reaches some definite position in the compression stroke. Adjusting the distributor on the engine so the spark occurs at this correct instant is called *ignition timing*. You adjust the distributor by turning it in its mounting. If you rotate the distributor in the direction opposite normal distributor-shaft rotation, you move the timing ahead. That is, the contact points open earlier (or the electric pulse from the pickup coil occurs earlier). This advances the spark, so the sparks appear at the spark plugs earlier. Turning the distributor in the opposite direction, or in the direction of distributor-shaft rotation, retards the sparks. The sparks appear at the plugs later.

1. *TIMING WITH A TIMING LIGHT* To time the ignition, check the markings on the crankshaft pulley with the engine running. Since the pulley turns rapidly, you cannot see the markings in normal light. But by using a special timing light, you can make the pulley appear to stand still. The timing light is a stroboscopic light. You use it by connecting the timing-light lead to the No. 1 spark plug, as shown in Fig. 11-13. Every time the plug fires, the timing light gives off a flash of light (Fig. 11-14). The light lasts only a fraction of a second. The repeated flashes of light make the pulley seem to stand still.

To connect the timing light, the spark-plug nipple is removed from the spark plug. A metal adapter is then installed between the spark-plug clip inside the nipple and the spark plug. The clip on the timing light is then attached to this adapter. Some timing lights do not require the adapter. These timing lights

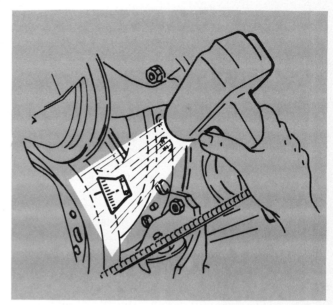

Fig. 11-14. The timing light flashes every time No. 1 spark plug fires.

have a type of spark-plug-lead connector which clamps around the spark-plug wire. Icepicks, pins, and wires should never be forced through the spark-plug nipple to connect the timing light.

To set the ignition timing, loosen the clamp screw that holds the distributor in its mounting. Then turn the distributor one way or the other. As you turn the distributor, the marking on the pulley will move ahead or back. When the ignition timing is correct, the markings will align with a timing pointer, or timing mark, as shown in Fig. 11-14. Tighten the distributor clamp.

2. *MONOLITHIC TIMING* Monolithic timing is a relatively new timing method developed by Ford. The method requires a special location indicator on the front end of the crankshaft. As the crankshaft rotates, this indicator produces an electromagnetic pulse in the monolithic timing equipment installed on the engine. The pulse triggers the timing light, and adjustment is made as already described.

The advantage claimed for the monolithic timing procedure is that the timing is done on the crankshaft, not on a pulley that is driven through a rubber ring. Here's why: The crankshaft pulley includes a torsional-vibration damper to reduce crankshaft vibrations. This damper works through a rubber ring that is between the driving flange on the crankshaft and the pulley itself. The rubber ring can reduce the accuracy of the setting because it allows the pulley to shift away from normal alignment with the crankshaft. Since the triggering device in the monolithic timing system is on the crankshaft itself, more accurate timing is claimed for this system.

CAUTION: When connecting a timing light, always connect the leads to the battery first. Then make the connection to the No. 1 spark plug. When disconnecting the timing light, always disconnect the tim-

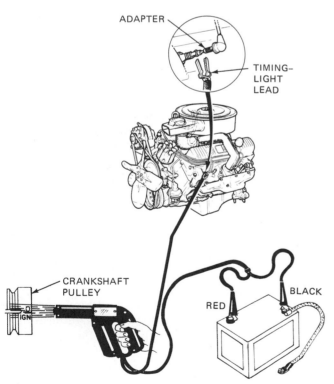

ADAPTER

TIMING–LIGHT LEAD

CRANKSHAFT PULLEY

RED

BLACK

Fig. 11-13. A timing light is used to check ignition timing.

ing-light lead from the No. 1 spark plug first. Then disconnect the battery leads. If you disconnect the battery leads first, you are apt to get a high-voltage shock when you touch the battery connections.

NOTE: There are other timing methods. Late-model Cadillacs can be timed without a timing light. A special probe-type advance meter is used. Another method, seldom used today, requires a test light connected across the points. With the engine not running but the timing marks aligned, the distributor is turned so that the points just open. This is shown by the test light coming on. Then the distributor clamp is tightened. Another method uses a piston-position gauge. It is inserted into the spark-plug hole to determine the exact position of the piston in No. 1 cylinder.

⊘ **11-13 Spark-Plug Service** Spark plugs will foul, or the electrodes will wear rapidly, if their heat range is wrong for the engine. (See Fig. 11-15, which illustrates spark-plug heat range.) Figure 11-16 relates spark-plug appearance to various conditions in the engine. To be cleaned, a spark plug is put into a spark-plug cleaner. The cleaner sends a blast of grit against the electrodes and insulator to clean them. After the cleaning, the spark-plug electrodes are filed flat with an ignition file. Then a special tool is used to adjust the electrode gap (Fig. 11-17).

The cost of labor is high, and the cost of spark plugs is relatively low. This has caused many service experts to recommend the installation of new plugs, rather than the cleaning and regapping of old plugs.

NOTE: The Delco-Remy High-Energy Ignition System requires special wide-gap spark plugs. The gap specified for some applications is 0.080 in [2.03 mm]. A standard plug cannot be satisfactorily adjusted to this wide a gap, because the outer electrode would be bent at a sharp angle. Always use the special plugs specified for the High-Energy Ignition System.

⊘ **11-14 Removing Spark Plugs from the Engine** Spark-plug manufacturers recommend installing new spark plugs at intervals of 10,000 mi [16,093 km]. This avoids loss of engine operating economy and atmospheric pollution, both caused by worn plugs. Before the plugs are removed, the area surrounding

them should be cleaned thoroughly, so that dirt will not fall into the cylinders. One method of doing this is to blow the dirt away with a compressed-air hose. Another is to loosen the plugs a little, and then start and run the engine for a few moments. This allows the leakage of compression to blow dirt away from around the plugs.

NOTE: See ⊘ 11-15 on the proper way to disconnect the high-voltage cables from the spark plugs. This must be done properly to avoid damaging the cables.

Some engines, such as the Chrysler "hemi" (hemispheric) engine, have the spark plugs mounted in wells. On these, the spark-plug covers must first be pulled out, with the cables. Then, a special spark-plug socket or a thin-walled socket must be used to reach down into the wells to loosen and remove the plugs.

⊘ **11-15 Ignition Wiring** An important part of ignition service is to inspect the wiring to make sure it is in good condition. Cracks and punctures in the secondary-wiring insulation can allow high-voltage leakage and engine miss, particularly under heavy load.

Visually inspect the secondary wiring for cracks, burned spots caused by the exhaust manifold, and brittleness. Feel the wiring to see if it is hard or crumbly. You can make a secondary-insulation check with an oscilloscope. If you do not have an oscilloscope, check the secondary-wiring insulation as follows: With the engine not running, connect one end of a test probe to a good ground such as the engine block. This leaves the other end with the test point free to probe. Disconnect the cable from a spark plug, and insulate the clip end from ground. Now start the engine, and move the test probe along the entire length of the wire. If there are punctures or cracks, a spark will jump through the insulation to the end of the test probe.

To remove a cable-and-nipple assembly from the distributor or coil tower, grasp the nipple firmly. Twist the nipple in the tower so that the cable and nipple can be turned freely. Then, grasping the nipple firmly, pull the cable-and-nipple assembly from the tower.

Here is the recommended way to install new cable assemblies. Grasp the nipple and clip end of the cable (Fig. 11-18). Gently push the cable clip into the cap tower. Pinch the larger diameter of the nipple to release trapped air. Then push the cable and nipple until the cable clip is fully entered into the cap terminal, and the nipple is all the way down around the terminal. Ford provides special insulated pliers to remove the cables from the spark plugs. Fig. 11-19 shows this special tool and how to use it. If the connector becomes loose on the coil terminal, the fit can be improved by squeezing the connector as shown in Fig. 11-20.

NOTE: If you are replacing a set of ignition cables, replace one cable at a time. This avoids mixing the

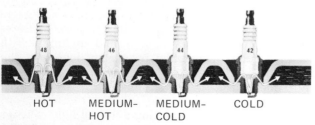

HOT   MEDIUM-   MEDIUM-   COLD
        HOT   COLD

Fig. 11-15. Heat ranges of spark plugs. The longer the heat path (indicated by arrows), the hotter the plug runs. (*AC Spark Plug Division of General Motors Corporation*)

NORMAL

Brown to grayish tan color and slight electrode wear. Correct heat range for engine and operating conditions.

RECOMMENDATION: Properly service and reinstall. Replace if over 10,000 miles of service.

SPLASHED DEPOSITS

Spotted deposits. Occurs shortly after long-delayed tune-up. After a long period of misfiring, deposits may be loosened when normal combustion temperatures are restored by tune-up. During a high-speed run, these materials shed off the piston and head and are thrown against the hot insulator.

RECOMMENDATION: Clean and service the plugs properly and reinstall.

CARBON DEPOSITS

Dry soot.

RECOMMENDATION: Dry deposits indicate rich mixture or weak ignition. Check for clogged air cleaner, high float level, sticky choke or worn breaker contacts. Hotter plugs will temporarily provide additional fouling protection.

HIGH-SPEED GLAZING

Insulator has yellowish, varnish-like color. Indicates combustion chamber temperatures have risen suddenly during hard, fast acceleration. Normal deposits do not get a chance to blow off, instead they melt to form a conductive coating.

RECOMMENDATION: If condition recurs, use plug type one step colder.

OIL DEPOSITS

Oily coating.

RECOMMENDATION: Caused by poor oil control. Oil is leaking past worn valve guides or piston rings into the combustion chamber. Hotter spark plug may temporarily relieve problem, but positive cure is to correct the condition with necessary repairs.

MODIFIER DEPOSITS

Powdery white or yellow deposits that build up on shell, insulator, and electrodes. This is a normal appearance with certain branded fuels. These materials are used to modify the chemical nature of the deposits to lessen misfire tendencies.

RECOMMENDATION: Plugs can be cleaned or, if replaced, use same heat range.

TOO HOT

Blistered, white insulator, eroded electrodes and absence of deposits.

RECOMMENDATION: Check for correct plug heat range, overadvanced ignition timing, cooling system level and/or stoppages, lean air-fuel mixtures, leaking intake manifold, sticking valves, and if car is driven at high speeds most of the time.

PREIGNITION

Melted electrodes. Center electrode generally melts first and ground electrode follows. Normally, insulators are white, but may be dirty due to misfiring or flying debris in combustion chamber

RECOMMENDATION: Check for correct plug heat range, overadvanced ignition timing, lean fuel mixtures, clogged cooling system, leaking intake manifold, and lack of lubrication.

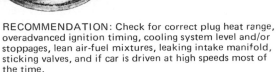

Fig. 11-16. Appearance of spark plugs related to causes. (*Champion Spark Plug Company*)

cables and connecting them to the wrong spark plugs. If all the cables have been removed, determine the direction in which the rotor turns and the firing order. From these, you will be able to figure out how the cables should be connected.

Never remove cable-and-nipple assemblies from the distributor or coil tower unless (1) the nipples are damaged, or (2) cable testing shows the cables are bad and must be replaced. You can ruin a cable by careless removal and installation.

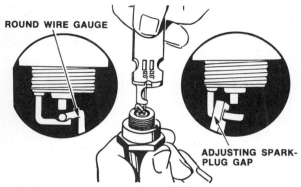

Fig. 11-17. Using a special gauge and adjusting tool to adjust the spark-plug gap.

CAUTION: Do not puncture cables or nipples with test probes. Puncturing the cable insulation or a nipple can ruin the cable. The probe can separate the conductor and cause high resistance. Also, breaking the insulation can result in high-voltage leakage to ground. Either of these can cause engine miss.

⊘ **11-16 Location of Secondary Wiring** The high-voltage cables, or secondary wiring, must be connected correctly between the distributor cap and the spark plugs. Also, the secondary wiring must be positioned correctly, and held apart by the plastic looms and grommets provided (see Fig. 11-21). Note how the cables are positioned and separated. Improper placement or the bundling of cables together can cause crossfiring. That is, the high-voltage surge leaks from one cable to another, causing the wrong spark plug to fire. This can cause engine miss or backfire.

⊘ **11-17 Causes of Ignition Failure** Most often, ignition failure results from normal wear of the con-

Fig. 11-18. Installing a cable and nipple on the distributor tower. (*Chrysler Corporation*)

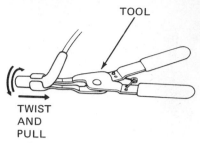

Fig. 11-19. Removing cables from spark plugs with a special tool. (*Ford Motor Company*)

tact points, spark plugs, and other components. Ignition failure can be classified under three headings, as follows:

1. Loss of energy in the primary circuit. This, in turn, may be caused by several conditions:
a. Resistance in the primary circuit, due to defective leads, bad connections, burned distributor contact points or switch, or open coil primary
b. Points not properly set
c. Discharged battery or defective alternator
d. Defective condenser (shorted, low insulation resistance, high series resistance)
e. Grounded primary circuit in the coil, wiring, or distributor
f. Defective pickup coil or pulse amplifier (electronic ignition)
2. Loss of energy in the secondary circuit:
a. Plugs fouled, broken, or out of adjustment
b. Defective high-voltage wiring, which allows high-voltage leaks

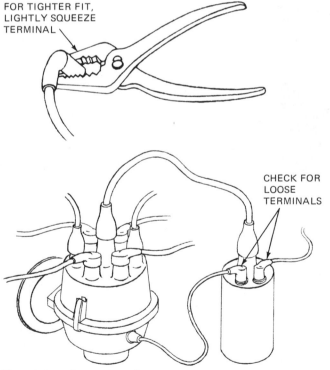

Fig. 11-20. Squeezing the connectors to original size to reestablish good fit. (*Ford Motor Company*)

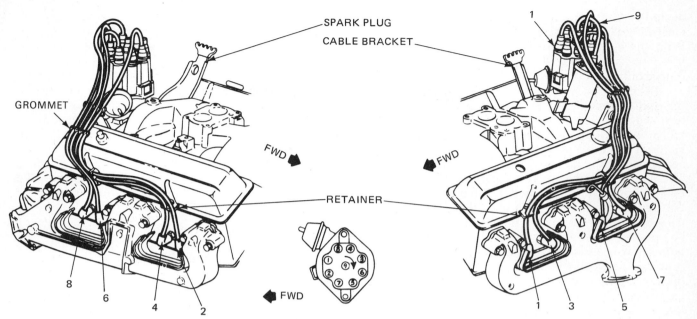

Fig. 11-21. Spark-plug-cable locations on a V-8 engine. (*Chevrolet Motor Division of General Motors Corporation*)

c. High-voltage leakage across the coil head, distributor cap, or rotor
d. Defective connections in the high-voltage circuits
e. Defective ignition coil
3. *Out of time:*
a. Timing not set properly
b. Distributor bearing or shaft worn, or shaft bent
c. Vacuum advance defective
d. Centrifugal advance defective
e. Preignition, due to plugs of wrong heat range, fouled plugs, etc.

⊘ 11-18 Quick Checks of Ignition System A number of quick checks can be made to determine whether the ignition system is at fault when the engine does not operate normally.
1. *ENGINE DOES NOT RUN* If the engine cranks at normal speed but does not start, the trouble could be in either the ignition or the fuel system. To check the ignition system, disconnect the lead from one spark plug (or from the center distributor-cap terminal). Hold it about ³⁄₁₆ in [4.76 mm] from the engine block. Crank the engine. If a good spark occurs, chances are that the ignition system is in reasonable condition (although the timing could be off). If no spark occurs, check the ignition system further.

Connect a test ammeter into the ignition-coil primary circuit, and watch it while cranking the engine. (The car ammeter can be used, where present, but it may not be sensitive enough to give a good reading.) If there is a small, steady reading that fluctuates somewhat, the primary circuit is probably all right. The trouble is probably a defective coil secondary or secondary leads, a defective condenser, or high-voltage leakage across the cap, rotor, or coil head.

If the ammeter shows a fairly high and steady reading, any one of the following could be the cause:

a. The contact points out of adjustment.
b. The condenser is shorted.
c. The coil primary circuit is grounded.
d. Pickup-coil circuit or pulse amplifier (electronic system) defective.

If there is no ammeter reading, the primary circuit is open. This could be due to out-of-adjustment contact points, a loose connection, defective wiring or switch, defective pulse amplifier (electronic system), or an open coil primary winding.
2. *ENGINE MISSES* Missing is caused by such defects in the ignition system as:

a. Worn or out-of-adjustment contact points
b. Defective condenser
c. Centrifugal or vacuum advance malfunctioning
d. Defective secondary wiring
e. Defective ignition coil
f. Poor connections
g. High-voltage leakage across the ignition-coil head, rotor, or cap
h. Defective spark plugs

The wrong ignition coil for the engine, or reversed connections to the ignition coil, may also cause missing. Putting a battery in backwards can also cause missing, because this reverses the polarity of the coil.

With reversed polarity, the electrons have to jump from the relatively cool outer electrode of the spark plug to the hot center electrode. This requires a considerably higher secondary voltage. It increases the possibility of the engine missing, especially at high speed. Normally, the coil and battery are connected so that electrons jump from the hot center electrode of the spark plug to the outer electrode. With the emitting electrode hot, the electrons can jump the spark-plug gap more easily. Voltage requirements are considerably lower.

Reversed polarity can be easily detected with the oscilloscope. If the polarity is reversed, the pattern is upside down. If an oscilloscope is not available, a reversed-polarity test can be made as follows. Hold an ordinary pencil tip between the high-voltage wire clip and the spark-plug terminal (Fig. 11-22). The spark should flare out between the pencil tip and the spark plug, as shown. If it flares out between the pencil tip and the wire clip, the polarity is reversed. Another test uses a neon bulb (NE-2 or similar) placed between the spark-plug terminal (high-voltage lead connected) and ground. With the engine running, the electrode in the neon bulb connected to the spark-plug terminal should glow. If the terminal connected to ground glows, the polarity is reversed. Reverse the coil primary leads to correct the polarity.

3. OVERHEATING AND SPARK KNOCK (DETONATION) These conditions may be caused by improper ignition timing.

⊘ **11-19 Ignition Service** With the oscilloscope (⊘ 11-5), you can fully check the operating condition of the ignition system. The scope face shows the pattern of voltages in the ignition system. Any variation from the normal pattern indicates trouble. The way the pattern varies from normal indicates the type and source of the trouble.

In addition, a mechanical check should be made to determine the condition of the battery and cables, ignition coil, distributor, ignition wiring, and spark

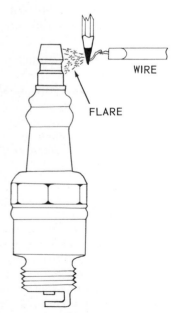

Fig. 11-22. Using a pencil tip to check the polarity of the ignition coil. If the flare is between the pencil tip and the plug, as shown, the coil is connected correctly.

plugs. Check the ignition wiring as discussed in ⊘ 11-15. The distributor cap and rotor and the ignition-coil head should be examined for cracks or carbonized paths that could allow high-voltage leakage. The distributor contact points should be examined, checked, and adjusted as necessary. Points that are burned or oxidized can be cleaned with a thin, fine-cut contact file or stone. Emery cloth must never be used. Particles of emery may become embedded and cause the points to burn away rapidly. On the full-vacuum-control distributor, the spark advance should be checked and adjusted as necessary. The distributor should be lubricated periodically.

Summary of Ignition Troubles
Various troubles that may occur in the components of the ignition system are discussed below.

1. Burned or oxidized contact points. It is normal for ignition-distributor contact points to burn away gradually, over a long period of time. Rapid burning or oxidizing of the points may be due to several conditions.

a. Excessive resistance in the condenser circuit, caused by high series resistance in the condenser or by a loose mounting or connection.
b. High voltage produced by a high-voltage-regulator setting.
c. Dwell angle too large (point opening too small). The points, closed too much of the total operating time, burn away rapidly.
d. Weak spring tension that causes the contact points to bounce and arc.
e. Oil or crankcase vapors entering the distributor housing are deposited on the point surfaces, causing them to burn rapidly. A glance at the breaker plate usually discloses this condition. It causes a black smudge on the breaker plate under the points. Clogged PCV valves or hoses and worn distributor bearings can cause this trouble.

2. Sooty, burned, or cracked spark-plug insulator. Spark plugs may fail for a variety of reasons. Spark-plug manufacturers usually recommend replacement of spark plugs at 10,000-mi [16,090-km] intervals. This helps to prevent failure and to maintain the engine at good operating efficiency. One cause of spark-plug trouble is the installation of plugs of the wrong heat range. (See ⊘ 11-13.) Cracked insulators are usually due to careless installation of the plugs or careless adjustment of the plug gaps.

⊘ **11-20 Distributor Lubrication** Many distributors have built-in lubrication and need no further lubrication. This is not so for the contact-point type, which may have a cam lubricator. On these, the lubricator should be turned 180° every 12,000 mi [19,308 km], and replaced every 24,000 mi [38,616 km]. Some Ford distributors are equipped with an oil cup which should get a few drops of SAE10W oil periodically.

⊘ **11-21 Distributor Removal and Replacement**
Distributor removal and replacement is a simple job if the engine is left undisturbed while the distributor is out. However, if the engine is cranked so that crankshaft and camshaft are turned with the distributor out, then the replacement job is a little more complicated.

1. Distributor removal Remove the air cleaner, and disconnect the vacuum hose or hoses from the distributor. Disconnect the primary lead running from the ignition coil to the distributor. Remove the distributor cap, and push the cap-and-wire assembly aside.

Scratch a mark on the distributor housing. Scratch another mark, which lines up with the first, on the engine block. These marks locate the position of the distributor housing in the block. Scratch a third mark on the distributor housing, exactly under the rotor tip. This mark locates the position of the rotor in the housing.

Remove the distributor hold-down bolt and clamp. Lift the distributor out of the block.

NOTE: If the engine is not cranked while the distributor is out, the distributor can be easily installed in the correct position. Simply align the marks on the distributor housing and cylinder block.

2. Distributor installation If the engine has been cranked with the distributor out, timing has been lost. The engine must be retimed. This is necessary to establish the proper relationship between the distributor rotor and the No. 1 piston.

Remove the No. 1 spark plug from the cylinder head. Place a shop towel over your finger, and cover the spark-plug hole. Crank the engine until you feel compression pressure on your finger.

Bump the engine with the starting motor until the timing marks on the crankshaft pulley and timing cover are aligned. This means that No. 1 piston is in firing position.

Now, the distributor can be installed in the cylinder block. Make sure to align the marks you made on the distributor housing and cylinder block. Check to make sure that the distributor gasket or rubber O ring is in place when you install the distributor.

NOTE: Three different distributor drives are shown in Fig. 11-23. You may have to turn the rotor slightly to engage the drive. Also, when the distributor goes down into place on the spiral-gear drive, the rotor will turn. So you must start with the rotor back of the proper position. Then it will turn into the correct position as the distributor goes down into place.

Make sure the distributor housing is fully seated against the cylinder block. If it is not, the oil-pump shaft is not engaging. Hold the distributor down firmly, and bump the engine a few times until the distributor housing drops into place.

Install, but do not tighten, the distributor clamp and bolt. Rotate the distributor until the contact

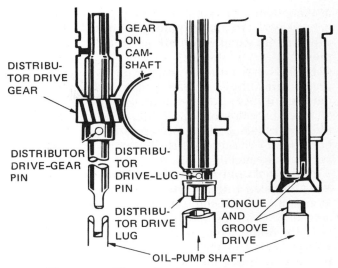

Fig. 11-23. Three distributor drive methods.

points just start to open, to fire No. 1 cylinder. Hold the distributor cap in place above the distributor. Make sure that the rotor tip lines up with No. 1 terminal on the cap. Install the cap with the wires. Connect the primary wire from the ignition coil to the distributor.

Start the engine. Set the ignition timing (⊘ 11-12). Connect the vacuum hose or hoses to the distributor. Replace the air cleaner.

CHAPTER 11 CHECKUP

NOTE: Since the following is a chapter review test, you should review the chapter before taking the test.

Now check up on how well you remember the material on ignition-system service. When you get into the shop, you must be familiar with the various ignition-system testers and how they are used. Take the quiz that follows to find out if you have the information firmly in mind.

⊘ **Completing the Sentences** The sentences below are incomplete. After each sentence there are several words or phrases, but only one of them correctly completes the sentence. Write each sentence in your notebook, ending it with the word or phrase that completes it correctly.

1. For testing ignition coils, most engineers now recommend the: (*a*) scope-type coil tester, (*b*) spark-gap tester, (*c*) neon-tube tester, (*d*) screwdriver tester.
2. A condenser should be checked for insulation resistance, series resistance, and: (*a*) parallel resistance, (*b*) volume, (*c*) capacity, (*d*) weight.
3. Contact-point opening can be measured with a dwell meter or: (*a*) an advance tester, (*b*) a vacuum gauge, (*c*) a feeler gauge, (*d*) a timing light.
4. Dwell is the number of degrees that the distributor cam rotates while the contact points are: (*a*) closed, (*b*) opened, (*c*) opening, (*d*) closing.

5. Point bounce and chatter at high speed are usually caused by: (a) excessive point pressure, (b) low point pressure, (c) excessive spark advance, (d) excessive dwell.

6. Engines have timing marks on the engine: (a) crankshaft pulley, (b) water-pump pulley, (c) alternator pulley, (d) power-steering pulley.

7. To adjust the ignition timing, you: (a) reposition the crankshaft pulley, (b) reposition the flywheel housing, (c) rotate the distributor, (d) connect the vacuum advance.

8. In the most commonly used method, ignition timing is adjusted with the engine: (a) idling, (b) running at intermediate speed, (c) running at fast idle, (d) shut off.

9. In the oscilloscope, the pattern pickup senses the voltage surges in the lead from the: (a) distributor primary terminal, (b) ignition switch, (c) coil high-voltage terminal, (d) battery.

10. When the patterns for the different cylinders follow one another across the oscilloscope-tube face, the arrangement is called the: (a) stacked pattern, (b) parade or display pattern, (c) imposed pattern, (d) superimposed pattern.

Reviewing Ignition Troubles Write, in your notebook, each procedure or answer called for below. Do not copy from the text. Instead, write the answers in your own words, just as you would explain them to a friend. This will help you remember the procedures and explanations.

1. List the various possible causes of ignition failure.
2. List the various engine troubles that might originate in the ignition system. Give the causes of each.
3. Explain how to make the spark test. Explain how to use the ammeter if no spark occurs, and the significance of the various ammeter readings.
4. List the causes of burned contact points.
5. Explain what is meant by spark-plug heat range.
6. Describe the appearance of a spark plug that has been running too hot. One that has been running too cold.
7. Explain the four things that should be tested when a condenser is checked.
8. What is the purpose of an oscilloscope? Describe how it it used.

9. What is wrong with using a feeler gauge to check the opening of worn contact points?
10. Describe several ignition-system troubles and the effect each has on the scope pattern.

Grouping Ignition Troubles There are two lists below. The first list includes the three basic causes of ignition trouble. The second list includes the various conditions causing these troubles. Your job is to put the two lists together properly. To do this, write the three basic "causes" in your notebook, leaving several spaces under each. Then write each item in the "conditions" list under the proper cause. For example, "Defective high-voltage wiring" would go under "Loss of energy in secondary circuit."

> *CAUSES*
> Loss of energy in primary circuit
> Loss of energy in secondary circuit
> Out of time
> *CONDITIONS*
> Defective high-voltage wiring
> Timing incorrectly set
> Centrifugal advance defective
> Points improperly set
> Discharged battery or defective alternator
> Excessive resistance in primary circuit
> Leakage across distributor cap or rotor
> Condenser shorted
> Vacuum advance defective
> Plugs fouled or broken
> Coil primary grounded
> Worn distributor bearing or shaft

SUGGESTIONS FOR FURTHER STUDY

All testing-equipment manufacturers issue detailed instructions on how to use their instruments. When you are in an automotive electrical-service shop or in the school automotive shop, study these instructions whenever you have a chance. Watch how the instruments are used. Another source of information on using testing instruments is automobile manufacturers' shop manuals. Be sure to study these manuals at every opportunity. Write, in your notebook, any important facts you learn.

chapter 12

ENGINE TROUBLE DIAGNOSIS

This chapter discusses various engine troubles and explains what may cause them. It also indicates cures for these troubles. In other words, the chapter covers engine trouble diagnosis or, as many call it, engine "troubleshooting." Earlier chapters describe the servicing and repair procedures required after a trouble has been traced to its cause.

⊘ **12-1 Trouble-Diagnosis Chart** The chart that follows lists various engine complaints, their possible causes, and checks or corrections to be made. The information in this chart will shorten the time you need to correct a trouble. If you follow a logical procedure, you can usually find the cause of trouble quickly. On the other hand, haphazard guesswork wastes time and effort.

NOTE: The troubles and possible causes are not listed according to how often they occur. That is, item 1 (or item a under "Possible Cause") does not necessarily occur more often than item 2 (or item b).

⊘ **12-2 Engine Will Not Turn Over** If the engine will not turn over when starting is attempted, turn on the headlights or dome light. Then try to start the engine. The lights will (1) stay bright, (2) dim considerably, (3) dim slightly, (4) go out, or (5) not burn at all.

1. If the lights stay bright, there is an open circuit in the starting motor or starting-motor circuit. Check as required. Also, the transmission may not be in neutral, or the neutral switch is out of adjustment. In addition, on some late-model cars, the ignition-interlock safety belts may not be fastened properly, or the system may be defective.

ENGINE TROUBLE-DIAGNOSIS CHART

(See ⊘ 12-2 to 12-19 for detailed explanations of the trouble causes and corrections listed below.)

COMPLAINT	POSSIBLE CAUSE	CHECK OR CORRECTION
1. Engine will not turn over (⊘ 12-2)	a. Run-down battery	Recharge or replace; start engine with jumper battery and cables
	b. Starting circuit open	Find and eliminate the open; check for dirty or loose cables
	c. Starting-motor drive jammed	Remove starting motor; free the drive
	d. Starting motor jammed	Remove for teardown and correction
	e. Engine jammed	Check engine to find trouble
	f. Transmission not in neutral, or neutral switch out of adjustment	Check and adjust if necessary
	g. Seat belt not fastened, or interlock faulty	Check interlock
	h. Also causes listed under item 3 below, "Engine turns over at normal speed but does not start"; driver may have run battery down trying to start	
2. Engine turns over slowly but does not start (⊘ 12-3)	a. Run-down battery	Recharge or replace; start engine with jumper battery and cables
	b. Defective starting motor	Repair or replace
	c. Bad connections in starting circuit	Check for loose or dirty cables; clean and tighten
	d. Also causes listed under item 3 below, "Engine turns over at normal speed but does not start"; driver may have run battery down trying to start	

COMPLAINT	POSSIBLE CAUSE	CHECK OR CORRECTION
3. Engine turns over at normal speed but does not start (⊘ 12-4)	a. Ignition system defective	Try spark test; check timing, ignition system
	b. Fuel pump defective or overchoking	Prime engine; check accelerator-pump discharge, fuel pump, fuel line, choke, carburetor
	c. Air leaks in intake manifold or carburetor	Tighten mounting; replace gaskets as needed
	d. Defect in engine	Check compression or leakage (⊘ 12-5), valve action, timing
	e. Ignition resistor burned out	Replace
	f. Plugged fuel filter	Clean or replace
	g. Plugged or collapsed exhaust system	Replace collapsed parts
4. Engine runs but misses on one cylinder (⊘ 12-6)	a. Defective spark plug	Clean or replace
	b. Distributor cap or spark-plug wire defective	Replace
	c. Stuck valve	Free valve; service guide
	d. Broken valve spring	Replace
	e. Burned valve	Replace
	f. Bent pushrod	Replace
	g. Flat cam lobe	Replace; camshaft
	h. Defective piston or rings	Replace; service cylinder wall as necessary
	i. Defective head gasket	Replace
	j. Intake-manifold leak	Replace gasket; tighten manifold bolts
5. Engine runs but misses on several cylinders (⊘ 12-6)	a. Defective distributor advance, coil, condenser	Check distributor, etc.
	b. Defective fuel system	Check fuel pump, flex line, carburetor
	c. Crossfiring plug wires	Replace; relocate
	d. Burned valves	Service
	e. Worn pistons and rings	Service
	f. Overheated engine	Check cooling system
	g. Manifold heat-control valve sticking	Free valve
	h. Restricted exhaust	Check tail pipe, muffler; eliminate restriction
6. Engine lacks power, acceleration, or high-speed performance, hot or cold (⊘ 12-8)	a. Ignition defective	Check timing, distributor, wiring, condenser, coil, plugs
	b. Fuel system defective; secondary throttle valves not opening	Check carburetor, choke, filter, air cleaner, fuel pump
	c. Throttle valve not opening fully	Adjust linkage
	d. Restricted exhaust	Check tail pipe, muffler; eliminate restriction
	e. Loss of compression	Check compression or leakage (⊘ 12-5)
	f. Excessive carbon in engine	Remove carbon
	g. Defective valve action	Check with compression, leakage, or vacuum tester (⊘ 12-5 and 12-7)
	h. Excessive rolling resistance from low tires, dragging brakes, wheel misalignment, etc.	Correct the defect causing rolling resistance
	i. Heavy oil	Use lighter oil
	j. Wrong or bad fuel	Use good fuel of correct octane
	k. Transmission not downshifting, or torque converter defective	Check transmission
7. Engine lacks power, acceleration, or high-speed performance, hot only (⊘ 12-8)	a. Engine overheating	Check cooling system (see item 9 below)
	b. Choke stuck partly open	Repair or replace
	c. Sticking manifold heat-control valve	Free valve
	d. Vapor lock	Use different fuel, or shield fuel line
8. Engine lacks power, acceleration, or high-speed performance, cold only (⊘ 12-8)	a. Automatic choke stuck open	Repair or replace
	b. Manifold heat-control valve stuck open	Free valve
	c. Cooling-system thermostat stuck open	Repair or replace
	d. Engine valves stuck open	Free valves; service valve stems and guides as needed
9. Engine overheats (⊘ 12-10)	a. Lack of coolant	Add coolant; look for leak
	b. Ignition timing late	Adjust timing
	c. Loose or broken fan belt	Tighten or replace
	d. Thermostat stuck closed	Replace

COMPLAINT	POSSIBLE CAUSE	CHECK OR CORRECTION
	e. Clogged water jackets	Clean out
	f. Defective radiator hose	Replace
	g. Defective water pump	Repair or replace
	h. Insufficient engine oil	Add oil
	i. High-altitude, hot-climate operation	Drive more slowly; keep radiator filled
	j. Defective fan clutch	Replace
	k. Valve timing late; slack timing chain has allowed chain to jump a tooth	Retime; adjust or replace
10. Rough idle (⊘ 12-11)	a. Carburetor idle adjustment incorrect	Readjust idle mixture and speed
	b. PCV valve stuck open	Replace
	c. Also causes listed under items 6 to 8 above, "Engine lacks power"	
11. Engine stalls cold or as it warms up (⊘ 12-12)	a. Choke valve stuck closed, or will not close	Open choke valve; free or repair automatic choke
	b. Fuel not getting to or through carburetor	Check fuel pump, lines, filter, float, idle system
	c. Manifold heat-control valve stuck	Free valve
	d. Throttle solenoid improperly set	Adjust
	e. Engine idling speed set too low	Increase idling speed to specified value
	f. Malfunctioning PCV valve	Replace
12. Engine stalls after idling or low-speed driving (⊘ 12-12)	a. Defective fuel pump	Repair or replace fuel pump
	b. Overheating	See item 9 above, "Engine overheats"
	c. High carburetor float level	Adjust
	d. Idling adjustment incorrect	Adjust
	e. Malfunctioning PCV valve	Replace
	f. Throttle solenoid improperly set	Adjust
13. Engine stalls after high-speed driving (⊘ 12-12)	a. Vapor lock	Use different fuel, or shield fuel line
	b. Carburetor venting or idle-compensator valve defective	Check and repair
	c. Engine overheating	See item 9 above, "Engine overheats"
	d. Malfunctioning PCV valve	Replace
	e. Improperly set throttle solenoid	Adjust
14. Engine backfires (⊘ 12-13)	a. Ignition timing off	Adjust timing
	b. Spark plugs of wrong heat range	Install correct plugs
	c. Excessively rich or lean mixture	Repair or readjust fuel pump or carburetor
	d. Engine overheating	See item 9 above, "Engine overheats"
	e. Carbon in engine	Clean out
	f. Valves hot or sticking	Adjust; free; clean; replace if bad
	g. Cracked distributor cap	Replace cap
	h. Inoperative antibackfire valve	Replace
	i. Crossfiring plug wires	Replace or reposition
15. Engine run-on or dieseling (⊘ 12-14)	a. Idle-stop or solenoid adjustment not correct	Adjust; fix solenoid
	b. Engine overheating	See item 9 above, "Engine overheats"
	c. Hotspots in cylinders	Check plugs, pistons, cylinders for carbon; check valves for defects and faulty seating
	d. Timing advanced	Adjust
16. Too much HC and CO in exhaust (⊘ 12-15)	a. Ignition miss	Check plugs, wiring, cap, coil, etc.
	b. Incorrect ignition timing	Time ignition
	c. Carburetor troubles	Check choke, float level, idle-mixture adjustment screw, etc., as listed in item 20 below
	d. Faulty air injection	Check pump, hoses, manifold
	e. Defective TCS system	Check system
	f. Defective catalytic converters	Replace converters or catalyst
17. Smoky exhaust:		
a. Blue smoke	Excessive oil consumption	See item 18 and ⊘ 12-16
b. Black smoke	Excessively rich mixture	See item 20 and ⊘ 12-18
c. White smoke	Steam in exhaust	Replace cylinder-head gasket; tighten cylinder-head bolts to eliminate coolant leakage into combustion chambers

COMPLAINT	POSSIBLE CAUSE	CHECK OR CORRECTION
18. Excessive oil consumption (⊘ 12-16)	a. External leaks	Replace seals; replace gaskets
	b. Burning oil in combustion chamber	Check valve-stem clearance, piston rings, cylinder walls, rod bearings
	c. High-speed driving	Drive more slowly
19. Low oil pressure (⊘ 12-17)	a. Worn engine bearings	Replace
	b. Engine overheating	See item 9 above
	c. Oil dilution or foaming	Replace oil
	d. Lubricating-system defects	Check oil lines, oil pump, relief valve
20. Excessive fuel consumption (⊘ 12-18)	a. Jackrabbit starts	Drive more reasonably
	b. High-speed driving	Drive more slowly
	c. Short-run operation	Make longer runs
	d. Excessive fuel-pump pressure or pump leakage	Reduce pressure; repair pump
	e. Choke partly closed after warm-up	Open; repair or replace automatic choke
	f. Clogged air cleaner	Clean
	g. High carburetor float level	Adjust
	h. Stuck or dirty float needle valve	Free and clean
	i. Worn carburetor jets	Replace
	j. Stuck metering rod or power piston	Free
	k. Idle too rich or too fast	Adjust
	l. Stuck accelerator-pump check valve	Free
	m. Carburetor leaks	Replace gaskets; tighten screws, etc.
	n. Cylinder not firing	Check coil, condenser, timing, plugs, contact points, wiring
	o. Automatic transmission slipping or not up-shifting	Check transmission
	p. Loss of engine compression (worn engine)	Check compression or leakage (⊘ 12-5)
	q. Defective valve action (worn camshaft, chain slack, jumped tooth)	Check with compression, leakage, or vacuum tester (⊘ 12-5 and 12-7)
	r. Excessive rolling resistance from low tires, dragging brakes, wheel misalignment, etc.	Correct the defects causing the rolling resistance
	s. Clutch slippage	Adjust or repair
21. Engine is noisy (⊘ 12-19)		
a. Regular clicking	Valve and tappet	Readjust valve clearance, or replace noisy hydraulic lifters
b. Ping or chatter on load or acceleration	Detonation due to low-octane fuel, carbon, advanced ignition timing, or causes listed under item 14 above, "Engine backfires"	Use high-octane fuel; remove carbon; adjust ignition timing
c. Light knock or pound with engine floating	Worn connecting-rod bearings or crankpin, misaligned rod, lack of oil	Replace or adjust bearings; service crankpins; replace rod; correct lack of oil
d. Light metallic double knock, usually most audible during idle	Worn or loose piston pin or lack of oil	Service pin and bushing; correct lack of oil
e. Chattering or rattling during acceleration	Worn rings, cylinder walls, low ring tension, broken rings	Service walls; replace rings
f. Hollow, muffled, bell-like sound, engine cold	Piston slap due to worn pistons, walls, collapsed piston skirts, excessive clearance, lack of oil, misaligned connecting rods	Replace or resize pistons; service walls; replace rods; correct lack of oil
g. Full, heavy, metallic knock under load or acceleration, especially when cold	Regular noise: worn main bearings; irregular: worn thrust-bearing knock on clutch engagement or on hard acceleration	Replace or service bearings and crankshaft
h. Miscellaneous noises	Rattles, etc., from loosely mounted accessories: alternator, horn, oil pan, front bumper, water pump, etc.	Tighten mounting

2. If the lights dim considerably, the battery may be run down. Or, there may be mechanical trouble in the starting motor or engine. If the battery tests okay, remove the starting motor for further checks. Try to turn the engine flywheel in the normal direction of rotation to see if the engine is jammed.

3. If the lights dim only slightly, listen for cranking action (sound of an electric motor running). If cranking is heard, the pinion if not engaging the flywheel (Bendix type), or the overrunning clutch is slipping. If the solenoid clicks but the starting motor does not rotate, the battery could be low; but the

trouble is probably in the starting motor. Remove it for service.

4. If the lights go out as cranking is attempted, there may be a bad connection in the main circuit, probably at a battery terminal.

5. If the lights burn dimly or not at all when they are turned on, even before cranking is attempted, the battery is probably run down.

⊘ **12-3 Engine Turns Over Slowly but Does Not Start** Causes of this condition could be a run-down battery, a defective starting motor, or mechanical trouble in the engine. Check the battery and starting-motor circuit. If they are normal, the trouble probably is in the engine (defective bearings, rings, and so on, that could produce high friction). Remember that, in cold weather, cranking speed is reduced by thickening of the engine oil and reduction of battery efficiency.

NOTE: If the battery is run down, the driver may have discharged it in attempting to start. The cause of starting failure could be as noted below.

⊘ **12-4 Engine Turns Over at Normal Cranking Speed but Does Not Start** This means the battery and starting motor are in normal condition. The cause of the trouble is probably in the ignition or fuel system. The difficulty could be due to overchoking.[1] Try cranking with the throttle wide open. If the engine does not start, disconnect the lead from one spark plug (or from the center distributor-cap terminal). Hold the lead clip about $3/16$ in [4.76 mm] from the engine block. Crank the engine to see if a good spark occurs. If no spark occurs, check the ignition system. If a spark does occur, the ignition system is probably okay (the timing could be off, however).

If the ignition system operates normally, the fuel system should be analyzed. First, prime the engine by operating the carburetor accelerator pump several times. Or remove the air cleaner, and squirt a small amount of gasoline into the carburetor air horn.

CAUTION: Gasoline is highly explosive. Keep back out of the way while priming the engine. The engine might backfire through the carburetor. Replace the air cleaner before cranking.

If the engine now starts and runs for a few seconds, the fuel system is probably faulty. It is not delivering fuel to the engine. Temporarily disconnect the fuel inlet to the carburetor. Hold a container under the fuel line to catch fuel, and crank the en-

[1] This applies to a cold engine. Failure to start with a hot engine may be due to a defective choke that fails to open properly as the engine warms up. This would cause flooding of the engine (delivery of too much gasoline). Open the throttle wide while cranking (this dechokes the engine), or open the choke valve by hand.

gine to see whether fuel is delivered. If it is not, the fuel pump is defective or the fuel line is clogged. If fuel is delivered, the fuel filter is probably at fault, the automatic choke is not working correctly, or possibly there are air leaks into the intake manifold or carburetor.

If the fuel and ignition systems seem okay on preliminary checks, check the mechanical condition of the engine with compression and leakage tests (⊘ 12-5).

⊘ **12-5 Cylinder Compression and Leakage Testers** These testers are used to determine whether the cylinder can hold compression, or whether there is excessive leakage past the rings, valves, or head gasket. The compression tester has been a basic engine-testing instrument for many years. Recently, the cylinder leakage tester has come into use. Some technicians believe it is more accurate in pinpointing defects in the cylinders.

The use of compression and leakage testers is described in detail in Chap. 13.

⊘ **12-6 Engine Runs but Misses** A missing engine is a rough engine. If one or more cylinders fail to fire, the engine is thrown out of balance. The result is roughness and loss of power. It is sometimes hard to track down a miss. The miss might occur at some speeds and not others. A miss may also skip around from cylinder to cylinder. The modern method of checking out a missing engine is to use an oscilloscope and a dynamometer. The oscilloscope is discussed in ⊘ 11-2 to 11-5. The dynamometer is discussed in Chap. 13. If these testing instruments are not available, then a test can be made as follows.

Use insulated pliers to disconnect each spark-plug wire in turn, to locate the missing cylinder. Removing the plug wire prevents the spark from reaching the plug, and the plug will not fire. If removing the wire changes the engine rhythm or speed, then the cylinder was delivering power before you removed the wire. But if there is no change in engine speed or rhythm, then that cylinder was missing before you removed the wire.

1. Check a missing cylinder further by disconnecting the spark-plug lead. Hold it close to the engine block while the engine is running. If no spark occurs, there is probably a high-voltage leak, due to a bad lead or a cracked or burned distributor cap. If a good spark occurs, install a new spark plug in the cylinder (or swap plugs between two cylinders). Then reconnect the lead, and see whether the cylinder still misses. If it does, the cause of the trouble is probably defective engine parts, such as valves or rings.

2. If the miss is hard to locate, perform a general tuneup (Chap. 13). This will disclose, and maybe eliminate, various causes of missing. These could include defects in the ignition system or fuel system, loss of engine compression, sticky or damaged engine valves, overheated engine, sticky manifold heat control, and clogged exhaust.

3. With most oscilloscopes, you can make a power-balance test that will quickly pinpoint the missing cylinder. When the oscilloscope is connected to the running engine, you turn a knob and the cylinders are shorted out, one by one, in the firing order. The scope shows which cylinder is shorted out. If shorting a cylinder changes the engine rpm as registered on the tester, you know the cylinder was delivering power. But if no change in rpm takes place, then you know that cylinder was not delivering power.

⊘ **12-7 Engine Vacuum Gauge** This is an important engine tester for tracking down troubles in an engine that runs but does not perform satisfactorily. It measures intake-manifold vacuum. The intake-manifold vacuum varies with different operating conditions, and with different engine defects. The manner in which the vacuum varies from normal indicates the type of engine trouble. Chapter 13 explains how to use the vacuum gauge.

⊘ **12-8 Engine Lacks Power** This is a general complaint that is often difficult to analyze. The best procedure is to do a tuneup job (Chap. 13). This will disclose various engine conditions that could cause loss of power. It is helpful to know whether the engine lacks power only when cold, only when hot, or when cold and when hot. A chassis dynamometer (Chap. 13) or an oscilloscope (⊘ 11-2 to 11-5) can be used to help locate the cause of the trouble.

1. *ENGINE LACKS POWER AND ACCELERATION, EITHER HOT OR COLD* The fuel system may not be enriching the mixture as the throttle is opened. This could be due to a faulty accelerator pump or a defective high-speed or main metering system in the carburetor. Also, the fuel system could be supplying an excessively lean or rich mixture. This could be due to a defective fuel pump, clogged lines, clogged filter, worn carburetor jets or lines, air leaks at the carburetor or manifold joints, malfunctioning PCV valve, and so on. Carburetor and fuel-system action can be checked with an exhaust-gas analyzer (Chap. 13).

Another condition could cause lack of power with the engine hot or cold. This is an improper linkage adjustment that prevents full throttle opening. Also, the ignition system may be causing trouble, owing to incorrect timing, a "weak" coil, reversed polarity, wrong spark-plug heat range, and so on. The wrong fuel or oil for the engine could reduce performance. In the engine, numerous conditions could cause loss of power: engine deposits (carbon), lack of compression (faulty valves, rings, worn cylinder walls, pistons), and defective bearings. A clogged exhaust (bent or collapsed exhaust pipe or tail pipe or clogged muffler) could create back pressure that would cause poor engine performance. Also, any sort of excessive rolling resistance would absorb engine power and hold down engine acceleration and speed. This would include dragging brakes,

underinflated tires, misaligned wheels, and excessive friction in the transmission or power train.

2. *ENGINE LACKS POWER ONLY WHEN HOT* The engine may be overheating (⊘ 12-10). Also, the automatic choke may not be opening normally as the engine warms up; the manifold heat-control valve may be stuck; or there may be a vapor lock in the fuel pump or line.

3. *ENGINE LACKS POWER WHEN COLD OR REACHES OPERATING TEMPERATURE TOO SLOWLY* The automatic choke may be leaning out the mixture too soon (before the engine warms up). The manifold heat-control valve may not be closed (so that insufficient heat reaches the intake manifold). Or, the cooling-system thermostat may be stuck open. In this case, coolant circulation goes on between the engine and radiator even with the engine cold, and so warm-up is delayed. Occasionally, engine valves may stick when the engine is cold; but the engine warms up, the valves become free and work normally.

⊘ **12-9 Exhaust-Gas Analyzer** At one time the major use of the exhaust-gas analyzer was to adjust the carburetor. Today, its major job is to check the emission controls on the car. If the emission controls are not working properly, there will be excess HC and CO in the exhaust. The exhaust-gas analyzer measures the amount of HC and CO in the exhaust gases coming out the tail pipe. Use of the exhaust-gas analyzer is discussed in Chap. 13.

⊘ **12-10 Engine Overheats** Most engine overheating is caused by loss of coolant through leaks in the cooling system. Other causes include a loose or broken fan belt, a defective water pump, clogged water jackets, a defective radiator hose, and a defective thermostat or fan clutch. Also, late ignition or valve timing, lack of engine oil, overloading the engine, or high-speed, high-altitude, or hot-climate operation can cause engine overheating. Also, freezing of the coolant could cause lack of coolant circulation so that local hot spots and boiling develop.

⊘ **12-11 Rough Idle** If the engine idles roughly but runs normally above idle, chances are the idle speed and idle mixture are incorrectly adjusted. A rough idle could also be due to other causes, such as a loose vacuum hose or one that is disconnected from the intake manifold.

⊘ **12-12 Engine Stalls** If the engine starts and then stalls, note whether the stalling takes place before or after the engine warms up, after idling or slow-speed driving, or after high-speed or full-load driving. Special note should be made of the PCV valve. If this valve becomes clogged or sticks, it will cause poor idling and stalling.

1. *ENGINE STALLS BEFORE IT WARMS UP* This could be due to an improperly set fast or slow idle,

or to improper adjustment of the idle-mixture screw in the carburetor. It could also be due to a low carburetor float setting or to insufficient fuel entering the carburetor. This condition could result from a faulty thermostatic air cleaner, dirt or water in the fuel lines or filter, a defective fuel pump, or a plugged fuel-tank vent. Also, the carburetor could be icing.

Certain ignition troubles could cause stalling after starting. But, as a rule, if an ignition problem is bad enough to cause stalling, it will also prevent starting. However, burned contact points might permit starting but could fail to keep the engine going. One other condition might be an open primary resistance wire. When the engine is cranked, this wire is bypassed. Then, when the engine starts and cranking stops, this wire becomes part of the ignition primary circuit. If the wire were open, the engine would stall at this time.

2. *ENGINE STALLS AS IT WARMS UP* This can result if the choke valve is stuck closed. The mixture becomes too rich for the hot engine, and the engine stalls. If the manifold heat-control valve sticks closed, the air-fuel mixture might become overheated and too lean, causing the engine to stall. If the hot-idle speed is set too low, the engine may stall as it warms up because the idle speed drops too low. Also, stalling may be caused by overheating of the engine, which could cause vapor lock.

3. *ENGINE STALLS AFTER IDLING OR LOW-SPEED DRIVING* This could occur if the fuel pump has a cracked diaphragm, weak spring, or defective valve. The pump fails to deliver enough fuel for idling or slow-speed operation (although it could deliver enough for high-speed operation). If the carburetor float level is set too high or the idle adjustment is too rich, the engine may "load up" and stall. A lean idle adjustment may also cause stalling. The engine may overheat during sustained idling or slow-speed driving. With this condition, air movement through the radiator may not be sufficient to keep the engine cool. Overheating, in turn, could cause vapor lock and engine stalling. (See ⊘ 12-10 for the causes of overheating.)

4. *ENGINE STALLS AFTER HIGH-SPEED DRIVING* This could occur if enough heat accumulates to cause a vapor lock. The remedy here would be to shield the fuel line and fuel pump, or use a less volatile fuel. Failure of the venting or idle-compensator valve in the carburetor may also cause stalling after high-speed operation. Excessive overheating of the engine is also a primary cause of stalling (⊘ 12-10).

⊘ **12-13 Engine Backfires** Most backfiring is caused by a faulty antibackfire valve. It could also be due to late ignition timing, or ignition crossfiring (caused by the spark jumping across the distributor cap or through the cable insulation). In addition, it could be due to spark plugs of the wrong heat range (which overheat and cause preignition), excessively rich mixtures (caused by fuel-pump or carburetor trou-

bles), overheating of the engine (⊘ 12-10), carbon in the engine, hot valves, or intake valves that stick or seat poorly. Carbon in the engine, if excessive, may retain enough heat to cause the air-fuel mixture to preignite as it enters the cylinder, so that backfiring occurs. Carbon also increases the compression ratio and, thus, the tendency for detonation and preignition. Hot plugs may cause preignition. Cooler plugs should be installed. If intake valves hang open, combustion may be carried back into the carburetor. Valves which have been ground excessively so that they have sharp edges, valves which seat poorly, and valves which are covered with carbon (so that they overheat) often produce backfiring.

⊘ **12-14 Engine Run-on or Dieseling** Modern engines, with their emission controls, require a fairly high hot idle for best operation. This makes run-on, or dieseling, possible. If there are hot spots in the combustion chambers, the engine can continue to run if the throttle is not completely closed. Enough air-fuel mixture could get past a slightly open throttle to keep the engine running. In the combustion chambers, the mixture would be ignited by the hot spots. Many engines have an idle-stop solenoid to close the throttle completely when the ignition switch is turned off.

If an engine runs on, or diesels, check the idle-stop solenoid (if present), to make sure it is releasing when the ignition is turned off. It could require adjustment to permit the throttle to close completely. Be sure the engine speed is not set too high. The trouble could also be due to advanced ignition timing. Correction of engine overheating is covered in ⊘ 12-10. Correcting hot spots may require spark-plug service, or removing the cylinder head for cleaning, plus valve service.

⊘ **12-15 Too Much HC and CO in Exhaust** If the exhaust-gas analyzer (Chap. 13) discloses that there is too much HC and CO in the exhaust, corrections must be made. Some states require exhaust-gas testing of all cars during state inspection. Cars that emit too much HC and CO must be repaired before they can be passed. This regulation is designed to get the smogmakers off the highways. Here are the possible causes. The corrections are obvious.

1. Missing due to ignition problems, such as faulty plugs, high-voltage wiring, distributor cap, ignition coil, condenser, or contact points. (Missing can also be caused by stuck or burned valves.)
2. Incorrect ignition timing.
3. Carburetor troubles such as a choke that sticks closed, worn jets, high float level, and other conditions listed in ⊘ 12-18.
4. A faulty air-injection system, which does not inject enough air into the exhaust manifold to completely burn the HC and CO. This could be caused by a faulty air pump or a leaking hose or air manifold.

5. A defective transmission-controlled spark system, which permits vacuum advance in all gear positions instead of in high and reverse only.

6. Defective catalytic converters, which must be replaced or serviced to restore the catalytic action.

⊘ **12-16 Excessive Oil Consumption** Oil is lost from the engine in three ways: by burning in the combustion chamber; by leakage in liquid form; and by passing out of the crankcase, through the crankcase ventilation system, in the form of mist or vapor.

External leakage can often be detected by inspecting the seals around the oil pan, valve-cover plate, and timing-gear housing, and the oil-line and filter connections.

Burning of oil in the combustion chamber gives the exhaust gas a bluish tint. Oil can enter the combustion chamber through the PCV system, through the clearance between intake-valve or exhaust-valve stems and valve guides, and past piston rings.

If intake-valve-stem clearance is excessive, oil is "pulled" through this clearance, and into the combustion chamber, on each intake stroke. The appearance of the intake-valve stem often indicates that this is occurring. Some of the oil remains on the underside of the valve and stem to form carbon. The remedy is to install valve seals or a new valve guide (and possibly a new valve).

Probably the most common cause of excessive oil consumption is passage of oil into the combustion chamber between the piston rings and the cylinder walls. This is often called "oil pumping." It is due to worn, tapered, or out-of-round cylinder walls or worn or carboned rings. In addition, when engine bearings are worn, excessive oil is thrown on the cylinder walls. The rings are not able to control all of it. Too much oil works up into the combustion chamber.

High speed must also be considered as a cause of excessive oil consumption. High speed means high temperatures and thus thin oil. More oil, and thinner oil, is thrown on the cylinder walls at high speed. The piston rings, moving at high speed, cannot function so effectively. So more oil works up into the combustion chamber. In addition, the churning effect of the oil in the crankcase creates more oil vapor and mist at high speed. More oil is thus lost through the crankcase ventilation system. Tests show that an engine uses several times as much oil at 60 mph [97 kmh] as at 30 mph [48 kmh].

⊘ **12-17 Low Oil Pressure** Low oil pressure is often a warning of a worn oil-pump or engine bearings. The bearings pass so much oil that the oil pump cannot maintain the proper oil pressure. Also, the end bearings will probably be oil-starved and may fail. Other causes of low oil pressure are a weak relief-valve spring, a worn oil pump, a broken or cracked oil line, and a clogged oil line. Oil dilution or foaming, sludge, insufficient oil, or oil made too thin by engine overheating can cause low oil pressure.

⊘ **12-18 Excessive Fuel Consumption** This condition can be caused by almost anything in the car, from the driver to underinflated tires or a defective choke. A fuel-mileage tester can be used to accurately check fuel consumption (Fig. 12-1). The compression or leakage tester and the vacuum gauge (Chap. 13) will help determine whether the trouble is in the engine, fuel system, ignition system, or elsewhere.[1] The exhaust-gas analyzer, dynamometer, and fuel-flow meter are also useful in analyzing the problem.

If the trouble seems to be in the fuel system, consider the following.

1. A driver who pumps the accelerator when idling, and insists on being the first to get away when the stoplight changes, uses excessive amounts of fuel.

2. Operation with the choke partly closed after warm-up results in excessive fuel consumption.

3. Short-run operation means the engine operates on warm-up most of the time. This means fuel consumption will be high.

These are vehicle operating problems. The only cure is to change the way the vehicle is driven. If the excessive fuel consumption is not due to any of these problems, then check the fuel pump for excessive pressure. High fuel-pump pressure causes a high float-bowl level and a rich mixture. Special gauges are used to check pump pressure (⊘ 10-8).

4. If excessive fuel consumption is not due to high fuel-pump pressure or to operating problems, the trouble is likely to be in the carburetor. It could be any of the following:

a. If the car is equipped with an automatic choke, the choke may not be opening rapidly enough during warm-up, or it may not be opening fully. This can be checked by removing the air cleaner and observing choke operation during warm-up.

b. A clogged air cleaner that does not admit sufficient air acts somewhat like a partly closed choke valve. The filter element should be cleaned or replaced.

c. A high float-bowl level will cause flooding and delivery of excessive fuel to the carburetor air horn. The needle valve may be stuck open or may not be seating fully. The float level should be checked and adjusted.

d. Fuel consumption will be excessive if the idle mixture is set too rich, or the idle speed too high. These should be checked and adjusted as necessary.

e. Where the accelerator-pump system has a check valve, failure of the check valve to close properly

---

[1] A rough test of mixture richness that does not require any testing instruments is as follows: Install a set of new or cleaned spark plugs of the correct heat range for the engine, and operate the car for 15 to 20 min. Then stop the car, and remove and examine the plugs. If they are coated with a black carbon deposit, the mixture is too rich. (See a to g under item 4.) Black exhaust smoke is another indication of an excessively rich mixture. The mixture is too rich to burn fully, so the exhaust gas contains "soot," or unburned fuel.

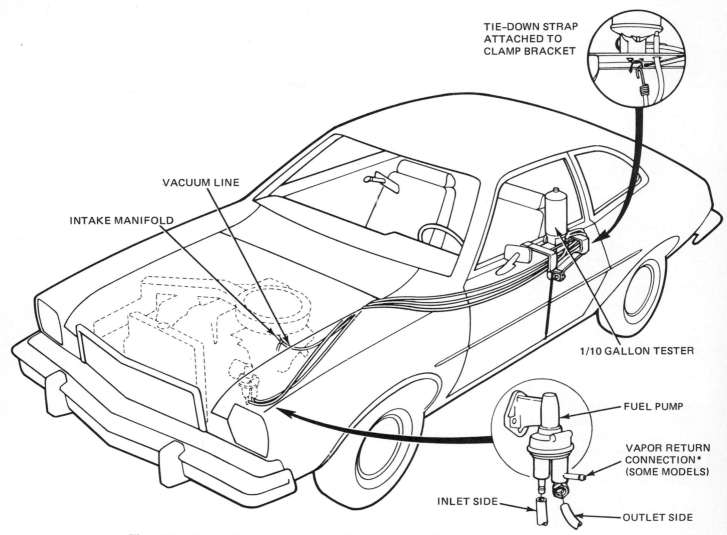

Fig. 12-1. Fuel-mileage tester. A small container holding exactly 1/10 gal (0.45 l) is mounted on the driver's door. (*Ford Motor Company*)

may allow fuel to feed into the carburetor air horn. The carburetor requires disassembly.

f. The metering rod may be stuck in the high-speed, full-throttle position, or the economizer valve may be held open. These permit the power system to function, supplying an excessively rich mixture. The carburetor requires disassembly for repair.

g. Worn jets, permitting the discharge of too much fuel, require replacement during carburetor rebuilding.

5. Faulty ignition can also cause excessive fuel consumption. The ignition system could cause engine miss, so that the engine fails to use all the fuel. This sort of trouble can also cause loss of power, acceleration, or high-speed performance (⊘ 12-8). Conditions in the ignition system that might add to the trouble include a "weak" coil or condenser, incorrect timing, faulty advance-mechanism action, dirty or worn plugs or contact points, and defective wiring.

6. Inferior engine action can produce excessive fuel

consumption. Examples are loss of engine compression from worn or stuck rings, worn or stuck valves, and a loose or burned cylinder-head gasket. Power is lost under these conditions, and more fuel must be burned to achieve the same speed. (Refer to Chap. 13 for compression and leakage checking procedures.)

7. Excessive fuel consumption can also result from conditions that hinder the movement of the car along the road. Such factors as low tires, dragging brakes, defective automatic transmission, and misalignment of wheels increase the rolling resistance of the car. The engine must use up more fuel to overcome this excessive rolling resistance.

⊘ **12-19 Engine Noises** Some engine noises have little meaning. Other noises may indicate serious engine trouble that requires prompt attention to prevent major damage to the engine. Various noises and their causes are described below, along with tests that may be necessary to confirm a diagnosis.

A listening rod or stethoscope is of help in locating the source of a noise (Fig. 12-2). The rod acts

Fig. 12-2. A mechanic's stethoscope being used to locate engine noise.

like a stethoscope. One end is placed at the ear, and the other end at some part of the engine. Noises from that part of the engine are carried along the rod to the ear. A long screwdriver or one of the engine stethoscopes now available can be used as a listening rod. When using the listening rod to locate the source of a noise, put the engine end at various places on the engine, until the noise is loudest. You can also use a piece of garden hose (about 4 ft [1.2 m] long) to locate engine noises. Hold one end of the hose to your ear, and move the other end of the hose around the engine until the noise is loudest. In this way you can, for example, locate a broken and noisy ring in a particular cylinder, or a main-bearing knock.

CAUTION: Keep away from the moving fan belt and fan when using a listening rod.

1. *VALVE AND TAPPET NOISE* This is a regular clicking noise that gets louder as engine speed increases. The cause is usually excessive valve clearance or a defective hydraulic valve lifter. A feeler gauge inserted between the valve stem and lifter or rocker arm reduces the clearance. If the noise also is reduced, then the cause is excessive clearance. The clearance should be readjusted. If inserting the feeler gauge does not reduce the noise, it is the result of such conditions in the valve mechanism as weak springs, worn lifter faces, lifters loose in the block, rough adjustment-screw face, and rough cams. Or else the noise is not from the valves at all. (See other conditions listed below.)

2. *DETONATION* Spark knock or detonation is a pinging or chattering sound most noticeable during acceleration or when the car is climbing a hill. Some spark knock is normal. When it becomes excessive,

it is due to the use of fuel with too low an octane rating, carbon deposits in the engine which increase compression ratio, advanced ignition timing, or the conditions described in ⊘ 12-13.

3. *CONNECTING-ROD NOISES* Connecting-rod noises usually have a light knocking or pounding character. The sound is most noticeable when the engine is "floating" (not accelerating or decelerating). The sound becomes more noticeable as the accelerator is eased off with the car running at medium speed. To locate connecting-rod noise, short out the spark plugs, one at a time. The noise will be considerably reduced when the cylinder that is responsible is not delivering power. A worn bearing or crankpin, a misaligned connecting rod, inadequate oil, and excessive bearing clearances cause connecting-rod noise.

4. *PISTON-PIN NOISE* Piston-pin noise is similar to valve and tappet noise, but it has a unique metallic double knock. It is usually most audible during idle, with the spark advanced. However, on some engines, the noise becomes most audible at car speeds of around 30 mph [48 km/h]. A check can be made by running the engine at idle with the spark advanced, and then shorting out spark plugs one at a time. Piston-pin noise is reduced somewhat when the plug in the noisy cylinder is shorted out. Causes of this noise are a worn or loose piston pin, a worn bushing, and lack of oil.

5. *PISTON-RING NOISE* Piston-ring noise is also similar to valve and tappet noise. It is a clicking, snapping, or rattling noise. This noise, however, is most evident on acceleration. Low ring tension, broken rings, worn rings, and worn cylinder walls produce this noise. Since the noise can sometimes be confused with other engine noises, a test can be made as follows: Remove the spark plugs, and add 1 to 2 fluid ounces [30 to 60 cc (cubic centimeters)] of heavy engine oil to each cylinder. Crank the engine for several revolutions, to work the oil down past the rings. The replace the plugs, and start the engine. If the noise has been reduced, the rings are probably at fault.

6. *PISTON SLAP* Piston slap is a muffled, hollow, bell-like sound. It is due to the rocking back and forth of the piston in the cylinder. If it occurs only when the engine is cold, it is not serious. When it occurs under all operating conditions, it should be checked further. It is caused by inadequate oil, worn cylinder walls, worn pistons, collapsed piston skirts, excessive piston clearances, and misaligned connecting rods.

7. *CRANKSHAFT KNOCK* This noise is a heavy, full, metallic knock. It is most noticeable when the engine is under a heavy load or accelerating, particularly when cold. When the noise is regular, it probably results from worn main bearings. When the noise is irregular and sharp, it is probably due to a worn end-thrust bearing. This latter condition, when bad, will usually produce the noise each time the clutch is released and engaged, and when the car is first accelerating.

8. *MISCELLANEOUS NOISES* Other noises result from loosely mounted accessory parts, such as the alternator, starting motor, horn, water pump, manifolds, flywheel, crankshaft pulley, and oil pan. Other automotive components, such as the clutch, transmission, and differential, may also develop noises.

CHAPTER 12 CHECKUP

NOTE: Since the following is a chapter review test, you should review the chapter before taking the test.

The chapter you have just completed is probably one of the hardest chapters in the book. At the same time, it is perhaps one of the most important chapters. For, to be an automotive emission control expert, you must know what troubles an engine might have, the causes of these troubles, and how to find the causes; that is, you need to be a good troubleshooter. The fact that you have come this far in the book shows that you have made an earnest start toward becoming that expert. The checkup that follows will help you determine how well you understand and remember the information you have been studying in this chapter. If any question stumps you, reread the pages that give you the answer.

⊘ **Correcting Troubles Lists** Each of the following lists contains one complaint followed by several causes. One of the causes does not belong. For example, check through the list "Engine will not turn over: run-down battery, worn rings, starting circuit open, engine jammed, starting motor jammed." You can see that "worn rings" does not belong, since it is the only condition that will not directly cause failure of the engine to turn over. Write each list in your notebook, but do not write the item that does not belong.

1. Engine lacks power, acceleration, or high-speed performance when cold: stuck valves, stuck manifold heat-control valve, vapor lock, stuck automatic choke.
2. Engine lacks power, acceleration, or high-speed performance when hot or cold: defective valve action, defective ignition system, defective fuel system, loss of compression, excessive carbon in the engine, run-down battery.
3. Engine lacks power, acceleration, or high-speed performance when hot only: overheating engine, defective choke, vapor lock, stuck manifold heat-control valve, incorrect idle adjustment.
4. Engine overheats: ignition timing late, loose fan belt, defective water pump, high altitude, clogged water jackets, defective radiator hose, defective fuel pump, defective thermostat, lack of water.
5. Engine stalls as it warms up: closed choke valve, stuck manifold heat-control valve, overheated engine, idling speed too low, defective head gasket.
6. Engine stalls after idling or low-speed driving: defective fuel pump, overheating, high float level, overcharged battery.
7. Engine stalls after high-speed driving: carburetor antipercolator defective, vapor lock, run-down battery.
8. Engine backfires: spark plugs of wrong heat range, overheated engine, hot valves, carbon in the engine, vapor lock, rich or lean mixture, ignition timing off.
9. Excessive oil consumption with blue exhaust smoke: burning oil in combustion chamber, clogged air cleaner, worn rings, worn valve guides, worn bearings.
10. Excessive fuel consumption with black exhaust smoke: clogged air cleaner, rich idle, worn carburetor jets, loss of engine compression, run-down battery, faulty ignition, defective valve action.

Completing the Sentences The following sentences are incomplete. After each sentence there are several words or phrases, but only one of them correctly completes the sentence. Write each sentence in your notebook, ending it with the word or phrase that completes it correctly.

1. An engine will not turn over with: (*a*) defective ignition coil, (*b*) a run-down battery, (*c*) a defective fuel pump, (*d*) valves that hang open.
2. An engine will turn over slowly because of: (*a*) a defective water pump, (*b*) vapor lock, (*c*) undersized battery cables, (*d*) excessive fuel-pump pressure.
3. Failure of an engine to start even though it turns over at normal cranking speed could be due to a: (*a*) run-down battery, (*b*) defective starting motor, (*c*) sticking engine valve, (*d*) defective ignition.
4. Missing in one cylinder is likely to result from: (*a*) clogged exhaust, (*b*) an overheated engine, (*c*) vapor lock, (*d*) a defective spark plug.
5. Irregular missing in different cylinders may result from: (*a*) a defective starting motor, (*b*) a defective carburetor, (*c*) an open cranking circuit, (*d*) a defective battery.
6. Loss of engine power as the engine warms up is most likely caused by: (*a*) vapor lock, (*b*) excessive rolling resistance, (*c*) the throttle valve not closing fully, (*d*) heavy oil.
7. An engine will lose power (hot or cold) if it has: (*a*) an incorrect idle adjustment, (*b*) an automatic-choke valve that is stuck open, (*c*) worn rings and cylinder walls, (*d*) a manifold heat-control valve that is stuck open.
8. An engine may stall as it warms up if the: (*a*) ignition timing is off, (*b*) choke valve sticks closed, (*c*) battery is run down, (*d*) throttle valve does not open fully.
9. An engine will overheat if the: (*a*) automatic choke sticks, (*b*) fan belt breaks, (*c*) fuel pump is defective, (*d*) battery is run down.
10. The most probable cause of an engine stalling after a period of idling or low-speed driving is: (*a*) loss of compression, (*b*) a defective fuel pump, (*c*) sticking engine valves, (*d*) a dead battery.

Troubleshooting Engine Complaints In servicing engines, you will come up against complaints of loss of power, high fuel consumption, knocking, and so on. You must know what to do to find the causes of these troubles. The following questions are stumpers that you might actually encounter in an automotive shop. In your notebook, write the procedures you would follow to find the causes of the various engine troubles. Do not copy from the text. Write the procedures in your own words, to help you remember them. If you are not quite sure of a procedure, turn back to the pages that give you the information.

1. You are called to check a car in which the engine will not turn over when the starting-motor switch is closed. You turn on the headlights and try to start the car. What are the five things that might happen to the headlights? List the probable causes of each.
2. What are the possible causes of the trouble when an engine turns over slowly but will not start? How would you locate the actual cause?
3. A car that will not start is pulled into your shop. You find that the engine turns over at normal speed but will not start. What ignition and fuel-system checks should you make?
4. In checking an engine, you find that one particular cylinder misses. What further checks can you make on this cylinder? What are the possible causes of the trouble?
5. What are the possible causes of the trouble when an engine miss is irregular and cannot be traced to any one cylinder?
6. List the possible causes of the trouble (and how to locate them) when an engine loses power as it warms up.
7. If an engine lacks power hot and cold, what are the possible causes of the trouble? How would you diagnose the trouble?
8. If an engine lacks power only when cold but seems to run normally when hot, what could the trouble be? What would you do to make sure?
9. What are three basic conditions under which an engine will stall? What are the causes of each condition? How can you tell which is the trouble?
10. List the possible causes of engine backfiring, and describe how to locate the actual cause.

SUGGESTIONS FOR FURTHER STUDY

There are two things you can do to learn more about the causes and effects of engine troubles. One is to carefully observe trouble-diagnosis procedures in the automotive shop. The other is to examine engine components after an engine is torn down. For instance, if you examine the pistons, rings, and cylinder walls of an engine which has lost compression and is using too much oil, you will quickly see why the engine lost compression and why it began to use too much oil.

It will be a great help to you, in the automotive shop, to know the trouble-diagnosis procedures outlined in this chapter. Thus, you should study these procedures carefully, and refer to the Engine Trouble-Diagnosis Chart over and over again. You may want to obtain the McGraw-Hill Automotive Troubleshooting Cards, which list troubles and their possible causes. Whenever you get a chance, as, for instance, when you are listening to music on the radio, eating lunch, or getting ready for bed, you can take out one of these cards and read it. You will soon know the troubleshooting procedures thoroughly.

Discuss the various methods of locating engine troubles with expert automotive mechanics and with your instructor. Ask them about their experiences in locating troubles: how often they find that loss of compression is due to worn rings, whether they find much valve-guide wear, and so on.

chapter 13

ENGINE TUNEUP AND TESTING INSTRUMENTS

This chapter describes the procedure known as engine tuneup. Tuneup usually begins with tests of the various components and accessory systems involved in engine operation. But tuneup goes further than just testing. It also includes readjusting or replacing parts as required to restore engine performance and to minimize exhaust pollutants. In some cases, serious problems that require major repair work may be uncovered during a tuneup. Previous chapters have described the various service jobs that may be performed on fuel and ignition systems.

In this chapter, we also describe the testing instruments used by automotive technicians to check the engine and its systems. Included is a review of some of the test instruments covered in earlier chapters. We include this to put together, in this chapter, the complete story of engine tuneup and testing instruments.

⊘ **13-1 Engine Testing Procedures** Engine testing procedures are of two types. One type is used when there is an obvious and specific trouble that seems related to the engine. For example, if there is a miss in the engine or a complaint of excessive fuel or oil consumption, then definite trouble-diagnosis checks are made to pinpoint the cause of trouble. This is often called "troubleshooting."

The second type of engine testing procedure is a general approach. Every engine component is tested as the procedure is carried out, and any wear, subnormal operation, or other defect is detected. This general approach is often referred to as "engine tuneup." By correcting troubles found during the testing procedure, the technician "tunes up" the engine—that is, improves engine performance.

Actually, both types of engine testing procedures have their place in the automotive business. When you encounter a specific trouble, you want to follow a specific procedure to find its cause so that you can correct it. On the other hand, it is often proper procedure to make a complete check of the engine and its components. Many automotive authorities recommend that the engine and its components be checked periodically (for example, every 10,000 mi [16,093 km] or at least once a year). Such an engine analysis will show up worn units or parts, or improper adjustments that soon might cause real trouble. Correction can then be made before serious trouble develops. In other words, the general proce-

dure eliminates trouble before it happens. This is called *preventive maintenance.* You prevent trouble by maintaining the engine in good operating condition.

⊘ **13-2 Engine Testing Instruments** The testing instruments we cover in this chapter are:

1. Tachometer, which measures engine speed in revolutions per minute
2. Cylinder compression tester, which measures the ability of the cylinders to hold compression
3. Cylinder leakage tester, which finds places where there is compression leakage
4. Vacuum gauge, which measures intake-manifold vacuum
5. Exhaust-gas analyzer, which measures the amount of pollutants in the exhaust gas
6. Ignition timing light, which is used to set the ignition timing and check the spark advance
7. Oscilloscope, which shows the overall operating condition of the ignition-system circuits
8. Chassis dynomometer, which checks the engine and its operating parts under operating conditions

There are also instruments that test the battery, starting motor, charging system, and cooling system. There are other instruments that test ignition coils, condensers, spark plugs, distributor contact-point dwell, and distributor advance mechanisms. We discussed many of these in Chap. 11.

⊘ 13-3 Tachometer The tachometer measures engine speed in revolutions per minute (rpm). It is a necessary instrument, because the idle speed must be adjusted to a specific rpm. Also, many tests must be made at specific engine speeds. The tachometer is connected to the ignition system and operates electrically.

The tachometer measures the number of times the primary circuit is interrupted. It translates this into engine rpm. The tachometer selector knob can be turned to 4, 6, or 8, the number of cylinders in the engine being tested. Figure 13-1 shows a tachometer connected to an engine.

Many high-performance cars have a tachometer mounted on the instrument panel, to indicate how fast the engine is turning. Then the driver can keep the rpms where the engine develops maximum torque. This lets the driver get the best performance from the engine. Many of these tachometers have a red line at the top rpm on the dial. The red line marks the danger point for engine speed. The driver should keep the engine below this speed.

Some car tachometers are mechanical instead of electrical. They are driven off a gear on the ignition distributor shaft. They operate somewhat like the speedometer.

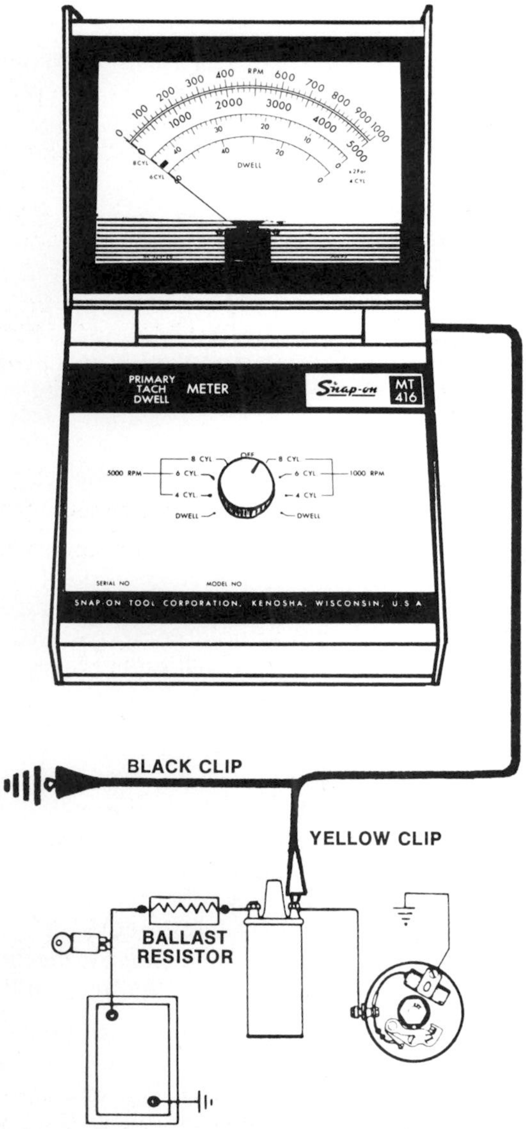

⊘ 13-4 Cylinder Compression Tester The cylinder compression tester measures the ability of the cylinders to hold compression. Pressure operates on a diaphragm in the tester. It causes the needle on the face of the tester to move around to indicate the pressure being applied. Figure 13-2 shows a compression tester being used to measure the pressure in an engine cylinder.

To use the tester, first remove all the spark plugs. A recommended way to do this is to disconnect the wires and loosen each plug one turn. Then reconnect the wires, and start the engine. Then run the engine for a few moments at 1,000 rpm. Finally, turn off the engine, and remove the plugs. This procedure allows the combustion gases to blow out of the plug wells any dirt that could fall into the cylinders when the spark plugs are removed. The gases also blow out of the combustion chambers any loosened carbon that was caked around the exposed threaded end of the plug. This prevents carbon and dirt particles from getting under a valve and holding the valve open during the compression test.

Next, screw the compression-tester fitting into the spark-plug hole of cylinder No. 1, as shown in Fig. 13-2. To protect the coil from high voltage, disconnect the distributor primary lead from the negative terminal of the coil. This is the small wire that goes from the coil to the distributor. Then, hold the throttle wide open, and operate the starting motor to crank the engine. The needle will move around to show the maximum compression pressure the cylin-

Fig. 13-1. A tachometer connected to an engine. (*Snap-on Tools Corporation*)

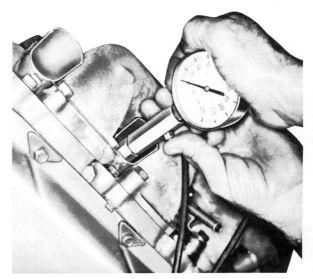

Fig. 13-2. A cylinder compression tester in use. (*Chevrolet Motor Division of General Motors Corporation*)

der is developing. Write down this figure. Then test the other cylinders in the same way.

⊘ 13-5 Results of the Compression Test

The manufacturer's specifications tell you what the compression pressure of the cylinders should be. If the test shows that the compression is low, there is leakage past the piston rings, valves, or cylinder-head gasket. To correct the trouble, you must remove the cylinder head and inspect the engine parts.

Before you do this, you can make one more test to pinpoint the trouble. Pour a small quantity of heavy oil into the cylinder, through the spark-plug hole. Then retest the compression. If the pressure increases to a more normal figure, the low compression is due to leakage past the piston rings. Adding the oil helps seal the rings temporarily so they can hold the compression pressure better. The trouble in this case is caused by worn piston rings, a worn cylinder wall, or a worn piston. The trouble could also be caused by rings that are broken or stuck in the piston-ring grooves.

If adding the oil does not increase the compression pressure, the leakage is probably past the valves. This could be caused by:

1. Broken valve springs
2. Incorrect valve adjustment
3. Sticking valves
4. Worn or burned valves
5. Worn or burned valve seats
6. Worn camshaft lobes
7. Dished or worn valve lifters

It may also be that the cylinder-head gasket is "blown." This means the gasket has burned away so that compression pressure is leaking between the cylinder head and the cylinder block. Low compression between two adjacent cylinders is probably caused by the head gasket blowing between the cylinders.

Whatever the cause—rings, pistons, cylinder walls, valves, or gasket—the cylinder head has to be removed.

⊘ 13-6 Cylinder Leakage Tester

The cylinder leakage tester does about the same job as the compression tester, but in a different way. It applies air pressure to the cylinder with the piston at top dead center (TDC) on the compression stroke. In this position, both valves are closed. Very little air should escape from the combustion chamber. Figure 13-3 shows a cylinder leakage tester. Figure 13-4 shows the tester connected to an engine cylinder, and how it pinpoints places where leakage can occur.

To use the tester, first remove all plugs, as we have explained. Then remove the air cleaner, the crankcase filler cap or dipstick, and the radiator cap. Set the throttle wide open, and fill the radiator to the proper level. You are now ready to begin.

Connect the adapter, with the whistle, to the spark-plug hole of cylinder No. 1. Turn the engine

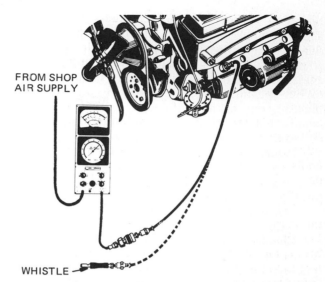

Fig. 13-3. Using a cylinder leakage tester. The whistle is used to locate TDC in the No. 1 cylinder. (*Sun Electric Corporation*)

over until the whistle sounds. When the whistle sounds, the piston is moving up on the compression stroke. Continue to rotate the engine until the TDC timing marks on the engine align. When the marks align, the piston is at TDC. Disconnect the whistle from the adapter hose, and connect the tester as shown in Figs. 13-3 and 13-4. Apply air pressure from

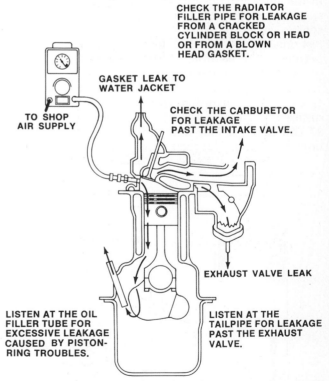

Fig. 13-4. How the cylinder leakage tester works. It applies air pressure to the cylinder through the spark-plug hole with the piston at TDC and both valves closed. Places where air is leaking can then be pinpointed, as shown. (*Sun Electric Company*)

the shop supply. Note the gauge reading, which shows the percentage of air leakage from the cylinder. Specifications vary, but if the reading is above 20 percent, there is excessive leakage. If the air leakage is excessive, check further by listening at the carburetor, tail pipe, and oil-filler pipe. If the air is blowing out of an adjoining spark-plug hole, it means that the head gasket is blown between the cylinders.

Figure 13-4 shows what trouble is indicated when you can hear air escaping at any of the three listening points. If air bubbles up through the radiator, then the trouble is a blown cylinder-head gasket or a cracked cylinder head. This allows leakage from the cylinder to the cooling system.

Check the other cylinders in the same manner. A special adapter supplied with the tester lets you quickly find TDC on the other cylinders. When you use the tester, follow the instructions that explain how to use the adapter.

⊘ **13-7 Engine Vacuum Gauge** The engine vacuum gauge is important for tracking down troubles in an engine that does not run as well as it should. This gauge measures intake-manifold vacuum. The intake-manifold vacuum changes with different operating conditions and with different engine defects. The way the vacuum varies from normal shows you what is wrong inside the engine.

Figure 13-5 shows the vacuum gauge connected to the intake manifold. With the gauge connected, start the engine. Operate it at idle and at other speeds, as explained in following paragraphs. The test must be made with the engine at operating temperature. The meanings of various readings are explained in following paragraphs (see Fig. 13-6).

A steady and fairly high reading on idle indicates normal performance. Specifications vary with different engines, but a reading somewhere between 17 and 22 in Hg [432 and 559 mm Hg] indicates the engine is okay. The reading will be lower at higher

altitudes because of the lower atmospheric pressure. For every 1,000 ft [305 m] above sea level, the reading will be reduced about 1 in Hg [25.4 mm Hg].

NOTE: The abbreviation "in Hg" stands for "inches of mercury." It refers to the way vacuums are measured. There is no mercury in the gauge.

A steady and low reading indicates late ignition or valve timing, or possibly leakage around pistons. Leakage around pistons—excessive blow-by—could be due to worn or stuck piston rings, worn cylinder walls, or worn pistons. Each of these conditions reduces engine power. With reduced power, the engine does not "pull" as much vacuum.

A very low reading indicates a leaky intake manifold or carburetor gasket, or possibly leaks around the carburetor throttle shaft. Air leaking into the manifold reduces the vacuum and engine power.

NOTE: Late-model engines, with high-lift cams and more valve overlap, may have a lower and more uneven intake-manifold vacuum. Also, certain automotive-engine emission controls lower intake-manifold vacuum.

A back-and-forth movement of the needle that increases with engine speed indicates weak valve springs.

Gradual falling back of the needle toward zero with the engine idling indicates a clogged exhaust line.

Regular dropping back of the needle indicates a valve sticking open or a plug not firing.

Irregular dropping back of the needle indicates that valves are sticking only part of the time.

Floating motion or slow back-and-forth movement of the needle indicates an air-fuel mixture that is too rich.

A test can be made for loss of compression due to leakage around the pistons. This would be the result of stuck or worn piston rings, worn cylinder walls, or worn pistons. Race the engine for a moment, and then quickly release the throttle. The needle should swing around to 23 to 25 in Hg [584 to 635 mm Hg] as the throttle closes, indicating good compression. If the needle fails to swing around this far, there is loss of compression. Further checks should be made.

⊘ **13-8 Exhaust-Gas Analyzer** As explained in Chaps. 7 to 9, several engine changes have been made, and several emission-control systems have been added to the automobile, to reduce the amounts of HC, CO, and NO_x emitted by the engine. The amounts of these pollutants in the exhaust gases are measured with an exhaust-gas analyzer. This tests the efficiency of the emission controls and the adjustments of the ignition system and carburetor (Fig. 13-7).

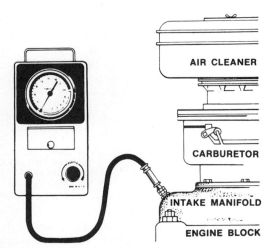

Fig. 13-5. A vacuum gauge connected to the intake manifold for a manifold-vacuum test. (*Sun Electric Corporation*)

	Reading	Diagnosis
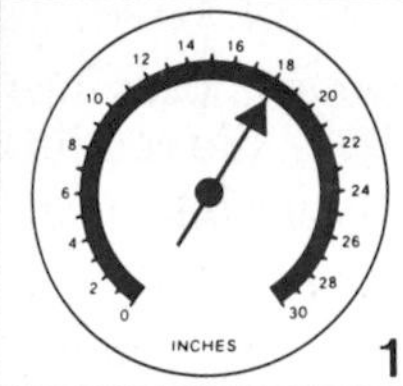 **1**	Average and steady at 17-21.	Everything is normal.
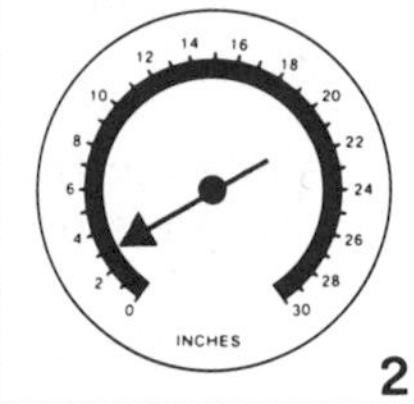 **2**	Extremely low reading—needle holds steady.	Air leak at the intake manifold or carburetor; incorrect timing.
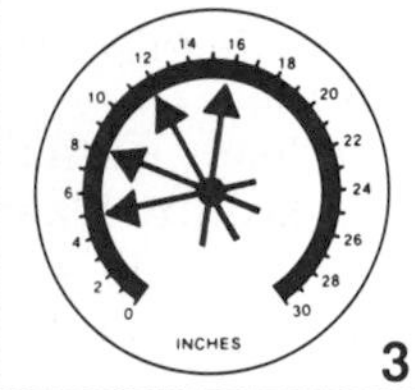 **3**	Needle fluctuates between high and low reading.	Blown head gasket between two side-by-side cylinders. (Check with compression test).
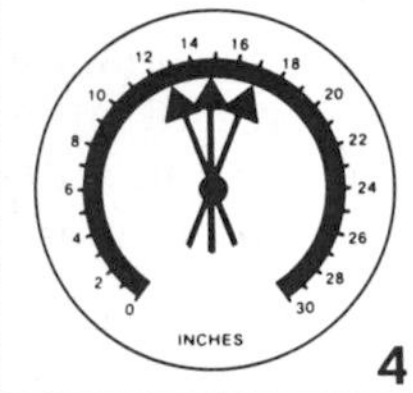 **4**	Needle fluctuates very slowly, ranging 4 or 5 points.	Carburetor needs adjustment, spark plug gap too narrow, sticking valves.
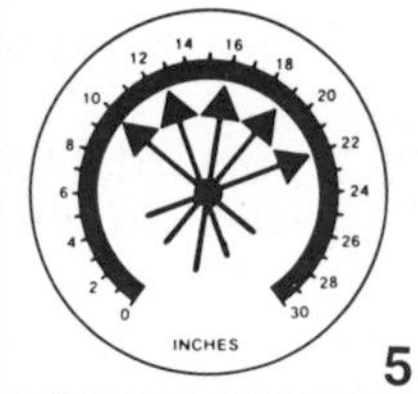 **5**	Needle fluctuates rapidly at idle—steadies as RPM is increased.	Worn valve guides.
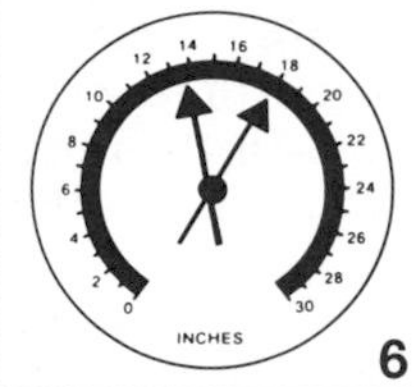 **6**	Needle drops to low reading, returns to normal, drops back, etc. at a regular interval.	Burned or leaking valve.
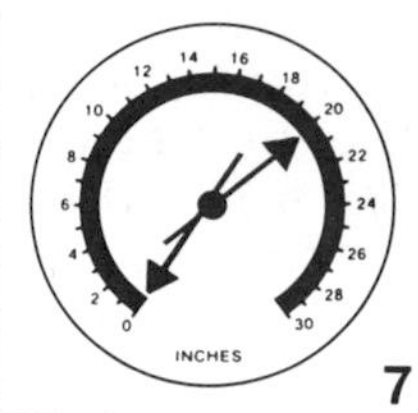 **7**	Needle drops to zero as engine RPM is increased.	Restricted exhaust system.
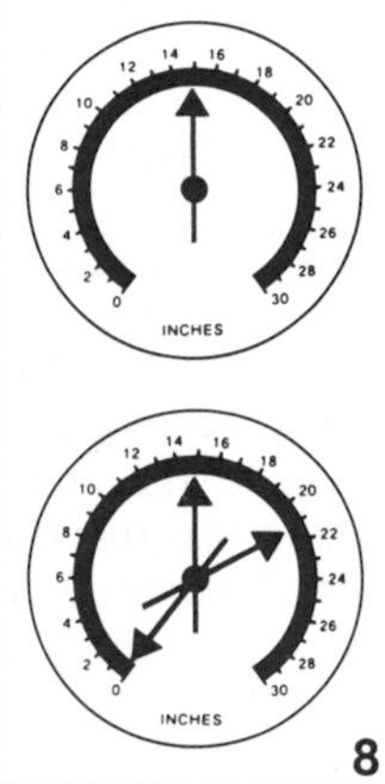 **8**	Needle holds steady at 12 to 16—drops to 0 and back to about 21 as you engage and release the throttle.	Leaking piston rings. (Check with compression test).

Fig. 13-6. Vacuum-gauge readings and their meanings. (*Champion Spark Plug Company*)

At one time, the major use of the exhaust-gas analyzer was to adjust the carburetor. Changing the carburetor adjustment changes the amount of HC and CO in the exhaust gas. Adjusting the idle-mixture screw, for example, can increase the richness of the idle mixture. This increases the amount of HC and CO in the exhaust gas. One of the anti-emission steps taken in the modern automobile is to get the idle mixture as lean as possible with a satisfactory idle. This reduces the amount of HC and CO in the exhaust.

Today, the exhaust-gas analyzer is used to check how well the emission controls on the car are working, as well as the idle adjustment. Figure 13-8 shows one type of exhaust-gas analyzer. To use it, you stick a probe into the tail pipe of the car (Fig. 13-9). The probe draws out some of the exhaust gas and carries it through the analyzer. Two dials on the face of the analyzer (Fig. 13-10) report how much HC and CO are in the exhaust gas. Federal and state laws set maximum legal limits on the amounts of HC and CO permitted in the exhaust.

To use the exhaust-gas analyzer, check the vehicle exhaust system to be sure it is free of leaks. A quick check is to block the tail pipe and listen for exhaust leaks anywhere in the system. If no leaks are heard, insert the exhaust-gas pickup probe at least 18 in [457.2 mm] into the tail pipe. Be sure the probe is securely in place.

Note that the engine to be tested should be at normal operating temperature. If the vehicle is equipped with a dual exhaust, insert the probe into the side opposite the exhaust-manifold heat valve.

To measure CO, run the engine at fast idle (1,500 to 2,000 rpm) for about 30 seconds. This will clear any excess fuel out of the engine. Then run the engine at the specified idle speed. Use the idle-speed adjustment screw as necessary to obtain the specified speed. Allow 10 seconds for the meter to stabilize after each adjustment, before reading the meter.

Read CO at idle on the CO meter. Be sure you are reading the correct scale on the meter. Write down the reading, so you will have a record of it (Fig. 13-11). Then run the engine at 2,500 rpm. Read the CO meter again, and write the reading in the proper space.

A good CO reading is within specifications at idle, and the same or lower at 2,500 rpm. A CO reading that is higher than specified at idle or that increases at 2,500 rpm is bad. In general, the higher the CO reading, the richer the air-fuel mixture. For tuneup testing, most vehicles with exhaust-emission controls should have less than 2.5 percent CO at idle. Vehicles without exhaust-emission controls should have less than 5 percent CO at idle.

To measure HC, run the engine at fast idle (1,500 to 2,000 rpm) for about 30 seconds. This will clear any excess fuel out of the engine. Then run the

Engine Tuneup and Testing Instruments 187

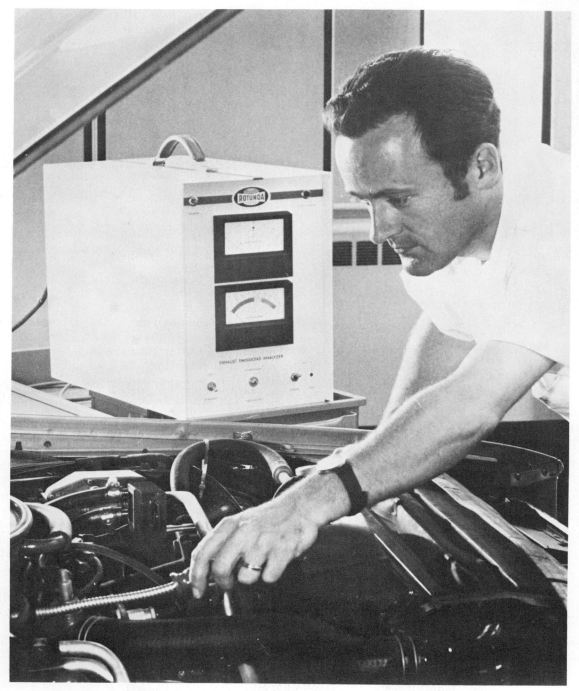

Fig. 13-7. Using an exhaust-gas analyzer to check the amounts of HC and CO in the exhaust gas while adjusting the carburetor. (*Ford Motor Company*)

engine at the specified idle speed. Read HC at idle on the HC meter. Be sure you are reading the correct scale on the meter. Write the reading in the proper space. Then run the engine at 2,500 rpm. Read the HC meter again, and write the reading in the proper space.

A good HC reading is within specifications at idle, and the same or less at 2,500 rpm. An HC reading that is higher than specified at idle or that increases at 2,500 rpm is bad. In general, the higher the HC reading, the more unburned air-fuel mixture is

passing out the tail pipe. For tuneup testing, most vehicles with exhaust-emission controls should have fewer than 300 ppm (parts per million) HC at idle. Vehicles without exhaust-emission controls should have fewer than 500 ppm HC at idle.

A different kind of tester is required for NO_x, but it works in the same general way. It draws exhaust gas from the tail pipe and runs the gas through the analyzer. The meter reports the amount of NO_x in the exhaust gas. Generally, NO_x testers are available only in testing laboratories. They are not widely

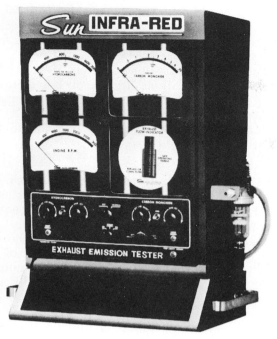

Fig. 13-8. Exhaust-emission analyzer. (*Sun Electric Corporation*)

used in the automotive service shop. Authorities say, however, that someday all well-equipped shops will have them.

⊘ **13-9 Ignition Timing Light** As you know, the sparks must jump across the plug gaps in the cylinders at exactly the right time. Adjusting the distribu-

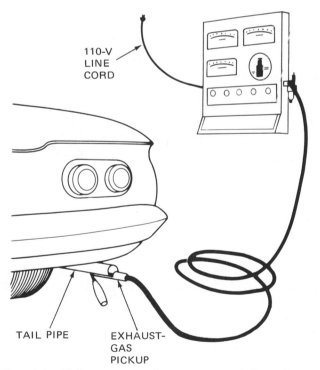

Fig. 13-9. Exhaust-gas analyzer connected for exhaust-gas test.

tor so that they do is called *ignition timing*. You can adjust the ignition timing by turning the distributor in its mounting. The procedure is described in ⊘ 11-12. You use a timing light (Fig. 11-13) to check the timing.

⊘ **13-10 Oscilloscope** The oscilloscope, described in ⊘ 11-2 to 11-5, is a high-speed voltmeter. It has a picture tube like that in a television set. The voltages in the ignition-system primary or secondary circuit are displayed on the tube. If there is trouble, the picture, or traces, show what is wrong. Besides showing what is wrong in the ignition system, the oscilloscope can also detect many engine troubles. For example, with loss of compression in a cylinder, the secondary voltage does not have to be as high as normally. This shows up on the trace for that cylinder, because the spike does not go as high as it would with normal compression.

⊘ **13-11 Dynamometer** The chassis dynamometer can test the engine power output under various operating conditions. It can duplicate any kind of road

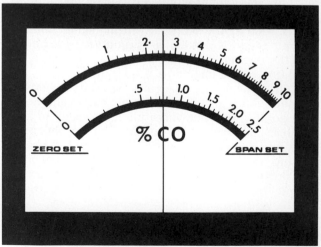

Fig. 13-10. HC and CO meter faces. (*Sun Electric Corporation*)

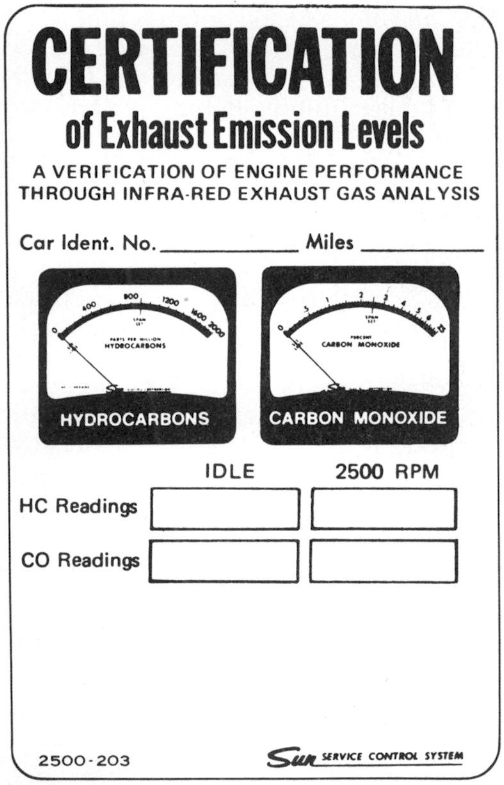

CERTIFICATION
of Exhaust Emission Levels
A VERIFICATION OF ENGINE PERFORMANCE THROUGH INFRA-RED EXHAUST GAS ANALYSIS

Car Ident. No. _____   Miles _____

HYDROCARBONS   CARBON MONOXIDE

	IDLE	2500 RPM
HC Readings		
CO Readings		

2500-203   *Sun* SERVICE CONTROL SYSTEM

Fig. 13-11. Sticker that can be attached to the car, on which to record readings of exhaust-emission levels. (*Sun Electric Corporation*)

test at any load or speed desired by the operator. The part of the dynamometer that you can see consists of two heavy rollers mounted at or a little above floor level. The car is driven onto these rollers (Fig. 13-12) so that the car wheels can drive the rollers. Next, the engine is started, and the transmission is put into gear. The car is then operated as if it were out on an actual road test.

Under the floor is a device that can place loads on the rollers. This allows the technician to operate the engine under various conditions. You can find out how the engine would do during acceleration, cruising, idling, and deceleration. The test instruments, such as the scope, dwell meter, tachometer, vacuum gauge, and exhaust-gas analyzer, are hooked into the engine. These instruments then show the condition of the engine as it operates.

The dynamometer can also be used to check the transmission and the differential. For example, the shift points and other operating features of an automatic transmission can be checked on the dynamometer. Special diagnostic dynamometers are becoming more popular. These units have many instruments attached; they have motored rollers that permit testing of wheel alignment, suspension, brakes, and steering.

⊘ **13-12 What Tuneup Is** Now that we have discussed (in this chapter and others) the test instruments used on an engine, let's see what a tuneup is.

Engine tuneup means different things to different people. To some, it means a light once-over check of the engine that takes in only the more obvious trouble spots. To others, it means use of the proper test instruments to do a careful, complete analysis of all engine components. In addition, it means adjusting everything to "specs" and repairing or replacing all worn parts. The latter is the proper meaning of engine tuneup. It is the procedure outlined in this chapter.

⊘ **13-13 Tuneup Procedure** An engine tuneup follows a fairly set procedure. Many mechanics use a printed form supplied by automotive or test-equipment manufacturers. By following the form and checking off the items listed, one by one, the mechanic is sure of not overlooking any part of the procedure. However, all tuneup forms are not the same. Figures 13-13 and 13-14 show two different forms. Different companies have different ideas about what should be done, and the order in which it should be done. In addition, the tuneup procedure depends on the equipment available. If the shop has an oscilloscope or a dynamometer, it is used as part of the tuneup procedure. If these test instruments are not available, then a tuneup is performed differently.

The procedure that follows includes car-care inspection. It lists all essential checks and adjustments, in what authorities believe is the most logical sequence.

⊘ **13-14 Tuneup and Car Care** The tuneup procedure restores driveability, power, and performance that have been lost through wear, corrosion, and deterioration of engine parts. These changes take

Fig. 13-12. An automobile in place on a chassis dynamometer. The rear wheels drive the dynamometer rollers, which are flush with the floor. At the same time, instruments on the test panel measure car speed, engine power output, engine vacuum, and so on. (*Sun Electric Corporation*)

CUSTOMER_____ PHONE_____ DATE_____

MAKE-YEAR MODEL_____ MILEAGE_____

SIGNATURE_____

Complete Engine Performance

TEST PROCEDURES
(USING A SUN INFRA-RED ENGINE PERFORMANCE TESTER)

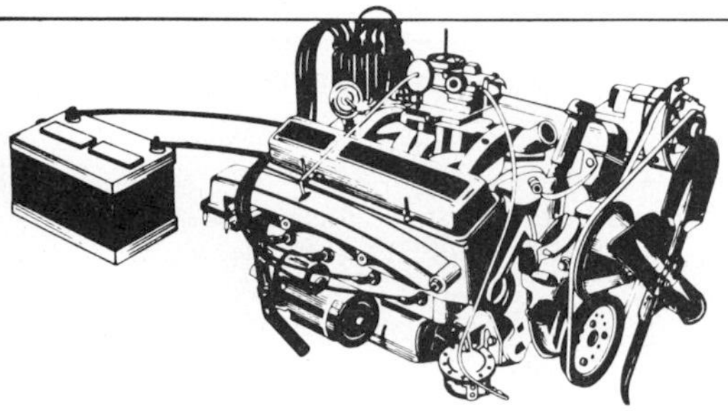

CUSTOMER'S COMMENTS: _____

_____

_____

_____

	TEST PROCEDURE	READ	SPECS.	RESULTS	GOOD	BAD
START	Cranking Voltage	Voltmeter				
	Cranking Coil Output	Scope (Display)				
	Cranking Vacuum	Vacuum Gauge				
IDLE	Idle Speed	Tachometer				
	Dwell	Dwell-Meter				
	Initial Timing	Timing Advance Unit				
	Hydrocarbons P.P.M.	Hydrocarbons Meter				
	Carbon Monoxide	Carbon Monoxide Meter				
	PCV Test	Carbon Monoxide Meter				
	Manifold Vacuum	Vacuum Gauge				
CRUISE	Dwell Variation	Dwell Meter				
	Coil Polarity	Scope (Display)				
	Spark Plug Firing Voltage	Scope (Display)				
	Maximum Coil Output	Scope (Display)				
	Secondary Circuit Insulation	Scope (Display)				
	Secondary Circuit Condition	Scope (Raster)				
	Coil and Condenser Condition	Scope (Raster)				
	Breaker Point Condition	Scope (Raster)				
	Cam Lobe Accuracy	Scope (Superimposed)				
	Hydrocarbons P. P.M.	Hydrocarbons Meter				
	Carbon Monoxide Percent	Carbon Monoxide Meter				
	Cylinder Power Balance	Tachometer	/////////////////			

Record R.P.M.	1	2	3	4	5	6	7	8

	TEST PROCEDURE	READ	SPECS.	RESULTS	GOOD	BAD
ACCEL-ERATION	Spark Plugs Under Load	Scope (Display)				
	Accelerator Pump Action	Carbon Monoxide Meter				
HIGH SPEED	Timing Advance	Timing Advance Unit				
	Charging Voltage	Voltmeter				
	Hydrocarbons P.P.M.	Hydrocarbons Meter				
	Carbon Monoxide Percent	Carbon Monoxide Meter				
	Exhaust Restriction	Vacuum Gauge				

Fig. 13-13. Printed form listing a test procedure which includes the use of the exhaust-gas analyzer. (*Sun Electric Corporation*)

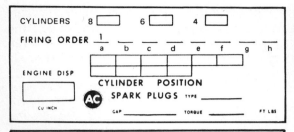

CYLINDERS	8 ☐	6 ☐	4 ☐

FIRING ORDER 1
          a b c d e f g h

ENGINE DISP _____

CYLINDER POSITION
(AC) SPARK PLUGS TYPE _____

CU INCH   GAP _____   TORQUE _____   FT LBS

AC **GM**
Diagnostic
TUNE-UP CENTER

DATE _____
CUST. NAME _____
ADDRESS _____
CITY _____
PHONE _____
CAR MAKE & YEAR _____
MILEAGE _____

ENGINE ANALYSIS

	TEST	SPECIFICAT'N	READ OUT	GOOD	BAD	AFFECTS	CORRECTIVE STEPS
2A-	Battery Voltage Under Light Load	11.5 to 12.4 V				Engine Starting	1. Note and proceed to Tests 3A, 3B, and 3C
2B-	Ignition Switch	Less than 1 V				Engine Starting	1. Check ignition switch. 2. Check starter motor solenoid by-pass circuit. Repair and/or replace as required.
2C-	Primary Resistor	4 - 8V				Overall Engine Performance	1. Check primary resistor and ignition switch. 2. Check starter motor solenoid by-pass circuit. Repair and/or replace as required.
3A-	Cranking Current	Refer to Operators Manual.				Engine Starting	
3B-	Cranking Volts	Not less than 9V				Engine Starting	Refer to Operator's Manual.
3C-	Cranking Speed	80 to 225 RPM				Engine Starting	
4A-	Engine Idle Speed					Gas Mileage, Idling Character- istics, Exhaust Emmission	1. Set idle speed according to manufacturer's specifications. 2. Perform PCV test, as outlined in manual.
4B-	Point Dwell					Passing Safety, Overall Engine Performance	Set dwell to specifications.
4C-	Dynamic Primary Resistance	Green band of Dynamic Primary Resistance scale				Starting, Acceleration, and Cruise Performance	1. Check distributor lead wire. 3. Check distributor ground. 2. Check breaker plate ground. 4. Check for resistance points.
4D-	Air/Fuel Ratio					Fuel Economy, Exhaust Emissions	1. Tune car to manufacturer's specifications. 2. Clean, adjust, and service carburetor, as required to manufacturer's specifications.
5	Power Balance 5A - B, - C, - D, - E, - F, - G, - H	Equal RPM fall off				Engine Idling Smoothness, Power Characteristics	1. Check ignition wires. 2. Make compression check. 3. Repair or replace, as required.
	Carburetor Balance -5J & - 5K	Equal RPM fall off				Exhaust Emissions, Engine Idling	1. Compare to Test 5-Power Balance. 2. Adjust idle mixture screws according to manufacturer's specifications.
6A-	Ignition Output Available	Scale reading in Green Band				Engine Starting, Passing Safety, Cruise Power	1. Set dwell to specifications. 3. Check coil polarity. 2. Check points and condenser. 4. Check with known good coil.
6B-	Coil Polarity	Scale reading in Green Band				Overall Engine Performance	Reverse coil "minus" and "plus" leads.
6C-	Ignition Output Required	Approximate Equal scale Readings in Green Band				Overall Engine Performance	Replace defective ignition wire(s), distributor cap, and/or spark plug(s).
6D-	Ignition Output Req. Under Load	Not more than 20 division increase				Passing Power, Acceleration, Engine Starting	1. Replace plugs. 2. Check all wiring.
7A-	Initial Ignition Timing					Engine Spark Knock, Power, Exhaust Emission, Economy	Adjust to manufacturer's initial timing specifications.
7B-	Mechanical Spark Advance @ 2000 RPM					Maximum Engine Power	If little or no advance is shown, check weights for binds.
7C-	Total Spark Advance @ 2000 RPM					Total Engine Efficiency Throughout Range of Operation	1. Check vacuum hoses for kinks, sharp bends, leaks or blockage. 2. Check for vacuum at vacuum outlet. 3. Check distributor vacuum unit. Repair or replace defective components.
8A-	Charging System					Starting Character- istics as related to Battery State of Charge and Battery Life	If above specifications, see manual notes. If below specifications, go to Step 8B and 8C.
8B-	Regulator Volts					Starting Character- istics as related to Battery State of Charge and Battery Life	If the indication is O.K. when button is depressed, regulator is O.K. If below green band, refer to notes in the Operators Manual.
8C-	Charging Amps	W/O AC 30 to 42 amp. W/AC 45 to 65 amp.				Starting Character- istics as related to Battery State of Charge, Operating Efficiency of Accessories and Battery Life	1. Check generator drive belt. 2. Check all wiring. 3. If generator output is within 10 amperes of rated output, the generator is O.K.: however, regulator adjustment or replacement is indicated.

Fig. 13-14. Printed tuneup form used for engine analysis and tuneup. (*AC-Delco Division of General Motors Corporation*)

place gradually in many automotive parts during normal car operation. Because of federal laws limiting automotive emissions, the tuneup procedure must include checks of all emission controls. Here is the procedure:

1. If the engine is cold, operate it for 15 to 20 min at 1,500 rpm, or until it reaches operating temperature.
2. Connect the oscilloscope, if available, and perform an electronic diagnosis. Check for any abnormal ignition-system conditions that appear on the pattern. Make a note of any abnormality and the cylinders in which it appears.
3. Remove all spark plugs. Fully open the throttle and choke valves. Disconnect the distributor primary lead from the coil, so the engine will not start.
4. Check the compression of each cylinder. Record the readings. If one or more cylinders read low, squirt about a tablespoon of engine oil through the spark-plug hole. Recheck the compression, and record the new readings.
5. Clean, inspect, file, gap, and test the spark plugs. Discard worn or defective plugs. Gap all plugs, old and new. Install the plugs.
6. Inspect and clean the battery case, terminals, cables, and hold-down brackets. Test the battery. Add water, if necessary. If severe corrosion is present, clean the battery and cables with a brush and a solution of baking soda and water.
7. Test the starting voltage. If the battery is in good condition but cranking speed is low, test the starting system.

8. If the battery is low, or the customer complains that the battery keeps running down, check the charging system (alternator and regulator). If the battery is old, it may have worn out. A new battery is then required.
9. Check the drive belts, and replace any in poor condition. If you have to replace one belt of a two-belt drive, replace both belts. Tighten the belts to the correct tension, using a tension gauge.
10. Inspect the distributor rotor, cap, and primary and high-voltage (spark-plug) wires (Fig. 13-15).
11. Clean or replace the distributor contact points. Adjust them by setting the point gap. Lubricate the distributor breaker cam if the specifications call for this. On a distributor with a cam lubricator, turn the lubricator 180° every 12,000 mi [19,311 km], and replace it every 24,000 mi [38,624 km].

NOTE: This step is not performed on an electronic ignition system. There are no contact points in the electronic distributor.

12. Check the centrifugal and vacuum advances. Set the contact dwell, and then adjust the ignition timing. Make sure the idle speed is not excessive, because this could produce centrifugal advance.
13. Use the oscilloscope to recheck the ignition system. Any abnormal conditions that appeared in step 2, above, should now have been eliminated.
14. Check the manifold heat-control valve. Lubricate it with heat-valve lubricant. Free up or replace the valve, if necessary.

INSPECTION OF DISTRIBUTOR-CAP TOWERS

CLEANING AND INSPECTION OF OUTSIDE OF DISTRIBUTOR CAP

CLEANING AND INSPECTION OF INSIDE OF DISTRIBUTOR CAP

REPLACING DISTRIBUTOR CAP

ROTOR INSPECTION

BLOWING OUT INSIDE OF DISTRIBUTOR CAP AND INSPECTION OF INSERT TERMINALS

CLEANING IGNITION COIL

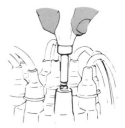
CLEANING TOWER INSERT

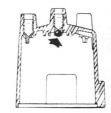
INSPECTION OF CARBON ROTOR BUTTON

Fig. 13-15. Checking and servicing a distributor cap and rotor. (*Chevrolet Motor Division of General Motors Corporation*)

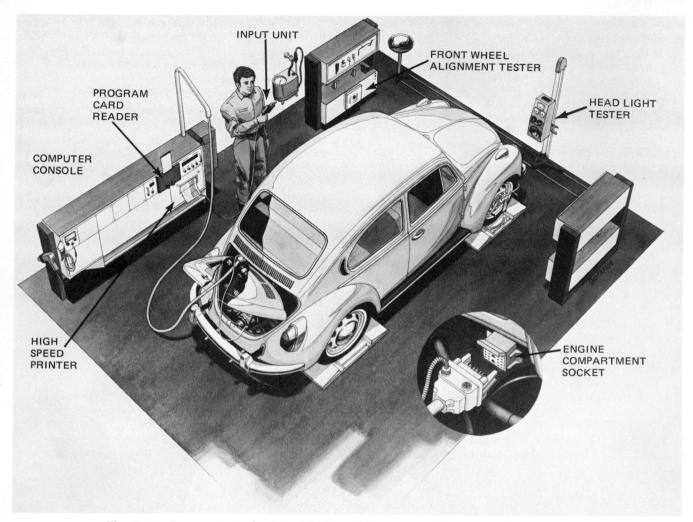

Fig. 13-16. A computerized automobile diagnostic system. (*Vokswagen of America, Inc.*)

15. Check the fuel-pump operation with a fuel-pump tester. Replace the fuel filter. Check the fuel-tank cap, fuel lines, and connections for leakage and damage.

16. Clean or replace the air-cleaner filter. If the engine is equipped with a thermostatically controlled air cleaner, check the operation of the control damper.

17. Check the operation of the choke and the fast-idle cam. Check the throttle valve for full opening, and the throttle linkage for free movement.

18. Inspect all engine vacuum fittings, hoses, and connections. Replace any brittle or cracked hose.

19. Clean the engine oil-filler cap, if a filter-type oil-filler cap is used.

20. Check the cooling system. Inspect all water hoses and connections, and the radiator, water pump, and fan clutch, if used. Check the strength of the anti-freeze, and record the reading. Pressure-check the system and the radiator cap. Replace any defective hose.

21. Check and replace the PCV valve, if necessary (see Chap. 14). Clean or replace the PCV filter, if

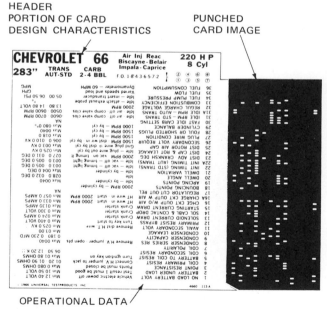

Fig. 13-17. Computer program card listing the specifications for a certain car. (*Universal Testproducts, Incorporated*)

required. Inspect the PCV hoses and connections. Replace any cracked or brittle hose.

22. If the engine is equipped with an air-pump type of exhaust-emission control, replace the pump-inlet air filter, if used. Inspect the system hoses and connections. Replace any brittle or cracked hose.

23. If the vehicle is equipped with an evaporative control system, replace the charcoal-canister filter.

24. Check the transmission-controlled vacuum spark-advance system, if the vehicle is so equipped.

25. On an engine equipped with an EGR system, inspect and clean the exhaust-gas recirculation valve. Inspect and clean the EGR discharge port.

26. Tighten the intake-manifold and exhaust-manifold bolts to the proper tension in the proper sequence.

27. Adjust the engine valves, if necessary.

28. Adjust the carburetor idle speed. Use an exhaust-gas analyzer, and adjust the idle-mixture screw. Check the CO and HC in the exhaust gas.

29. Road-test the car on a dynamometer or on the road. Check for driveability, power, and idling. Any abnormal condition should be noted on the repair order before you return the car to the customer.

30. Check the door-jamb sticker to determine if the engine is due for a change of oil and oil filter. Also

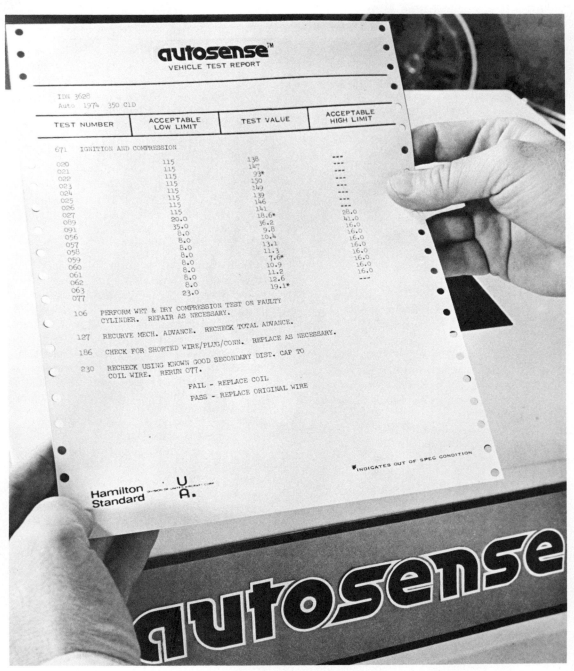

Fig. 13-18. The computer printout tells the mechanic and the customer what work is needed. (*Hamilton Standard Division of United Aircraft Corporation*)

note the schedule for chassis lubrication. Recommend an oil change and a lube job if they are due. Note that car manufacturers recommend changing the oil filter every time—or every other time—the oil is changed.

NOTE: Items 31 to 36 are not actually part of the tuneup job. They are included here so you will have the complete car-care program all in one place.

31. Check the brakes for even braking and adequate braking power.
32. Check the steering system for ease and smoothness of operation. Check for excessive play in the system. Record any abnormal conditions.
33. Check the tires for inflation and for abnormal wear. Abnormal wear can mean suspension trouble, and a front-alignment job should be recommended.
34. Check the suspension system for looseness, excessive play, and wear.
35. Check the front wheels and ball joints for excessive wear and loose bearings. Adjust the bearings, if necessary.
36. Check the headlights and horns to make sure

Fig. 13-19. Sensor panel (called the Electro Sensor Panel, or ESP, by the manufacturer). (*Toyota Motor Sales, Limited*)

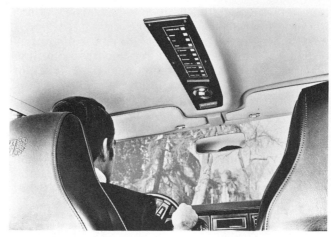

Fig. 13-20. Location of the sensor panel in the car. (*Toyota Motor Sales, Limited*)

they are in good working order. Check all other lights. Replace any burned-out lights. Check the headlight alignment, if possible.

NOTE: As you can see, the comprehensive list above covers about everything on the vehicle that could cause trouble. The complete procedure therefore will uncover any problems that might affect driveability and performance. If all necessary corrective steps are taken, new-car performance will be restored to the vehicle.

⊘ **13-15 Engine Computer Diagnosis** Figure 13-16 shows a computerized diagnostic system introduced by Volkswagen. Wiring and sensors built into the car are connected to the computer through a socket in the engine compartment. With a special program card for each year and model of car, more than 70 items are checked. One type of card is shown in Fig. 13-17. Automatic computer sequences compare the operation of car components with standard values read from the program card. The electric system

Fig. 13-21. Connections from the sensor panel to the 11 service areas. (*Toyota Motor Sales, Limited*)

and engine compression are among the items that are automatically checked. The results of the tests are recorded by a high-speed printer. Figure 13-18 shows the printout from another type of engine diagnostic computer. This printed record tells the mechanic and the customer what work is needed to bring the car up to specifications.

One further refinement has been suggested. This is to put into the computer information on the costs of parts and repair operations. Then the computer could print out, along with the test information, the cost of fixing any troubles. That is, it would print out the costs of parts and labor. It has also been suggested that the computer could be programmed to

1976 CADILLAC — COMPLETE VEHICLE MAINTENANCE SCHEDULE

When To Perform Services (Months or Miles whichever occurs first)	Item No.	Services (For Details, See Numbered Paragraphs)	Mileage When Service Is To Be Performed					
			7.5	15.0	22.5	30.0	37.5	45.0
Section A – Lubrication and General Maintenance								
Every 6 Months or 7,500 Miles	A-1	*Chassis Lubrication	X	X	X	X	X	X
	A-2	●*Fluid Levels Check	X	X	X	X	X	X
	A-3	*Engine Oil Change	X	X	X	X	X	X
At 1st Oil Chg. — Then Every 2nd	A-4	*Oil Filter Change	X		X		X	
See Explanation	A-5	Tire Rotation (Steel Belted Radial)	X		X		X	
	A-6	Rear Axle Lube Change						
Every 12 Months	A-7	Air Conditioning Check	yrly.		yrly.		yrly.	
Every 12 Months or 15,000 Miles	A-8	*Cooling System Check		X		X		X
		*–Coolant Change				X		
See Explanation	A-9	Wheel Bearing Repack				X		
Every 30,000 Miles	A-10	Final Drive Boots & Seals Check (Eldorado)				X		
Every 100,000 Miles	A-11	*Auto. Trans. Fluid & Filter Change						
Section B – Safety Maintenance								
Every 6 Months or 7,500 Miles	B-1	Owner Safety Checks	X	X	X	X	X	X
	B-2	Tire, Wheel and Disc Brake Inspection	X	X	X	X	X	X
	B-3	*Exhaust System Check	X	X	X	X	X	X
	B-4	Suspension and Steering Check	X	X	X	X	X	X
	B-5	Brake and Power Steering Check	X	X	X	X	X	X
Every 12 Months or 15,000 Miles	B-6	*Drive Belt Check		X		X		X
	B-7	Drum Brake and Parking Brake Check		X		X		X
	B-8	Throttle Linkage Check		X		X		X
	B-9	Underbody Flush & Check		X		X		X
	B-10	Bumper Check		X		X		X
Section C – Emission Control Maintenance								
At First 6 Months or 7,500 Miles – Then at 18 Month/22,500 Mile Intervals as Indicated in Log	C-1	Air Cleaner Check	X		X			X
	C-2	Carburetor Choke (Except Fuel Injection)	X		X			X
	C-3	Engine Idle Speed Adjustments	X		X			X
	C-4	EFE System Check (Except Fuel Injection)	X		X			X
	C-5	Carburetor (Or Fuel Injection Throttle Body) Mounting Torque	X		X			X
	C-6	Vacuum Advance System & Hoses Check	X		X			X
Every 12 Months or 15,000 Miles	C-7	Fuel Filter Replacement		X		X		X
	C-8	PCV System Check & Filter Service		X		X		X
		– PCV Valve Replacement				X		
Every 18 Months or 22,500 Miles	C-9	Spark Plug Wires Check			X			
Every 22,500 Miles	C-10	Spark Plug Replacement			X			X
	C-11	Engine Timing Adjustment & Dist. Check			X			X
Every 24 Months or 30,000 Miles	C-12	ECS System Check & Filter Replacement				X		
	C-13	Fuel Cap, Tank and Lines Check				X		
Every 30,000 Miles	C-14	Air Cleaner Element Replacement				X		

●Also A Safety Service   *Also An Emission Control Service

Fig. 13-22. Complete vehicle maintenance schedule for a new car having the latest emission controls. (*Cadillac Motor Car Division of General Motors Corporation*)

schedule the work, depending on the technicians and space available in the shop.

Some car manufacturers are beginning to use on-the-car diagnostic or trouble-indicating devices. A recent innovation in indicating devices is the sensor panel introduced by Toyota in 1974 (Fig. 13-19). This panel is installed on the roof of the car above the driver (Fig. 13-20). It is connected to sensors in the light circuits, brakes, windshield washer, battery, cooling-system radiator, and engine crankcase (see Fig. 13-19). The sensor panel has 11 warning lights which come on if something needs attention. For example, if any of the four lights at the top of the panel (LICENSE, BRAKE, TAIL, HEAD) comes on, it indicates trouble in that light circuit. If one headlight burns out, HEAD comes on to warn the driver of the trouble. The four FLUID LEVEL lights (W-WASHER, BATTERY, RADIATOR, ENGINE OIL) indicate low fluid level in these four areas. That is, if the engine oil level becomes low, the ENGINE OIL light comes on. The BRAKE section of the panel warns of low brake fluid, loss of vacuum in the power-brake unit, and excessive brake-lining wear. Figure 13-21 shows how the 11 warning lights are connected by sensors to the service areas.

According to some experts, the day is coming when a general tuneup procedure, such as we discussed in this chapter, will not be used. They see preventive maintenance, as part of a complete vehicle maintenance schedule (Fig. 13-22), evolving into *predictive* maintenance. That is, computers and on-the-car indicating devices will tell the driver when service on a part or system is needed or due.

CHAPTER 13 CHECKUP

NOTE: Since the following is a chapter review test, you should review the chapter before taking the test.

The material presented in this chapter is designed to acquaint you with the procedures and instruments used to tune and test engines. Now find out how well you remember this material by taking the following test. If you cannot answer a question, turn back into the chapter and reread the pages that give you the information you need.

Completing the Sentences The sentences that follow are incomplete. After each sentence there are several words or phrases, but only one of them correctly completes the sentence. Write each sentence in your notebook, ending it with the word or phrase that completes it correctly.

1. Two types of engine testing procedures are: (*a*) trouble diagnosis and fault-finding, (*b*) trouble diagnosis and tuneup, (*c*) preventive maintenance and tuneup, (*d*) fault-finding and roadside service.
2. The general procedure which eliminates trouble

before it happens is called: (*a*) preventive maintenance, (*b*) trouble diagnosis, (*c*) a timing test, (*d*) checking dwell.
3. When the tachometer is connected between the distributor primary terminal and ground, it indicates: (*a*) engine speed, (*b*) engine vacuum, (*c*) engine compression, (*d*) engine horsepower.
4. If pouring heavy oil into a cylinder increases the compression pressure, then the chances are that the loss of compression is due to leakage: (*a*) past the valves, (*b*) past the head gasket, (*c*) past the piston rings, (*d*) past the oil pump.
5. If the vacuum-gauge needle swings around to 23 to 25 in Hg [584 to 635 mm Hg] as the throttle is quickly closed after the engine has been raced, it indicates: (*a*) stuck valves, (*b*) low compression, (*c*) satisfactory compression, (*d*) leaky valves.
6. A steady but low vacuum reading with the engine idling indicates that the engine: (*a*) is losing power, (*b*) has a stuck valve, (*c*) exhaust line is clogged, (*d*) is idling too fast.
7. A very low vacuum reading with the engine idling indicates: (*a*) stuck valves, (*b*) air leakage into manifolds, (*c*) loss of compression, (*d*) faulty piston rings.
8. A valve that sticks open or a spark plug that is not firing causes the vacuum-gauge needle to: (*a*) oscillate slowly, (*b*) drop back regularly, (*c*) fall back slowly to zero, (*d*) read too high.
9. The exhaust-gas analyzer determines the air-fuel-mixture ratio by analyzing the: (*a*) fuel charge, (*b*) compression ratio, (*c*) compression mixture, (*d*) exhaust gas.
10. The device which can give a very close approximation of a road test in the shop is called the: (*a*) engine dynamometer, (*b*) chassis dynamometer, (*c*) tachometer, (*d*) engine tester.

Unscrambling the Test Instruments Following are two lists. The first list includes various test instruments discussed in the chapter. The second list contains the uses of these instruments, but not in the same order. To unscramble the lists, match each item in the "test instruments" list with its use from the "purposes" list. Write each pair in your notebook. For instance, the first test instrument listed is "Compression tester." When you look down the purposes list, you come to "Checks cylinder compression." So you put the two together and write "compression tester checks cylinder compression."

Compression tester
Tachometer
Vacuum gauge
Exhaust-gas analyzer
Timing light

PURPOSES
Analyzes exhaust gas
Checks intake-manifold vacuum
Checks ignition timing
Checks engine speed
Checks cylinder compression

SUGGESTIONS FOR FURTHER STUDY

Test-instrument manufacturers issue printed information on how to use their instruments and what the test results mean. If you can find this printed information at your local service station or garage or in your school shop, you will find it of considerable interest. You should also examine test instruments in the shop, and watch carefully to see how they are used. In this connection, we give a word of caution. These instruments can be damaged by careless handling and by improper connecting. Therefore, you must know what you are doing before you attempt to use the test instruments. Carefully study the information on how to use the instruments before you attempt to use any test instrument.

PART FIVE

SERVICING AUTOMOTIVE EMISSION CONTROLS

In previous chapters we discussed the various pollutants given off by the automobile. We also described the emission-control devices used on modern cars to reduce or eliminate these pollutants. In Part Five we explain how to check these controls, perform maintenance services, and make whatever corrections are necessary. Also covered in Part Five are the installation and servicing of smog devices on used cars. The last chapter presents a review of automotive emission standards. There are four chapters in Part Five.

⊘ **CHAPTER 14** Servicing PCV and Evaporative Control Systems

⊘ **CHAPTER 15** Servicing Exhaust Control Systems

⊘ **CHAPTER 16** Retrofit Smog Devices for Used Cars

⊘ **CHAPTER 17** Automotive Emissions: a Summary

chapter 14

SERVICING PCV AND EVAPORATIVE CONTROL SYSTEMS

This chapter discusses service procedure for the PCV system and the evaporative control system. As you will see, these systems require very little in the way of service; they are relatively troublefree in operation.

⊘ **14-1 Positive Crankcase Ventilation** We described the PCV system in Chap. 5. It is illustrated in Figs. 5-2 to 5-19. Briefly, the system carries filtered air from the carburetor air filter through the crankcase. This air picks up blow-by and gasoline vapors and carries them to the intake manifold. The air then flows through the engine, where the blow-by and gasoline vapors are burned.

The PCV valve is spring-loaded. At low speeds and idle, when intake-manifold vacuum is high, the vacuum holds the valve nearly closed. In this position, the valve passes only a small amount of air. This prevents the idle air-fuel mixture from being upset and producing poor idling. Then, when the throttle is opened wider and engine speed increases, the intake-manifold vacuum drops. Now, with less

vacuum, the PCV valve opens, allowing more air to flow through the crankcase.

⊘ **14-2 PCV-System Trouble-Diagnosis Chart** The chart that follows lists the various PCV-system complaints, their possible causes, and checks or corrections to be made. The information in the chart will shorten the time you need to correct a trouble. If you follow a logical procedure, you can locate the cause of the trouble quickly. On the other hand, haphazard guessing wastes time and effort.

NOTE: The troubles and possible causes are not listed according to how often they occur. That is, item 1 (or item a under "Possible Cause") does not necessarily occur more often than item 2 (or item b).

PCV-SYSTEM TROUBLE-DIAGNOSIS CHART

(See ⊘ 14-3 to 14-6 for detailed explanations of the causes and corrections listed below.)

COMPLAINT	POSSIBLE CAUSE	CHECK OR CORRECTION
1. Rough idle, frequent stalling (⊘ 14-3)	a. PCV valve plugged	Replace PCV valve
	b. PCV valve stuck open	Replace PCV valve
	c. Restricted PCV air filter	Replace filter; clean system
2. Vapor flow from air cleaner (⊘ 14-4)	a. PCV valve plugged or stuck in backfire position	Replace PCV valve
	b. PCV valve stuck in idle position	Replace PCV valve
3. Oil in air cleaner (⊘ 14-5)	a. PCV valve plugged	Replace PCV valve
	b. Leak in crankcase ventilation system	Clean PCV system; inspect and correct leaks to atmosphere
	c. Cylinder-head oil-return holes clogged	Remove valve cover; inspect and clean holes
	d. Valve-cover oil baffle restricted	Remove valve cover; inspect and repair baffle
4. Excessive oil sludging or dilution (⊘ 14-6)	a. Clogged hoses or fittings	Clean hoses and fittings
	b. Clogged or stuck PCV valve	Replace PCV valve

⊘ **14-3 Rough Idle, Frequent Stalling** Probably the most common problem with the PCV system is sticking of the PCV valve. The driver's complaint depends on the position in which the valve is stuck, but the correction is always the same: Replace the PCV valve.

As oil vapor and blow-by gases pass through the PCV valve, some carbon and sludge remain in the valve. At an average speed of 25 mph [40 km/h], in a car traveling 12,000 mi [19,312 km], about 115,200 ft³ [3,262 m³] of gases from the crankcase could pass through a PCV valve. This gas contains blow-by, sludge, acids, oil, and other contaminants.

When the valve plugs completely, the engine develops rough idle and often stalls. This results from the blow-by and crankcase vapors discharging irregularly into the air cleaner through the tube, or hose, which connects the crankcase (usually through the valve cover) with the air cleaner. This backflow into the air cleaner gets heavier at wide-open throttle.

If the engine operates normally, and blow-by is found to discharge from the air cleaner, the PCV valve is stuck in the idle or minimum-flow position.

When the PCV valve sticks in the intermediate position, the engine idles rough and stalls frequently. But when it runs, it runs at about the speed of fast idle. When the valve sticks in the open, or maximum-flow position, too much air is drawn through the crankcase into the intake manifold. This causes excessive leanout of the air-fuel mixture. Idle is rough, and high-speed miss and power loss may result.

Many problems may be caused by the PCV filter, even though it is now usually located inside the air cleaner. Often, the PCV air filter does not receive regular maintenance. Remove the filter from the air cleaner, or from the separate housing, and check the filter for damage, dirt, and clogging. If the filter is clean, then clean the tube and fittings leading to the filter.

⊘ **14-4 Vapor Flow from Air Cleaner** A plugged PCV valve, or one that is stuck in the engine-off or backfire position, can cause crankcase vapors to flow from the tube at the air cleaner. When the PCV valve is shut completely, crankcase vapors cannot get to the intake manifold. So after the engine fills with vapors and blow-by, the excess flows to the air cleaner through the fresh-air tube. As mentioned in ⊘ 14-3, if the engine runs normally, and blow-by vapors discharge from the air cleaner under heavy throttle, the PCV valve is stuck in the idle or minimum-flow position. To correct a sticking PCV valve, replace it.

⊘ **14-5 Oil in Air Cleaner** An accumulation of oil in the air cleaner, or on the air-cleaner element, indicates that a large volume of crankcase vapors is flowing into the air cleaner. The large vapor flow carries oil mist from the crankcase. This condition often is found on worn engines having a high blow-by rate. The problem gets worse when the PCV valve becomes plugged.

Oil to lubricate the valve train drains down to the crankcase through holes in the cylinder head. Sludge may clog these holes. Then oil is drawn easily through the tube that, on many engines, connects the valve cover and the oil cleaner. Some engines have a valve-cover oil baffle to prevent oil from passing to the air cleaner.

⊘ **14-6 Excessive Oil Sludging or Dilution** A fairly large quantity of water and liquid gasoline appear in the crankcase of a cold engine. One of the jobs of the PCV system is to remove these crankcase contaminants before the rotating crankshaft mixes them with the oil. If they are not removed, they form sludge and dilute the oil. If any part of the line to the intake manifold clogs, or the PCV valve clogs or sticks, these contaminants remain in the engine. To correct the problem, there must be free flow through the PCV system. This usually means cleaning the hoses and fittings or replacing the PCV valve (⊘ 14-9).

⊘ **14-7 PCV-System Service Intervals** The PCV valve should be checked periodically. It should be routinely replaced at specified intervals. Recommendations are:

American Motors: Replace the PCV valve every 30,000 mi [48,280 km].
Ford: Replace the PCV valve every 24,000 mi [38,624 km] or 24 months, whichever comes first.
Chevrolet (GM) and Chrysler: Check the PCV valve every 12 months or 15,000 mi [24,140 km], and replace it every 24 months or 30,000 mi [48,280 km].

⊘ **14-8 Testing the PCV System** Here is a simple way to check the PCV system and the PCV valve: Remove the valve or valve connection with the engine running. Feel for a slight vacuum pull against your hand when you place it over the opening. If there is no vacuum action, or if you can feel a positive pressure, then something is wrong. The PCV valve should be checked. Toyota recommends checking the PCV valve by blowing through it from each end (Fig 14-1). Air should pass freely in the direction of the intake manifold, and should be restricted (but not blocked) in the opposite direction. All hoses and connections should be checked for free flow.

Special testers are available which can be used to check the operation of the PCV valve. If the valve becomes clogged, it will cause engine loping (speeding up and slowing down) and rough idle. The PCV valve cannot be cleaned. A clogged or sticking PCV valve must be replaced. Thus, for engine loping and rough idle, install a new PCV valve. If the idling

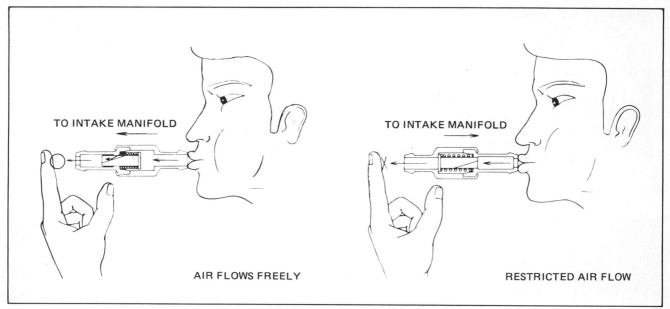

TO INTAKE MANIFOLD

AIR FLOWS FREELY

TO INTAKE MANIFOLD

RESTRICTED AIR FLOW

Fig. 14-1. Quick check for a plugged PCV valve. (*Toyota Motor Sales, Limited*)

improves, leave the new PCV valve in. If the loping or rough idle persists, check for restrictions in the lines. A test can be made to pinpoint the trouble with a PCV tester (Fig. 14-2), as follows:

1. With the engine at operating temperature, remove the oil-filler cap and dipstick. Plug the dipstick tube with the hole plug (Fig. 14-2).
2. With the tester body and proper tester adaptor attached to the hose, as shown, insert the adaptor into the oil-filler opening. Turn the selector knob to the correct setting for the engine under test.
3. Start the engine, and let it idle. Hold the tester body upright, and note the color displayed in the tester windows. Figure 14-3 shows what various colors mean, and the connections to be made.

A second type of tester is shown in Fig. 14-4. It is used as follows:

1. With the engine at normal operating temperature, remove the oil-filler cap. Hold the tester over the opening in the valve cover. Make sure that there is a

tight seal between the cover and the tester. An air leak here will prevent tester operation.
2. Start the engine, and operate it at idle. Note the position of the ball. If the ball settles in the GOOD (green) area, the system is functioning properly. If it settles in the REPAIR (red) area, check the system components as previously noted.

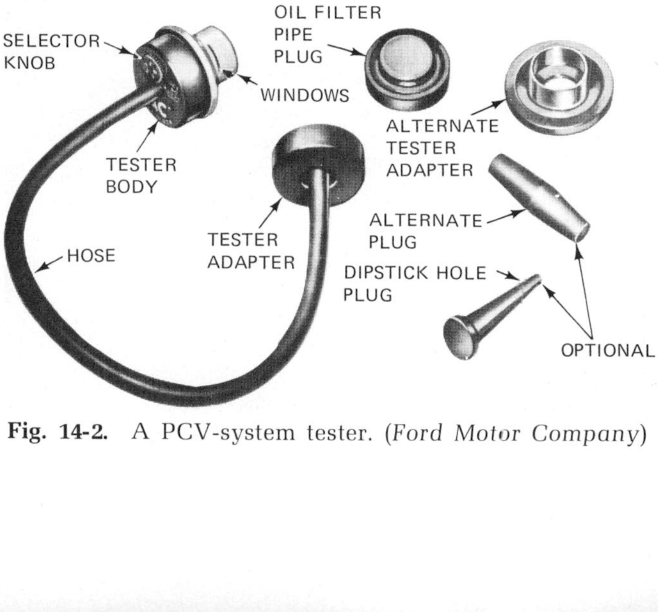

COLOR	CAUSE
Green	System operating properly
Green and yellow	Regulator valve or system partially plugged Slight kink in tester hose Slight engine blow-by Plugs from kit or engine vacuum lines not properly sealed Tester knob improperly set
Yellow	Regulator valve or system partially plugged Tester hose kinked or blocked Blow-by at maximum capacity of regulator valve Plugs from kit or engine vacuum lines not properly sealed Tester knob improperly set
Yellow and red	Regulator valve or system partially or fully plugged More engine blow-by than regulator valve can handle Vent hose plugged or collapsed
Red	Regulator valve or system fully plugged or stuck Vent hose plugged or collapsed Extreme blow-by

SELECTOR KNOB

OIL FILTER PIPE PLUG

WINDOWS

ALTERNATE TESTER ADAPTER

TESTER BODY

HOSE

TESTER ADAPTER

ALTERNATE PLUG

DIPSTICK HOLE PLUG

OPTIONAL

Fig. 14-2. A PCV-system tester. (*Ford Motor Company*)

Fig. 14-3. The colors displayed by the tester, and the conditions they indicate. (*Ford Motor Company*)

Servicing PCV and Evaporative Control Systems 205

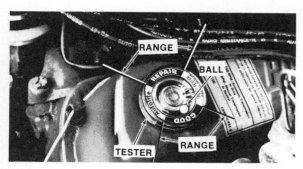

Fig. 14-4. The PCV tester on the valve cover, ready for a test. (*Ford Motor Company*)

Chrysler's recommended test does not require a tester. Instead, remove the PCV valve from the rocker-arm cover with the engine idling. The valve should hiss, and you should be able to feel a strong vacuum when a finger is placed over the valve inlet. Then reinstall the PCV valve, and remove the crankcase-inlet air cleaner. Hold a piece of stiff paper over the opening of the rocker-arm cover. After a few moments, the paper should be sucked against the opening. Then stop the engine; remove the PCV valve from the rocker-arm cover, and shake it. It should click or rattle, showing the valve is free. If the

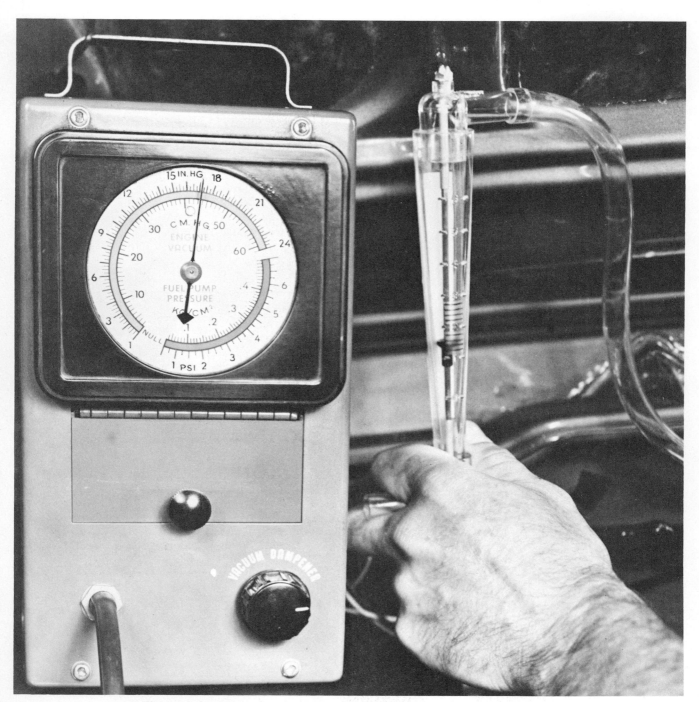

Fig. 14-5. A PCV-valve flow-rate tester. (*American Motors Corporation*)

system does not meet these tests, replace the PCV valve and try the test again. If the system still does not pass the test, the hose may be clogged. It should be cleaned out or replaced. Or it may be necessary to remove the carburetor and clean the vacuum passage with a ¼-in [6.35-mm] drill. Also, clean the inlet vent, on the crankcase-inlet air cleaner, that is connected by the hose to the carburetor air cleaner.

Chevrolet offers still another method. With the engine running at idle, remove the PCV valve from the valve-cover grommet, with hose attached. Block the opening of the valve, and note the change in engine speed. A decrease of less than 50 rpm indicates a plugged PCV valve. You should use a tachometer when making this test, to get an accurate reading of the change in engine rpm.

American Motors recommends checking the flow rate of the PCV valve. To do this, a special tester (Fig. 14-5) is required. With the engine idling, the PCV valve is removed from the intake manifold or valve cover and connected to the tester. The airflow through the valve (the flow rate) can be observed on the special tester and compared to specifications (Fig. 14-6). A PCV valve which allows too much or too little airflow must be replaced.

⊘ **14-9 Servicing the PCV System** The PCV valve must be replaced at regular intervals (⊘ 14-7) and whenever it clogs or sticks. When you install a new PCV valve (Fig. 14-7), inspect and clean the system thoroughly. This includes all hoses, grommets, and connectors. To clean the hoses, soak then in mineral spirits (Fig. 14-8). Then clean the insides with a brush, and wash the outsides. Thoroughly clean all connectors, especially the elbow connection. Wash the oil-filler cap in mineral spirits, and shake it dry. Some types of oil-filler caps must not be dried with compressed air.

After all parts of the PCV system are clean, inspect them carefully. Replace any component that shows signs of damage, wear, or deterioration. Be

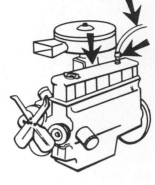

IN A V–8 ENGINE THE PCV VALVE IS LOCATED IN:
1. ROCKER-ARM COVER
2. REAR OF ENGINE
3. CARBURETOR BASE

IN A SIX-CYLINDER ENGINE THE PCV VALVE IS LOCATED IN:
1. ROCKER-ARM COVER
2. CARBURETOR BASE
3. HOSE

Fig. 14-7. PCV-valve locations.

sure the grommet that the PCV valve fits into (Fig. 14-8) is not damaged or torn. Replace any cracked or brittle hose with hose of a similar type. Replace any component, hose, or fitting that does not allow a free flow of air after cleaning.

⊘ **14-10 Servicing the PCV Filter** Fresh ventilation air must be filtered before it enters the crankcase. There are two different methods in use. In one method, the carburetor air-cleaner filter does the cleaning. In this system, the hose for the crankcase ventilation air is connected to the downstream, or clean-air, side of the carburetor air filter. No special service is required. The second method of cleaning the crankcase ventilation air is to use a separate filter, called a PCV filter. This filter, shown in Figs. 5-12 and 14-9, mounts on the inside of the air-cleaner housing. Ventilation air comes into the air cleaner through the inlet or snorkel. It then passes through the PCV filter and into the crankcase.

Whenever the PCV system is serviced, the PCV filter must also be checked. To check the filter shown in Fig. 14-9, remove the retainer clip. Then remove the air-cleaner cover, and take out the PCV filter.

ENGINE MANIFOLD VACUUM (In. Hg.)	Air Flow (CFM)	
	Black Valve	**Silver Valve**
20	1.35-1.65	1.3-1.7
18	1.35-1.65	1.3-1.7
16	1.35-1.65	1.3-1.7
14	1.35-1.65	1.3-1.7
12	1.35-2.2	1.3-1.7
10	1.8 -2.9	1.3-1.7
8	2.5 -3.5	1.3-1.7
6	2.9 -4.0	1.3-1.7
3	3.3 -4.4	1.7

Fig. 14-6. Chart showing how many cubic feet per minute (cfm) of air should flow through a PCV valve at various vacuums. (*American Motors Corporation*)

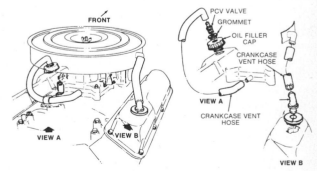

Fig. 14-8. A PCV system in assembled and exploded views. (*Ford Motor Company*)

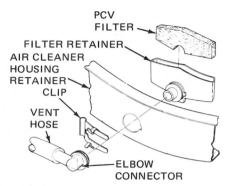

Fig. 14-9. A PCV-filter location inside the air cleaner. (*Ford Motor Company*)

Check it for damage, dirt buildup, and clogging. If the filter is clean, reinstall it in the air cleaner. A dirty or damaged PCV filter must be replaced.

⊘ **14-11 Evaporative Control Systems**   In Chap. 6 we described evaporative control systems. Figures 6-1 to 6-24 show the construction and operation of the various systems and components. Briefly, the evaporative control system limits fuel-vapor (HC) losses from the fuel tank and carburetor float bowl into the atmosphere. This is done by catching and storing the fuel vapors in a charcoal canister (or, in some cars, the engine crankcase) while the engine is off. When the engine is started, the stored fuel vapor passes to the carburetor air cleaner. From there, the vapor is drawn into the engine and burned.

⊘ **14-12 Evaporative-Control-System Trouble-Diagnosis Chart**   The chart that follows lists the various complaints that can be caused by the evaporative control system, their possible causes, and checks or corrections to be made. The information in the chart will shorten the time you need to correct a trouble. If you follow a logical procedure, you can locate the cause of the trouble quickly. On the other hand, haphazard guessing wastes time and effort.

NOTE: The troubles and possible causes are not listed according to how often they occur. That is, item 1, (or item a under "Possible Cause") does not necessarily occur more often than item 2 (or item b).

EVAPORATIVE-CONTROL-SYSTEM TROUBLE-DIAGNOSIS CHART

(See ⊘ 14-13 to 14-16 for detailed explanations of the causes and corrections listed below.)

COMPLAINT	POSSIBLE CAUSE	CHECK OR CORRECTION
1. Fuel odor, or loss of fuel (⊘ 14-13)	a. Overfilled fuel tank	Drain excess fuel; fill tank to proper level
	b. Leaks in fuel, vapor, or vent line	Repair or replace defective line
	c. Wrong or faulty fuel cap	Install correct cap
	d. Faulty liquid-vapor separator	Replace
	e. Fuel volatility too high	Use proper fuel
	f. Vapor-line restrictor missing	Replace
	g. Canister drain cap or hose missing	Replace
2. Collapsed fuel tank (⊘ 14-14)	Wrong fuel-tank cap, stuck relief valve	Replace cap; repair relief valve; repair or replace fuel tank
3. Excess pressure in fuel tank (⊘ 14-15)	a. Plugged or pinched vent lines	Repair
	b. Plugged liquid-vapor-separator outlet	Replace liquid-vapor separator
	c. Plugged charcoal canister	Replace canister
4. Improper engine idling (⊘ 14-16)	a. Improper purge-hose routing	Correct hose routing
	b. Disconnected purge hose	Connect
	c. Plugged canister filter	Replace
	d. High-volatility fuel	Use proper fuel
	e. Vapor-line restrictor missing	Replace

⊘ **14-13 Fuel Odor, Loss of Fuel**   Any noticeable fuel odor usually means that liquid gasoline or fuel vapor is escaping. This may occur when some fuel is spilled in filling the tank with gasoline. But after the cap is installed on the tank of a car, no fuel vapor should escape, and no odor should be noticeable. Overfilling of the fuel tank can cause a loss of liquid gasoline and vapor. Filling the tank, waiting several minutes, and then topping off the filler neck is an improper fueling procedure. It causes leakage. Evaporative control systems have many pipes and hoses through which ventilation air, fuel vapor, and liquid gasoline must flow. Pinched, plugged, disconnected, and leaky lines cause fuel odor.

When you order gasoline, you have no control of the volatility of the fuel you select. However, fuel volatility is adjusted seasonally by the refiner. Winter grades of gasoline are more volatile than summer grades. In unseasonably hot weather, the service station may be pumping a fuel that is too volatile for the temperature. As a result, part of the gasoline evaporates too quickly, overloading the evaporative control system. This allows some gasoline vapor to escape into the atmosphere, where you can smell it.

⊘ **14-14 Collapsed Fuel Tank** Deformation, or "caving-in," of the fuel tank may result from either of two causes. The wrong fuel-tank cap may get installed on the tank filler neck, or the tank vacuum-relief valve may stick closed.

Different fuel tanks can have the same size filler-neck opening. On some cars without evaporative controls, vacuum venting was provided by a small hole through the cap. On other precontrolled cars the cap was sealed, but there was a separate vent line to the atmosphere.

Evaporative controls first began to appear on California cars in 1970 (1971, nationwide). The filler-neck size did not change, but the cap did. Cars began using caps that incorporated two valves. One valve is the pressure-relief valve, which prevents pressure in the tank from rising too high. The second valve is the vacuum-relief valve. It opens to allow enough air to enter the tank to replace the gasoline pumped from the tank by the fuel pump. Other cars use a sealed cap, and have separate vacuum- and pressure-relief valves.

If a sealed cap is placed on a late-model car that requires a cap with pressure and vacuum valves, a collapsed fuel tank can result. As the gasoline is pumped from the tank, a vacuum develops in it. Then, the atmospheric pressure of about 15 lb [6.8 kg] on every square inch (6.45 cm^2) of tank surface becomes too great for the tank to support. The tank collapses or caves in at the sides. Depending on how badly the tank deforms, it may or may not have to be replaced.

⊘ **14-15 Excess Pressure in Fuel Tank** Some pressure can be expected in the fuel tank of a car with evaporative controls. The pressure may be most noticeable as the sound of rushing air, or the feel of air moving past your hand, while you remove the fuel-tank cap. This condition may be even more noticeable when the weather turns unseasonably hot and the tank contains a high-volatility or winter-blend fuel.

Excessive pressure may develop in the tank because of plugged or pinched lines, or from a plugged liquid-vapor separator or charcoal canister. (Internal plugging of the charcoal canister may occur.) Pressure can also develop in the fuel tank if the pressure-relief valve in the tank cap sticks closed. In this case, the problem is solved by installing a new cap of the proper type.

⊘ **14-16 Improper Engine Idling** Many different engine-idling problems can result from faulty or improper connection of a hose in the evaporative control system. The correction, of course, is to repair or reroute the hose. Another cause of improper engine idling can be a dirty or plugged air filter for the charcoal canister. Most manufacturers recommend inspection and, if necessary, replacement of the filter every 12 months or 12,000 mi [19,312 km], or every 24 months or 24,000 mi [38,624 km]. A plugged filter (often caused by excessive driving under dusty conditions, or oil or water getting into it) must be replaced.

A fuel too volatile for the outside temperature, or a missing restrictor in the vapor line, will also cause improper engine idling.

⊘ **14-17 Evaporative Control System Service Intervals** Evaporation control systems require little in the way of service. The troubles that can occur are discussed in ⊘ 14-12 to 14-16. About the only periodic service required is to replace the filter, which is located in the bottom of the canister, at specified intervals. Recommendations are:

American Motors: Replace the filter every 30,000 mi [48,280 km].
Chevrolet (GM): Replace the filter every 24 months or 30,000 mi [48,280 km], whichever comes first.
Chrysler: Replace the filter every 15,000 mi [24,140 km].
Ford: Inspect the evaporative-emission converter every 20 months or 20,000 mi [32,187 km], whichever comes first.

⊘ **14-18 Servicing Evaporative Control Systems** No testers are needed to check evaporative control systems. Almost all problems can be found by visual inspection. Problems are also indicated by a strong odor of fuel. Some experts suggest that an infrared exhaust analyzer can be used to quickly detect small vapor losses from around the fuel tank, canister, air cleaner, lines, or hose. Any loss will register on the HC meter of the exhaust analyzer.

Figure 14-10 is a schematic view of the two types of evaporative control systems. The left view shows the commonly used canister storage system, and the right view shows the crankcase storage system. Note that the crankcase storage system requires an airtight crankcase to prevent the escape of HC vapor while it is stored there. Crankcase leaks also can be detected with an infrared exhaust analyzer.

Most problems with evaporative control systems are obvious and can be noticed during an inspection. Typical defects are damaged lines, liquid-fuel and vapor leaks, and missing parts. The filler cap can be damaged or corroded so that its valves fail to work properly. A problem with the fuel-tank cap could result in deforming of the tank. This could also occur when the wrong cap is installed on the tank. Be sure that the fuel-tank filler cap is of a type specified by the manufacturer for the vehicle, and that the cap seals the fuel tank.

To service the evaporative control system, inspect the fuel-tank cap (Fig. 14-11). Check the condition of the sealing gasket around the cap (see Fig. 6-21). If the gasket is damaged, replace the cap. Check the filler neck and tank for stains resulting from fuel leakage. Usually, you can trace a stain back to its origin. Then fix the cause of the leak. This may

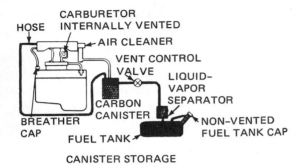

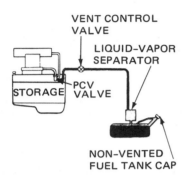

CRANKCASE STORAGE

Fig. 14-10. Canister and crankcase types of fuel-vapor storage systems. (*Ford Motor Company*)

require replacing a gasket, clamp, or hose, or replacing the tank.

Inspect all lines and connections in the fuel and evaporative control systems (Fig. 14-11) for damage and leakage. Perform any necessary repairs. Check all clamps and connections for tightness.

NOTE: The hoses used in evaporative control systems are specially made to resist deterioration from contact with gasoline and gasoline vapor. When you replace a hose, make sure the new hose is specified by the manufacturer for use in evaporative control systems. Sometimes this type of hose is marked EVAP.

Check the charcoal-canister lines for liquid gasoline (Fig. 14-12). If any is present, replace the liquid-vapor separator (Fig. 14-11) or the liquid check valve.

⊘ **14-19 Servicing the Canister Filter** At scheduled intervals (⊘ 14-17), inspect and replace the filter in the canister (Fig. 14-13). Servicing evaporative control systems is very simple, and no special tools are required. To replace the canister filter, remove the canister, turn it upside down (Fig. 14-13), and remove the bottom cover. Pull out the old filter with your fingers, and insert the new filter. If the canister itself is cracked or internally plugged, a new canister assembly should be installed.

⊘ **14-20 Ford Auxiliary Fuel Tanks** Some 1975 and later models of Ford-built cars are equipped with a separate auxiliary fuel tank (Fig. 14-14). On these cars, the fuel-tank filler tube feeds into the auxiliary fuel tank. When you fuel the car, gasoline enters the auxiliary tank and then flows into the main tank, until both tanks are filled. Fuel for driving comes from the main tank. Fuel drains from the auxiliary tank into the main tank as the car is driven. Each tank has its own vapor separator and a line which

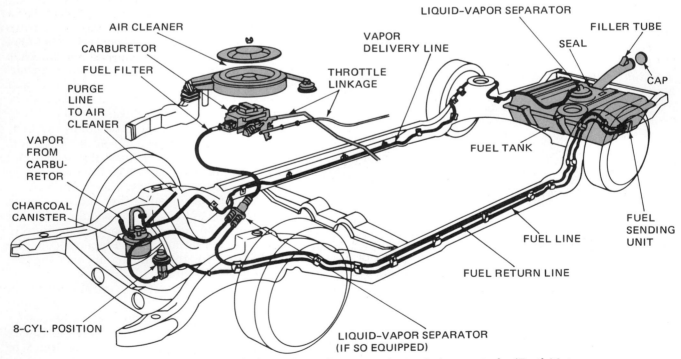

Fig. 14-11. Automotive fuel system with evaporative emission controls. (*Ford Motor Company*)

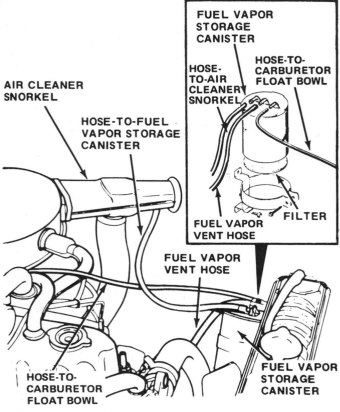

Fig. 14-12. Location and hose connections for a fuel-vapor storage canister. (*American Motors Corporation*)

connects it to the charcoal canister. The vapor separators are identical and of the single-orifice type (Fig. 14-15).

The vapor separator has a float valve in it (Fig. 14-15). If liquid gasoline reaches the valve opening inside the vapor separator, the float rises, closing off the opening. Shown on the right in Fig. 14-15 is a new type of vapor separator introduced by Ford in 1976. In incorporates an internal spring inside the float, to seal the opening any time the car rolls 90°. For example, if the car rolls over on its side or top in a collision, the float valve shuts so no gasoline can escape through the separator or the line connected to it. All the vapor separators shown in Fig. 14-15 are installed by pushing the separator into a rubber grommet mounted in the top of the tank, in much the same way as a PCV valve is installed. Never insert a sharp object between the tank seal and the push-in type of separator during removal or installation. It could damage the grommet, and liquid-fuel and vapor leakage could occur.

The auxiliary fuel tank is made of polyethylene. It can be cleaned with a solution of detergent and water.

NOTE: Ford auxiliary fuel tanks must not be steam-cleaned or exposed to extreme heat from any source. The tanks are made of plastic and can be destroyed by heating or steam-cleaning.

Cars equipped with auxiliary fuel tanks are required to comply with state and federal laws prohibiting excessive evaporative emissions, just like other late-model cars. Service procedures on the Ford auxiliary fuel tank, and cars equipped with them, are routine. A plugged, damaged, or defective vapor separator must be replaced. An auxiliary tank must be replaced if damaged, although it can be cleaned with a solution of detergent and water if dirty or contaminated. Each tank is connected through a vapor separator to the carbon canister. Many of these cars are equipped with a nylon carbon canister which has shoulders on the tube nipples (Fig. 14-16). The shoulders cause the hoses connecting to the canister-tube system to hold better. Notice that this late-model canister (Fig. 14-16) has a different shape from other canisters shown in Chap. 6 and in this chapter. However, it has the same connections to the fuel-vapor sources, and it works in the same way.

Fig. 14-13. Replacing the air filter in the charcoal canister.

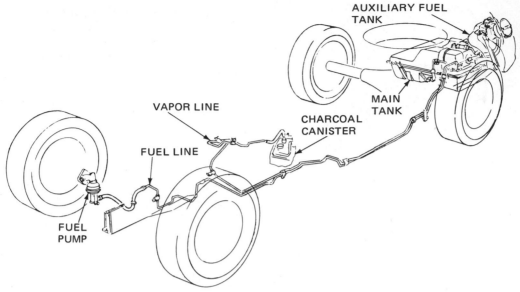

Fig. 14-14. Auxiliary-fuel-tank installation on a late-model car. (*Ford Motor Company*)

Service procedures for cars with auxiliary fuel tanks are the same as for other cars equipped with evaporative control systems. Reread ⊘ 14-11 to ⊘ 14-19 for details on their operation and service procedures.

CHAPTER 14 CHECKUP

NOTE: Since this is a chapter review test, you should review the chapter before taking the test.

You are making good progress in your study of automotive emission control service. In this chapter

you learned about servicing PCV and evaporative control systems. The following quiz covers the material in the chapter, including the trouble-diagnosis charts. The ability to diagnose troubles caused by emission controls is of great value to the service technician. To see how far you have come in acquiring that ability, answer the questions below.

Completing the Sentences The sentences below are incomplete. After each sentence there are several words or phrases, but only one of them correctly completes the sentence. Write each sentence in your notebook, ending it with the word or phrase that completes it correctly.

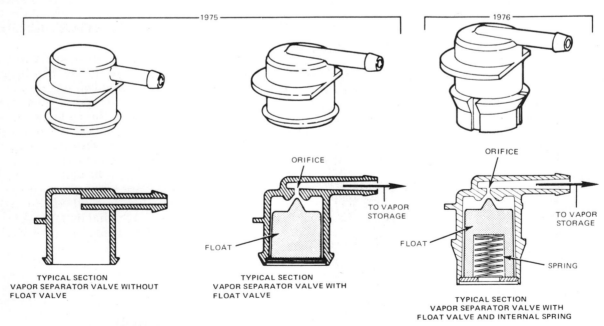

Fig. 14-15. Different types of vapor-separator valves which mount in a grommet in the top of the fuel tank. (*Ford Motor Company*)

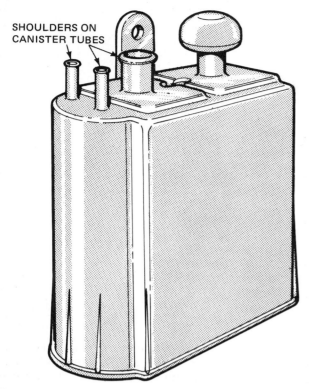

SHOULDERS ON
CANISTER TUBES

Fig. 14-16. Late-model nylon-type carbon canister which has shoulders on the nipples to secure the hoses better. (*Ford Motor Company*)

1. A complaint of rough idle and frequent stalling can be caused by: (*a*) high idle speed, (*b*) a plugged air cleaner, (*c*) a gasoline with too low a volatility, (*d*) a PCV valve that is stuck open.
2. Clogged cylinder-head oil-return holes may cause: (*a*) rough idle with frequent stalling, (*b*) vapor flow from the air cleaner, (*c*) oil in the air cleaner, (*d*) excessive engine sludging.
3. Ford recommends replacing the PCV valve every: (*a*) 30,000 mi [48,280 km], (*b*) 24,000 mi [38,624 km], (*c*) 15,000 mi [24,140 km], (*d*) month.
4. A quick check for a PCV valve, according to Chrysler, is to: (*a*) shake the valve, (*b*) soak the valve, (*c*) replace the valve, (*d*) disassemble the valve.
5. The PCV filter is located in the: (*a*) intake manifold, (*b*) valve cover, (*c*) crankcase, (*d*) air cleaner.
6. A collapsed fuel tank can be caused by: (*a*) overfilling the tank, (*b*) running out of gasoline, (*c*) unseasonably hot weather, (*d*) the wrong fuel-tank cap.
7. Chevrolet recommends replacing the filter in the charcoal canister every: (*a*) 30,000 mi [48,280 km], (*b*) 15,000 mi [24,140 km], (*c*) 20,000 mi [32,187 km], (*d*) 12 months.

8. To service evaporative control systems, you need: (*a*) tuneup instruments and meters, (*b*) no special tools, (*c*) metric tools, (*d*) an oscilloscope.
9. Stains around the fuel-tank filler neck indicate: (*a*) excess pressure in the tank, (*b*) a plugged canister filter, (*c*) fuel leakage, (*d*) water in the fuel tank.
10. The late-model Ford cars which use two vapor separators have: (*a*) an auxiliary fuel tank, (*b*) fuel injection, (*c*) two canisters, (*d*) two fuel gauges.

Correcting Lists The purpose of this exercise is to enable you to spot the unrelated trouble, test instrument, or cause in a list. For example, check through the list "shoes, pants, shirt, milk, tie, coat." You can see that "milk" does not belong, because it is the only thing named that you could not put on and wear. Each of the following lists contains one unrelated item. Write each list in your notebook, but do not write the item that does not belong.

1. Troubles in the PCV system can be caused by the PCV valve, hose and connections, engine condition, and charcoal canister.
2. Test instruments for PCV systems include the tachometer, PCV tester, timing light, and PCV-valve flow gauge.
3. Possible causes of rough engine idling are a PCV valve plugged shut, low engine oil level, PCV valve stuck open, and restricted air filter.
4. Possible causes of oil in the air cleaner are a PCV valve stuck open, plugged PCV valve, clogged cylinder-head oil-return holes, and restricted valve-cover oil baffle.
5. Possible causes of fuel odor in a car are a stuck PCV valve, overfilled fuel tank, gasoline of too high a volatility, wrong fuel-tank cap, and faulty liquid-vapor separator.

SUGGESTIONS FOR FURTHER STUDY

In your notebook, draw lines to divide two pages into three parts each, the way the trouble-diagnosis charts in this chapter are divided. Label one page "PCV System," and the other page "Evaporative Control System." Then, label the columns with the headings "Complaint," "Possible cause," and "Check or correction." Every time you finish working on a PCV system or an evaporative control system, fill in one line of the chart. After you have entered this information for a few jobs, you will see that some troubles occur more often than others. From your chart, you will be able to tell what these troubles are, and the service or repairs needed to correct them.

chapter 15

SERVICING EXHAUST CONTROL SYSTEMS

In this chapter we discuss service procedures for the most widely used exhaust-emission control systems. Service procedures for other exhaust-emission controls may be found in the manufacturers' service manuals. In general, exhaust-emission controls require little in the way of service. However, many different types of driver complaints may be traced to malfunctions of these devices.

⊘ **15-1 Air Injection** In ⊘ 9-1 we discussed the air-injection system. It treats the exhaust gas to control HC and CO emissions. Figure 15-1 illustrates this system. Let us briefly review the operation of the air-injection system (Fig. 15-2): An air-injection pump pushes air through the air lines and the air manifold into a series of air-injection tubes. These tubes are located opposite the exhaust valves. In the exhaust manifold, the oxygen in the air helps to burn

any HC and CO in the exhaust gas. The check valve (Fig. 15-2) prevents any backflow of exhaust gases to the air pump in case of backfire. The air-by-pass valve operates during engine deceleration, when intake-manifold vacuum is high. The bypass valve momentarily diverts air from the air pump to the air cleaner, instead of to the exhaust manifold. This tends to prevent backfiring in the exhaust system.

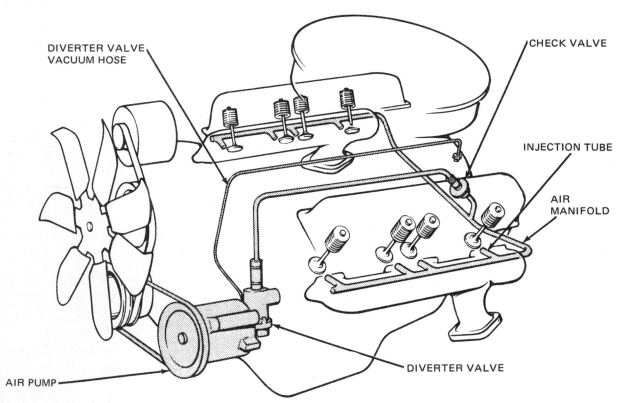

Fig. 15-1. Simplified view of an air-injection system on a V-8 engine. (*Chrysler Corporation*)

⊘ 15-2 An Air-Injection-System Trouble-Diagnosis Chart The chart that follows lists the various air-injection-system complaints, their possible causes, and checks or corrections to be made. The information in the chart will shorten the time you need to correct a trouble. If you follow a logical procedure, you can locate the cause of the trouble quickly. On the other hand, haphazard guessing wastes time and effort.

NOTE: The troubles and possible causes are not listed according to how often they occur. That is, item 1 (or item a under "Possible Cause") does not necessarily occur more often than item 2 (or item b).

AIR-INJECTION-SYSTEM TROUBLE-DIAGNOSIS CHART

(See ⊘ 15-3 to 15-7 for detailed explanations of the causes and corrections listed below.)

COMPLAINT	POSSIBLE CAUSE	CHECK OR CORRECTION
1. Excessive belt noise (⊘ 15-3)	a. Loose belt	Tighten belt
	b. Seized air pump	Replace air pump
2. Excessive air-pump noise (⊘ 15-4)	a. Leaking, loose, or disconnected hose	Replace or properly connect hose
	b. Hose touching other engine parts	Adjust hose position
	c. Diverter-valve failure	Replace diverter valve
	d. Check-valve failure	Replace check valve
	e. Pump mounting bolts loose	Retorque all mounting bolts
	f. Centrifugal fan damaged	Replace centrifugal fan
	g. Air pump seized or binding	Replace air pump
	h. Cup plug missing from cover	Replace plug
	i. Bent or misaligned pulley	Replace or align pulley
3. No air supply (⊘ 15-5)	a. Loose or broken belt	Tighten or replace belt
	b. Leak in hose	Locate source of leak and correct
	c. Leak at hose fitting	Replace or tighten hose clamps
	d. Diverter-valve failure	Replace diverter valve
	e. Check-valve failure	Replace check valve
	f. Air-pump failure	Replace air pump
4. Backfire in exhaust system (⊘ 15-6)	a. Diverter valve defective	Replace diverter valve
	b. Wrong hose on diverter valve	Correct hose routing
	c. No vacuum to diverter valve	Locate and repair cause of no vacuum
5. High HC and CO levels (⊘ 15-7)	a. Air supply leaks	Locate and repair
	b. Low air-pump output	Replace air pump
	c. Plugged air-injection tubes	Clean or replace injection tubes.

⊘ 15-3 Excessive Belt Noise For proper operation of the air pump, the air-pump drive belt must be in good condition and adjusted to the specified tension. The belt should be checked and tightened to the specified tension at least every 12 months or 12,000 mi [19,312 km].

If the air pump seizes, the belt may slide in the pump pulley, making noise. As the pump is not repairable, replace the pump. Check the condition of the belt before tightening it.

⊘ 15-4 Excessive Pump Noise During normal operation, the air-injection system is not completely noiseless. The normal noise from the pump rises in pitch as engine speed increases. A quick check to determine if the air pump is the source of excessive engine-compartment noise is to remove the pump drive belt and operate the engine. If the noise cannot be heard, the problem is in the air-injection system. When the belt is removed, and the pump is turned by hand, the pump frequently squeaks. This is normal, and does not indicate a defective pump. Do not oil or lubricate the pump in any way. The only serviceable part of the pump is the centrifugal filter

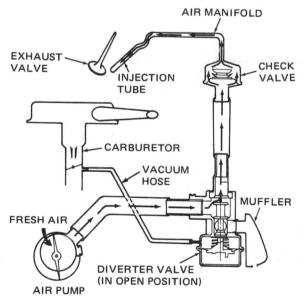

Fig. 15-2. Schematic view of the air-injection system. (*Chevrolet Motor Division of General Motors Corporation*)

fan. Until properly "broken in," a new pump may make some chirping noises. A continuous knocking noise indicates rear-bearing failure; this may result from excessive drive-belt tension. As you can see in ⊘ 15-2, any abnormal noise from the pump requires that it be replaced.

⊘ 15-5 No Air Supply

This problem often is the result of the pump not turning. If the drive belt breaks or works loose, the pump cannot turn. Another possible reason for no air supply is seizure, or failure, of the pump. Servicing of the air pump is limited to replacement of the centrifugal-fan filter. Do not disassemble the air pump for any reason. When servicing the pump filter, do not clamp the pump in a vise or hammer on the pump. Be careful, when adjusting the drive belt, not to pry on the pump housing. If a pry bar must be used to properly tension the belt, pry as close to the rear of the pump cover as possible.

NOTE: See ⊘ 15-9 which describes this procedure.

⊘ 15-6 Backfire in Exhaust System

A backfire in the exhaust system, especially on deceleration, may be caused by failure of the diverter valve. In order for a backfire to occur, an excessively rich mixture must get into the exhaust system. This happens on deceleration. Then, when the fresh air being pumped into the exhaust manifold by the air-injection system hits the hot, rich mixture in the exhaust gas, backfire occurs. Under normal conditions, the diverter valve acts during deceleration to divert the air supply from the air pump into the atmosphere or the air cleaner. Without the fresh air from the air pump, the fuel-rich exhaust gas does not explode, so no backfire takes place. Failure of the diverter valve to operate may be caused by a disconnected, plugged, or leaking vacuum hose.

⊘ 15-7 High HC and CO Levels

An engine equipped with an air-injection system has a higher than allowable amount of HC and CO leaving the combustion chamber. It is the job of the air-injection system to provide additional air to the exhaust gases, so that the excess amounts of HC and CO become harmless water and carbon dioxide. When an engine with an air-injection system has high levels of HC and CO in the exhaust, the air-pump air may not be getting into the exhaust manifold. If any air hose or the air manifold leaks, air from the pump cannot reach the injection tubes (Fig. 15-2). High levels of HC and CO result. The same thing happens when the injection tubes become clogged with carbon. This problem may be corrected by removing and cleaning the tubes. A small drill, turned back and forth between the fingers, can be used to remove the carbon and open the tube.

There are many reasons why an engine could have high levels of HC and CO. To determine if the cause is the air-injection system, make the quick test of the air injection system outlined in ⊘ 15-8. If the air-injection system is okay, refer to Chap. 12, "Engine Trouble Diagnosis." If the air-injection system is not working, continue testing the system as outlined in ⊘ 15-2 and 15-8.

NOTE: A defective air pump cannot cause poor idle, stalling, or driveability complaints. Check the air-injection system following the procedure outlined in this and previous sections. If the air-injection system is okay, refer to Chap. 12, "Engine Trouble Diagnosis."

⊘ 15-8 Testing the Air-Injection System

Figures 9-1, 15-1, and 15-2 show the air-injection system. A quick check of air-pump operation can be made by temporarily disconnecting the hose from the pump outlet, air manifold, or check valve (Fig. 15-3). Then run the engine at about 1,500 rpm. When you

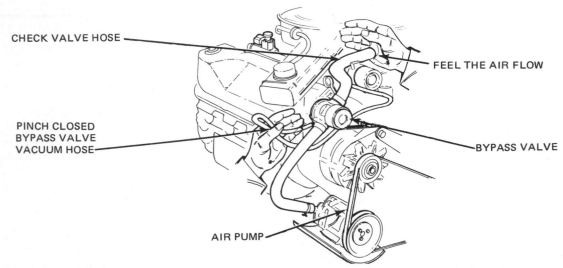

Fig. 15-3. Make a quick check of the air-injection pump by removing the hose from the check valve and feeling for airflow from the hose. (*Ford Motor Company*)

hold your hand to the disconnected hose, you should feel airflow. If you do not, test the air pump and the diverter valve further.

NOTE: As you can see in Fig. 15-3, Ford uses a bypass valve instead of a diverter valve. Each valve is a different type of antibackfire valve.

If you feel air flowing from the hose, accelerate the engine. If the pump is operating satisfactorily, the airflow should increase as engine speed increases. If the airflow does not increase, either the air-pump belt tension is too low, or there is trouble in the pump. Also, the pressure-relief valve may be stuck open. In this case, you will hear the air leaking out. The remedy is to replace the pump.

Ford recommends checking the bypass valve when the pump checks okay and there is trouble in the air-injection system. For the bypass-valve check, the engine must be at normal temperature, the transmission in neutral, and the engine speed at 1,500 rpm. Pinch the bypass-valve vacuum hose shut (Fig. 15-3) for 8 s (seconds). Then release the hose. Air should flow momentarily from the bypass-valve vent instead of from the check-valve hose.

A similar quick check of the diverter valve can be performed by pinching the diverter-valve vacuum hose shut (Figs. 15-1 and 15-2) for at least 1 s. Then release the hose. Air should exhaust from the lower portion of the diverter valve for about 4 s if the diverter valve is functioning properly.

If the diverter valve fails the test, check the condition and routing of all lines, especially the diverter-valve vacuum line. All lines must be fastened securely, without any crimps or leaks. If the diverter valve does not operate, disconnect the vacuum line from the valve. With the engine running, place your finger over the end of the vacuum line (Fig. 15-4). You should feel vacuum. If not, the wrong line may be connected to the diverter valve, or the line is plugged between the disconnected end and the intake manifold.

Fig. 15-4. When the diverter valve fails to operate, remove the vacuum hose from the valve, and feel for vacuum. (*Chevrolet Motor Division of General Motors Corporation*)

A quick check of the diverter valve can be made with the engine at normal temperature and running at idle speed. No air should be escaping through the muffler (Fig. 15-4), or silencer, on the diverter valve. Quickly open and close the throttle. A short blast of air should discharge through the diverter-valve muffler for at least 1 s. This short discharge of air can be felt and heard; it makes a buzzing noise. If no air discharge occurs, the diverter valve is defective and must be replaced.

A brittle, burned, or charred hose connecting the diverter valve to the check valve (Figs. 15-1 and 15-2) indicates the check valve is defective and must be replaced. If check-valve leakage is suspected, remove the hose from the check valve with the engine running at 1,500 rpm. No exhaust noise should be heard. Using a shop towel or rag to protect your hand from the heat, hold your hand over the check-valve opening for about 15 s. No exhaust pressure should be felt. If there is any exhaust leakage back through the valve, replace it.

⊘ **15-9 Servicing the Air-Injection System** In general, no routine service is required on the air-injection system. Hoses should be inspected and replaced, if required, whenever a tuneup is performed. Some systems use a separate filter to clean the air entering the pump. On these systems, the filter should be checked every year or every 12,000 mi [19,312 km] of operation. It should be cleaned or replaced as necessary. All late-model air pumps use a centrifugal filter. It is replaced only in case of mechanical damage; the procedure is covered in ⊘ 15-10.

The air-pump drive belt should be checked periodically to make sure it is in good condition and at the proper tension (Fig. 15-5). The engine should be hot when the check is made. Inspect the belt for adjustment, wear, cracks, and brittleness. Install a new belt if necessary. Proper belt tension is important. A loose belt does not turn the air pump. This causes high exhaust-emission levels, and may result in noise. A tight belt overloads the rear bearing in the air pump. If the bearing becomes noisy or fails, replacement of the air pump is necessary. When tightening the belt, do not pry against the pump housing. It is aluminum and will deform and break easily. Ford recommends the use of a special pump belt-tension adjuster (Fig. 15-6) to hold the proper belt tension while the air-pump mounting bolts and adjusting-arm bolts are tightened.

⊘ **15-10 Replacing Air-Pump Centrifugal Filter Fan** Should the centrifugal filter fan on the air pump (Fig. 15-7) become damaged, the fan must be replaced. Remove the drive belt from the air pump. Then remove the pulley-attaching screws, and pull the pulley off the rotor shaft (Fig. 15-7). Pry the outer disk loose, and remove it. Note in Fig. 15-7 that the fan blades are exposed after the outer disk is removed. Grasp the blades of the fan with pliers, and pull the fan from around the drive hub (Fig. 15-8). Position the new fan, and draw it into place using the pulley and pulley-attaching bolts as an installing tool. Tighten the bolts alternately, to install the fan evenly. When the fan is in position, it should look as shown in Fig. 15-7. In its proper position, the outer edge of the fan slips into the pump housing. A slight interference with the pump-housing bore is normal. When a new fan is installed, it may squeal for the first 20 to 30 mi [32 to 48 km], until its outer-diameter sealing lip has seated.

Fig. 15-5. Use a belt-tension gauge to check the adjustment of the air-pump drive belt. (*Chevrolet Motor Division of General Motors Corporation*)

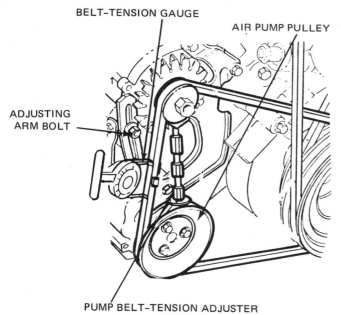

BELT–TENSION GAUGE

AIR PUMP PULLEY

ADJUSTING ARM BOLT

PUMP BELT–TENSION ADJUSTER

Fig. 15-6. A pump belt-tension adjuster can be used to hold the air pump in place while the adjusting bolts are tightened. (*Ford Motor Company*)

REAR COVER

VENT HOLE (DO NOT OIL)

OUTER DISK

HOUSING

FILTER FAN

DRIVE HUB

ROTOR SHAFT

Fig. 15-7. An air pump using a centrifugal filter fan. (*Chevrolet Motor Division of General Motors Corporation*)

⊘ **15-11 Transmission-Controlled Spark System** The transmission-controlled spark (TCS) system is an exhaust-emission control system that allows vacuum to the distributor vacuum-advance mechanism only when the transmission is in high gear. We discussed the operation of the system in detail in ⊘ 8-11. Figures 8-19 to 8-23 show the condition of the system during cold-engine startup and in each gear position.

Using the TCS system to control distributor vacuum advance reduces the emission of unburned HC and reduces the formation of NO_x. This is done by retarding the spark, thereby reducing the peak combustion temperature during the power stroke. There are several variations of the basic TCS system. Some systems include a time-delay relay to provide vacuum advance during cold starts, and a tempera-ture-override switch to restore full vacuum advance should the engine begin to overheat. This could occur, for example, during long periods of engine idling.

⊘ **15-12 TCS-System Trouble-Diagnosis Chart** The chart that follows lists the various TCS-system complaints, their possible causes, and checks or corrections to be made. The information in the chart will shorten the time you need to correct a trouble. If you follow a logical procedure, you can locate the cause of the trouble quickly. On the other hand, haphazard guessing wastes time and effort.

NOTE: The troubles and possible causes are not listed according to how often they occur. That is, item 1 (or item a under "Possible Cause") does not necessarily occur more often than item 2 (or item b).

TCS-SYSTEM TROUBLE-DIAGNOSIS CHART

(See ⊘ 15-13 to 15-15 for detailed explanations of the causes and corrections listed below.)

COMPLAINT	POSSIBLE CAUSE	CHECK OR CORRECTION
1. Engine stalls at idle, car creeps excessively at idle, high idle speed, engine diesels (⊘ 15-13)	Defective or improperly adjusted idle-stop solenoid	Adjust or replace idle-stop solenoid
2. Poor high-gear performance, stumble or stall on cold start, excessive fuel consumption, backfire during deceleration (⊘ 15-14)	a. Inoperative vacuum-advance solenoid b. Time relay does not energize c. Temperature switch defective d. Transmission switch inoperative	Check vacuum source; replace solenoid Check wiring; replace relay Replace temperature switch Replace transmission switch
3. High HC and NO_x emissions, distributor vacuum advance at all times (⊘ 15-15)	a. Transmission switch defective b. Vacuum-advance solenoid defective c. Time relay defective d. Temperature switch defective	Replace transmission switch Replace vacuum-advance solenoid Replace time relay Replace temperature switch

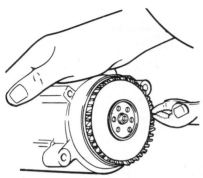

Fig. 15-8. Removing the centrifugal filter fan. (*Ford Motor Company*)

◇ **15-13 Engine Stalls at Idle** General Motors includes the idle-stop solenoid as part of the TCS system. We discussed the antidieseling, or idle-stop, solenoid in ◇ 7-17. On engines equipped with this device, when there is a problem with high or low idle speed, or dieseling when the ignition is turned off, the operation and adjustment of the idle-stop solenoid should be checked.

◇ **15-14 Poor High-Gear Performance** As listed in item 2 of the Trouble-Diagnosis Chart, there are several problems related to engine performance that can be caused by troubles in the TCS system. Before testing the components of the system, check for a blown fuse, loose connection, broken wire, broken or disconnected hose, proper electrical ground, and proper routing and connection of hoses. Note in the chart that failure of any electrical device in the TCS system can cause a complaint of this type. To determine if a problem does exist, test the system as outlined in ◇ 15-16.

◇ **15-15 High HC and NO$_x$ Emissions** At idle and in lower gears, high HC and NO$_x$ emissions may be caused by distributor vacuum advance. If there is distributor vacuum advance at all times, follow the procedure in ◇ 15-16 to determine if the TCS system has failed. On manual-transmission cars, the transmission switch is opened or closed by gear position, or the position of the shifter shaft. Some automatic transmissions are equipped with a switch which opens or closes in relation to car speed. The switch opens or closes at about 36 mph [58 km/h]. The switch is operated by governor oil pressure. A governor oil pressure of 1 psi [0.07 kg/cm²] is approximately equal to a car speed in direct drive of 1 mph [1.6 km/h].

◇ **15-16 Testing the TCS System** Typical TCS systems are shown in Figs. 8-19 to 8-23 and 15-9.

A complaint of engine stall at idle, excessive creep at idle, high idle speed, or dieseling indicates a problem with the idle-stop solenoid (Fig. 15-10). Check for free movement of the plunger in the idle-stop solenoid. Then check for an incorrectly ad-

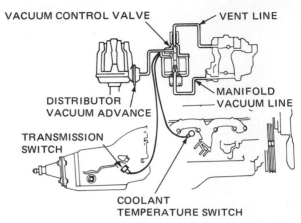

Fig. 15-9. Layout of the transmission-controlled spark (TCS) system on the engine and transmission. (*Chevrolet Motor Division of General Motors Corporation*)

justed plunger. Check that the solenoid energizes when the ignition is turned on, and deenergizes when the ignition is turned off. Replace or adjust the idle-stop solenoid as necessary.

Distributor vacuum advance at all times is probably caused by a defective transmission switch. Jack up the drive wheels, and place stands under the vehicle. With the engine warm and running, put the transmission in low forward gear. The advance solenoid should de-energize. If the solenoid energizes, disconnect the wire from the transmission switch (Fig. 15-11). If the solenoid de-energizes when the wire is disconnected, replace the transmission switch.

Poor high-gear performance, stumble or stall on cold start, excessive fuel consumption, or popping in the exhaust during deceleration may be caused by a malfunction in a TCS-system component. First check for a blown fuse, loose connection, broken

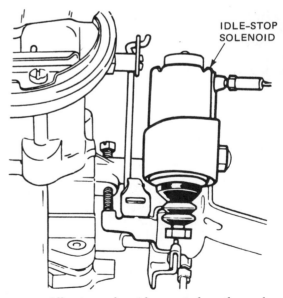

Fig. 15-10. Idle-stop solenoid mounted on the carburetor to prevent engine dieseling when the ignition is turned off. (*Echlin Manufacturing Company*)

Transmission Switch

Fig. 15-11. TCS-system transmission-switch location on a manual transmission. (*Chevrolet Motor Division of General Motors Corporation*)

wire, broken or disconnected hose, proper ground at all components, and proper routing of hoses.

The problem could be caused by an inoperative vacuum-advance solenoid. Check the intake-manifold vacuum hose at the solenoid for vacuum. If it is okay, then connect a vacuum gauge to the distributor vacuum-advance port on the solenoid valve. With 12 V applied to the solenoid, the solenoid should be energized. The vacuum gauge should show vacuum at the distributor port.

Check for an inoperative time relay (Figs. 8-22 and 15-12). Remove the temperature-switch connector (Fig. 15-13). Check the relay to make sure it is cool; then turn the ignition on. The solenoid should energize for 20 s and then de-energize. If the solenoid does not de-energize, remove the blue lead from the time relay. The solenoid will not de-energize if the relay is defective.

Check for an inoperative temperature switch (Fig. 15-13). On a cold engine, the vacuum-advance solenoid should be energized. If it is not, disconnect and ground the wire from the cold terminal of the temperature switch. If the solenoid energizes, the temperature switch is bad and should be replaced. If the temperature switch is okay, proceed to the next step.

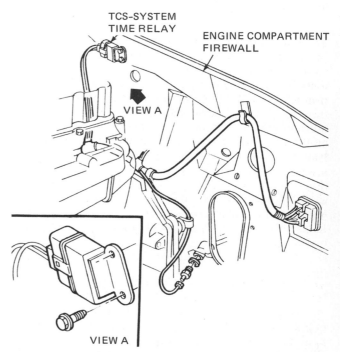

Fig. 15-12. Location of the TCS-system time relay. (*Chevrolet Motor Division of General Motors Corporation*)

Fig. 15-13. Temperature switch for the TCS system. (*Chevrolet Motor Division of General Motors Corporation*)

Check for an inoperative transmission switch (Fig. 15-11). Jack up the drive wheels, and place stands under the vehicle. With the engine warm and running, put the transmission in high gear. The solenoid should be energized. If it is not, remove and ground the connector at the switch. Replace the switch if the solenoid energizes.

⊘ **15-17 Servicing the TCS System** The TCS system does not require regular service. However, every 12 months or 12,000 mi [19,312 km], or whenever a tuneup is performed, the operation of the system should be checked, and the idle-stop solenoid adjusted.

⊘ **15-18 Ford Transmission-Regulated Spark (TRS) System** A Ford transmission-regulated spark (TRS) system is shown in Figs. 8-24 and 15-14. The TRS system is similar in operation to the General Motors TCS system. Both systems prevent vacuum advance

when the car is operating in lower gears. However, the TRS system allows vacuum advance when the outside air temperature is below about 60°F [15.6°C]. Ford mounts the temperature switch in the door pillar. Recall from your study of the TCS system (⊘ 8-11) that it allows vacuum advance when the engine coolant is cold (Fig. 15-13).

A quick check of the TRS system can be made as shown in Fig. 15-14, by connecting a vacuum gauge into the vacuum-advance line. With the air temperature about 65°F [18.3°C] or higher, run the engine at 1,500 rpm. In NEUTRAL or PARK, the gauge should show no vacuum to the distributor. With the manual transmission in high gear (clutch disengaged), at 1,500 rpm, the vacuum gauge should show 6 in Hg [152.4 mm Hg] of vacuum or more. At idle, in reverse gear (with foot brake applied), the vacuum gauge should show 6 in Hg [152.4 mm Hg] of vacuum or more. If the tests show no vacuum when there should be vacuum, check for vacuum in the hose to the carburetor. Then test the solenoid vacuum valve.

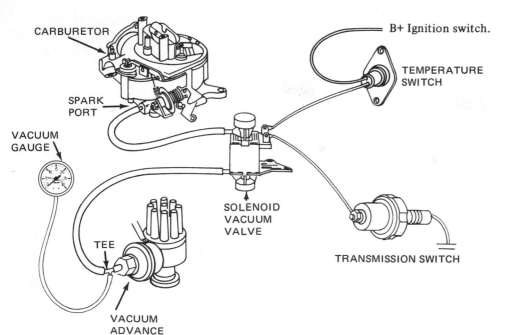

Fig. 15-14. Transmission-regulated spark (TRS) system components. (*Ford Motor Company*)

⊘ **15-19 Chrysler Orifice Spark-Advance Control (OSAC) System** In addition to the TCS and TRS systems, there are other vacuum-advance control systems. Most are especially tailored for the engines and vehicles with which they are used. Late-model cars produced by Chrysler use an orifice spark-advance control (OSAC) system (Fig. 15-15). The OSAC valve (Figs. 15-16 and 15-43) includes a very small hole, or orifice. This delays any change in the application of vacuum to the distributor by about 17 s (27 s on some engines), between idle and part throttle. There is thus a delay in vacuum advance until acceleration is well under way. Acceleration is a critical time, during which vacuum advance could produce high NO_x.

A thermal ignition control (TIC) valve (Figs. 15-15 and 15-17), or thermostatic vacuum switch (also called by Ford a ported vacuum switch or PVS), is used on some engines to reduce the possi-

bility of engine overheating. When the engine-coolant temperature at idle reaches 225°F [107.2°C], the valve opens and allows manifold vacuum to the distributor. This action bypasses the OSAC system. Advancing the spark increases the idle speed, which provides additional cooling. When the engine has cooled to normal temperature, the TIC valve closes, restoring normal operation of the OSAC system. Figure 15-18 shows a similar system used by Ford to restore vacuum advance when the engine coolant overheats.

Little service is required on the OSAC system. Every 15,000 mi [24,140 km], Chrysler recommends inspecting the hose connections between the valve, carburetor, and distributor. Any cracked or brittle hoses should be replaced. Then inspect the OSAC valve (Fig. 15-16) for airtight fittings and hoses, and free operation.

To test the OSAC valve, use a T fitting to con-

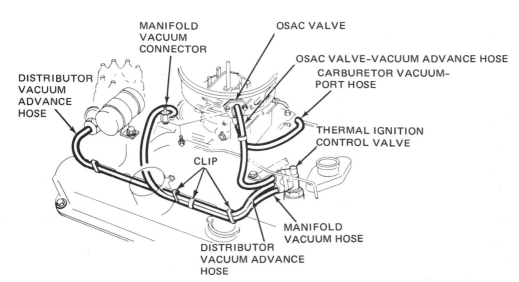

Fig. 15-15. Vacuum-hose routing on an engine equipped with an orifice spark-advance control (OSAC) valve. (*Chrysler Corporation*)

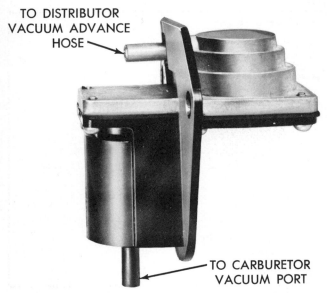

Fig. 15-16. OSAC valve. (*Chrysler Corporation*)

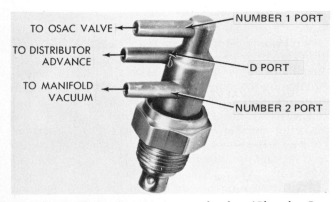

Fig. 15-17. Thermal ignition control valve. (*Chrysler Corporation*)

nect a vacuum gauge into the distributor vacuum-advance hose. Set the parking brake, and run the engine at 2,000 rpm in neutral. If the vacuum gauge immediately shows manifold vacuum or shows no vacuum, the OSAC valve is not operating and must be replaced. Normal operation of the OSAC valve will show a gradual increase in the gauge vacuum reading, from zero to a normal level in about 20 s.

To test the thermal ignition control valve (Fig. 15-17), adjust the engine idle speed to 600 rpm. Disconnect the hose from the No. 2 valve port, and plug the open end of the hose. Check the idle speed. No change in idle speed indicates the valve is not leaking. If the idle speed drops 100 rpm or more, replace the valve. Next, reconnect the vacuum hose to the No. 2 valve port. Cover the radiator to increase the engine temperature. Be careful not to overheat the engine. When the coolant temperature reaches about 225°F [107.2°C]—about the time the gauge indicator reaches the top of its normal bar—the engine speed should increase 100 rpm or more. If no increase occurs, the valve is defective and must be replaced. Then uncover the radiator, and idle the engine until the engine temperature returns to normal. Readjust the idle rpm.

⊘ **15-20 Ford Spark-Delay Valve** Ford uses a system somewhat similar to the Chrysler OSAC system. The Ford system is called the spark-delay valve system. Operation of the valve is shown in Fig. 15-19. It delays vacuum advance during some vehicle acceleration conditions. As shown in Fig. 15-19, the spark-delay valve is connected in series with the vacuum hose from the vacuum-advance port in the carburetor and the distributor vacuum-advance mechanism. During mild acceleration, the vacuum to the distributor can increase only gradually. This is

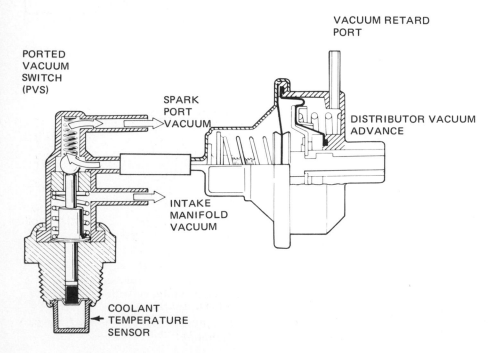

Fig. 15-18. Actions of the ported vacuum switch (PVS) in turning the distributor vacuum advance on and off. (*Ford Motor Company*)

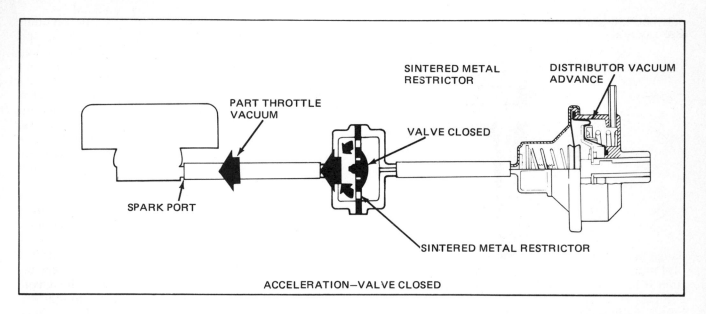

ACCELERATION—VALVE CLOSED

DECELERATION—VALVE OPEN

Fig. 15-19. The two positions of the spark-delay valve. (*Ford Motor Company*)

because the spark-delay valve only allows the vacuum to pass through slowly. Depending on the valve, vacuum spark advance is delayed between 1 and 28 s. During deceleration or heavy acceleration, the difference in pressure across the spark-delay valve is great enough to open it (Fig. 15-19). The opening of the valve instantly cuts off the vacuum spark advance.

Along with the spark-delay valve on some engines, Ford uses a delayed-vacuum-bypass (DVB) system (Fig. 15-20). It works to bypass the spark-delay valve, and restore vacuum advance, when the outside temperature is below about 65°F [18.3°C].

If an engine equipped with a spark-delay valve develops poor acceleration or surge, check that the spark-delay valve is the right one for the engine. Then check the operation of the valve with the vacuum pump on the distributor tester. Connect the black side of the valve to the vacuum hose from the distributor tester (Fig. 15-21). Connect a vacuum

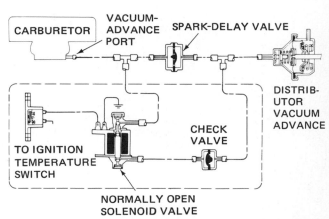

Fig. 15-20. Delay-valve bypass (DVB), used on some engines. (*Ford Motor Company*)

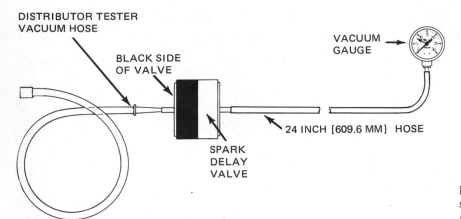

Fig. 15-21. Testing a spark-delay valve. (*Ford Motor Company*)

gauge to the color side of the valve. Apply 10 in Hg [254 mm Hg] of vacuum to the valve. Measure the time it takes for the gauge reading to go from 0 to 8 in Hg [203.2 mm Hg] of vacuum. The time must be between the minimum and maximum times listed in the chart in Fig. 15-22. If the spark-delay valve does not test within specifications, replace it with the proper valve.

The delayed-vacuum-bypass system may cause problems such as poor throttle response and poor cold-engine performance. To check out a complaint of poor throttle response, test the check valve for free flow and no flow, as shown in Fig. 15-23. Replace the check valve if it fails either test. Poor cold-engine performance may be caused by a check

valve that was installed backward or a temperature switch that is stuck closed. To test the temperature switch, remove it from the car and hold it in your hand to warm it. Connect an ohmmeter to the temperature switch. The ohmmeter should read zero, since in warm weather the switch contacts close. Then place the switch in a cup of ice water. The switch contacts should open, and the ohmmeter should show infinity (an open circuit). The temperature switch can also be tested in the car. Warm the switch with a sponge soaked in hot water; cool the switch by spraying it with a can of aerosol spray. If the temperature switch fails either test, replace it. The solenoid valve may be tested by procedures given in the Ford shop manual.

| VALVE COLOR | TIME IN SECONDS | |
	MINIMUM	MAXIMUM
Black & Gray	1	4
Black & Brown	2	5
Black & White	4	12
Black & Yellow	5,8	14
Black & Blue	7	16
Black & Green	9	20
Black & Orange	13	24
Black & Red	15	28

Fig. 15-22. Chart showing the time delays for different spark-delay valves. (*Ford Motor Company*)

⊘ **15-21 Exhaust-Gas Recirculation (EGR)** We discussed exhaust-gas recirculation in ⊘ 8-9. Figure 8-15 shows a schematic view of an EGR system. Figure 8-16 shows a sectional view of an EGR valve. Figures 15-24 and 15-25 show typical applications of the EGR system on a V-8 engine and on a six-cylinder engine. Note, in Fig. 15-25, that the thermostatic switch is called a coolant temperature-override switch.

To review briefly, exhaust-gas recirculation is used on many late-model cars to reduce nitrogen

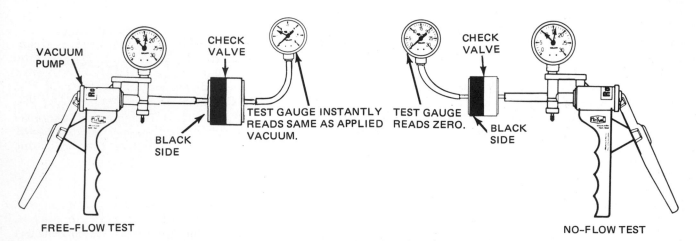

Fig. 15-23. Testing the DVB check valve. (*Ford Motor Company*)

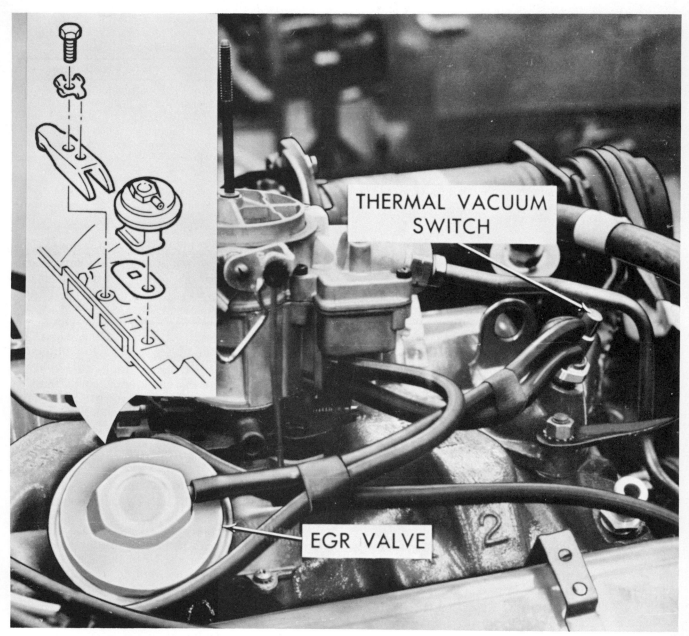

Fig. 15-24. Exhaust-gas recirculation (EGR) system on a V-8 engine. (*Chevrolet Motor Division of General Motors Corporation*)

oxide (NO_x) emissions from the engine exhaust. Air is about 80 percent nitrogen. During the combustion process, at temperatures above 2,500°F [1,371°C], some of the nitrogen and oxygen unite to form NO_x. In the engine cylinders, combustion temperatures may go above 4,000°F [2,204°C]. Formation of NO_x can be decreased by reducing peak flame, or combustion, temperatures. Exhaust gases are almost totally inactive, or inert. This means they neither burn nor support combustion. When some exhaust gas is mixed with the fresh air-fuel charge going into the cylinders, the inert exhaust gas absorbs some of the heat of combustion. This lowers the combustion temperature and, in so doing, reduces the amount of NO_x formed in the engine.

⊘ 15-22 Exhaust-Gas-Recirculation-System Trouble-Diagnosis Chart The chart that follows lists the various EGR-system complaints, their possible causes, and checks or corrections to be made. The information in the chart will shorten the time you need to correct a trouble. If you follow a logical procedure, you can locate the cause of the trouble quickly. On the other hand, haphazard guessing wastes time and effort.

NOTE: The troubles and possible causes are not listed according to how often they occur. That is, item 1 (or item a under "Possible Cause") does not necessarily occur more often than item 2 (or item b).

EXHAUST-GAS-RECIRCULATION-SYSTEM TROUBLE-DIAGNOSIS CHART

(See ⊘ 15-23 to 15-26 for detailed explanations of the causes and corrections listed below.)

COMPLAINT	POSSIBLE CAUSE	CHECK OR CORRECTION
1. Engine idles rough and stalls (⊘ 15-23)	a. EGR-valve vacuum hose misrouted	Correct EGR-valve hose routing
	b. Leaking EGR valve	Clean or replace EGR valve
	c. Incorrect idle speed	Set idle speed; check EGR valve
	d. Wrong vacuum to EGR valve	Check vacuum at carburetor EGR port
	e. Failed EFE-EGR thermal vacuum switch	Check vacuum to and from switch
	f. Leaking EGR-valve gasket	Tighten attaching bolts; if not loose, replace gasket
2. Poor part-throttle performance, poor fuel economy, engine runs rough on light acceleration (⊘ 15-24)	a. EGR-valve vacuum hose misrouted	Correct EGR-valve hose routing
	b. Defective EFE-EGR thermal vacuum switch	Check vacuum to and from switch
	c. Deposits in EGR passages	Clean passages
	d. Sticking or binding EGR valve	Clean or replace EGR valve
3. Engine stalls on deceleration (⊘ 15-25)	EGR vacuum line restricted	Remove restriction; check EGR valve for deposits
4. Detonation at part throttle (⊘ 15-26)	Insufficient exhaust-gas recirculation	Check hoses, EGR valve, and thermal vacuum switch

⊘ **15-23 Engine Idles Rough and Stalls** This condition may be caused by incorrect hose connections or a leaking EGR valve. The EGR valve is operated by "ported vacuum." That is, the vacuum source for the EGR valve is a port in the carburetor, located above the throttle valve. Unless the throttle is open to a position equivalent to about 20 mph [32 km/h] under light acceleration, practically no vacuum appears at the carburetor port. Without vacuum, a spring in the valve holds it closed. Therefore, at idle or closed throttle, no exhaust gas should recirculate into the engine. A misrouted vacuum hose connected to the EGR valve from a source of intake-manifold vacuum would open the valve, allowing exhaust-gas flow. This would excessively dilute the air-fuel mixture, and result in rough idle and stalling.

There are other ways in which exhaust gas can leak into the intake manifold. If the EGR-valve bolts work loose, the exhaust gas can flow between the EGR valve and its gasket. To correct this problem, tighten the bolts. If the bolts are not loose, but a leak is suspected, remove the valve and inspect the gasket. It may be damaged and require replacement. While the EGR valve is removed, check it for leakage. The problem could be caused by deposits on the valve which prevent it from seating.

⊘ **15-24 Poor Part-Throttle Performance** Basically, the EGR system is controlled by carburetor ported vacuum and engine-coolant temperature. A problem with any part of these controls may cause the complaints listed in item 2, and others. A defective thermal vacuum switch may stick in the open position, allowing exhaust gas to recirculate when the engine is cold. This may cause poor part-throttle performance, as well as rough engine operation. Deposits in the EGR passages, and a sticking or binding EGR

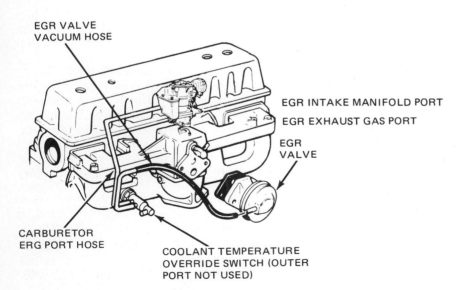

EGR VALVE VACUUM HOSE

EGR INTAKE MANIFOLD PORT
EGR EXHAUST GAS PORT
EGR VALVE

CARBURETOR ERG PORT HOSE

COOLANT TEMPERATURE OVERRIDE SWITCH (OUTER PORT NOT USED)

Fig. 15-25. Exhaust-gas recirculation (EGR) system on a six-cylinder engine. (*American Motors Corporation*)

valve, may cause mileage complaints. With some exhaust-gas recirculation during the wrong modes of engine operation, the driver must open the throttle wider to obtain the power needed. As a result, more fuel is used and fuel economy is poor.

⊘ **15-25 Engine Stalls on Deceleration** Engine stalling on deceleration can be caused by failure of the EGR valve to close promptly. Vacuum for controlling the EGR valve comes from a carburetor vacuum port above the throttle valve. When the throttle is released, the EGR valve should close almost immediately. This cuts off exhaust-gas recirculation. However, if the EGR vacuum line is restricted, the vacuum in it will decrease slowly. This will keep the EGR valve open with exhaust gas flowing into the intake manifold long enough to stall the engine. Likewise, if there are deposits on the EGR valve so it does not close completely and some exhaust gas continues to flow, the engine may stall.

⊘ **15-26 Detonation at Part Throttle** Detonation, or pinging, of an engine at part throttle may be caused by insufficient exhaust-gas recirculation. Recall from ⊘ 8-1 that detonation occurs when the air-fuel mixture in the combustion chamber overheats and explodes spontaneously before the flame from the spark plug reaches it. In an engine designed to work with exhaust-gas recirculation, some of the heat of combustion is absorbed by the recirculated exhaust gases. Should a vacuum hose crack or become disconnected, or the thermal vacuum switch stick closed, no exhaust-gas recirculation will occur. The engine will ping, or detonate, during the modes of engine operation when there should be exhaust-gas recirculation.

⊘ **15-27 Testing the EGR system** Some EGR valves have the valve stem visible under the diaphragm, or vacuum actuator (Fig. 15-26). A quick check of this type valve can be made with the engine warmed up and idling. With the transmission in neutral, abruptly open the throttle until the engine accelerates to about 2,000 rpm. If the EGR valve is operating, you will see the stem (and the groove in it) move up as the valve opens. If the stem does not move, check the EGR valve further, as explained below.

The setup recommended by Ford for a quick check of the EGR valve, on the car, is shown in Fig. 15-27. Check all hose connections in the EGR system. Then, with the engine warmed up and idling, connect the vacuum tester to the EGR valve. Apply 8 in Hg [203.2 mm Hg] of vacuum to the valve. If there is no change in idle condition or rpm, the EGR valve is restricted and should be cleaned. If the valve is not dirty, it is defective and must be replaced. However, if the engine idle gets rough when the vacuum is applied, and the rpm drops or the engine stalls, the EGR valve is okay.

General Motors recommends checking the EGR

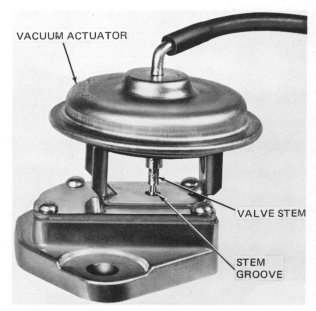

Fig. 15-26. EGR valve with exposed valve stem. (*Chrysler Corporation*)

valve in a similar manner, by connecting a hose from the intake manifold to the EGR valve. The engine must be warmed up and running at fast idle. If the valve is good, the engine speed should drop at least 100 rpm on a car with manual transmission, and at least 250 rpm on a car with automatic transmission. Otherwise, clean or replace the valve.

To check the thermal vacuum switch, which Ford calls a ported vacuum switch (PVS) valve (Fig. 15-28), remove both hoses from the valve. Connect a vacuum tester to the lower port, and a vacuum gauge to the upper port (Fig. 15-28). When the engine is cold, with the coolant temperature 50°F [10°C] or less, apply vacuum to the valve. If the valve is working properly, no reading should appear on the vacuum gauge. (This closed position of the PVS valve prevents exhaust-gas recirculation on a cold engine.) If the gauge shows a vacuum reading, the PVS valve is defective and must be replaced.

Next, operate the engine until it warms up. Then apply vacuum to the valve (Fig. 15-28). The vacuum gauge should register. If the gauge does not register a vacuum, replace the PVS valve.

NOTE: Chevrolet points out that leakage of up to 2 in [50.8 mm] of vacuum in 2 min through a thermal vacuum switch is okay. This does not indicate the switch is defective.

⊘ **15-28 EGR-System Service Intervals** There are differences in manufacturers' recommended service intervals for EGR systems. When the engine is operated with leaded gasoline, the EGR system should be checked for proper operation every 12 months or 12,000 mi [19,312 km]. For engines operated on unleaded gasoline, the EGR system is checked every 24 months or 24,000 mi [38,624 km]. Some cars man-

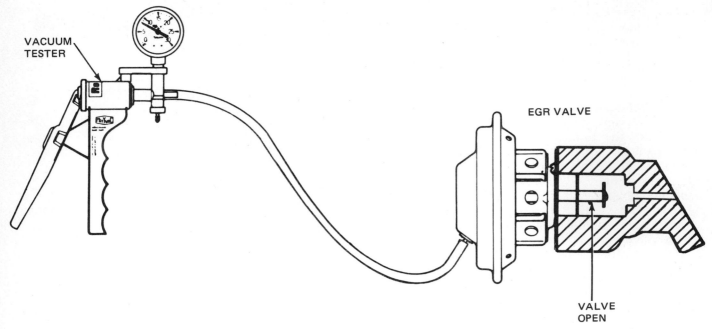

Fig. 15-27. Testing the EGR valve. (*Ford Motor Company*)

ufactured by Chrysler have an EGR-maintenance reminder light on the instrument panel. The light comes on automatically at 15,000 miles [24,140 km] to remind the driver to have the EGR system checked. Many late-model cars do not require regular EGR-system service. Instead, if a trouble develops in the EGR system, a diagnosis is performed (⊘ 15-22), along with the needed test or service.

⊘ **15-29 Servicing the EGR System** A sticking EGR valve should be inspected for deposits. If there is

more than a thin film of deposits, clean the EGR valve. Remove any deposits from the mounting surface and from around the valve and seat. The method of cleaning depends on the type of valve (Fig. 15-29). General Motors recommends cleaning an EGR valve from a V-8 engine by holding the valve assembly in your hand and tapping the protruding stem lightly with a plastic hammer. Then lightly tap the sides of the valve. Shake out the loose particles. If you are not certain of the type of valve or how to clean it, refer to the manufacturer's shop manual.

NOTE: Do not clamp the EGR valve in a vise, or wash the EGR valve in solvent. Either may damage the valve and diaphragm.

Figure 15-30 shows an exploded view of the spacer-entry EGR system. Figure 15-31 shows sectional views of the intake-manifold floor-entry EGR system. Whenever an inspection shows a buildup of deposits in any of the passages, they should be cleaned. Deposits can be loosened with a round wire

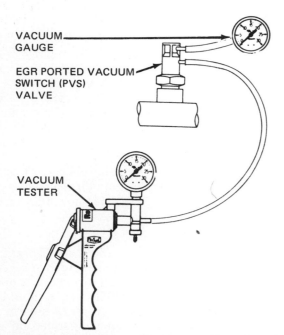

Fig. 15-28. Testing the EGR-system PVS valve. (*Ford Motor Company*)

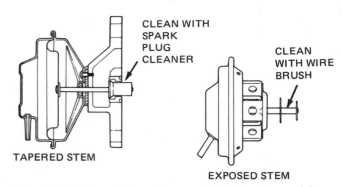

Fig. 15-29. Two different types of EGR valves and how to clean them. (*Ford Motor Company*)

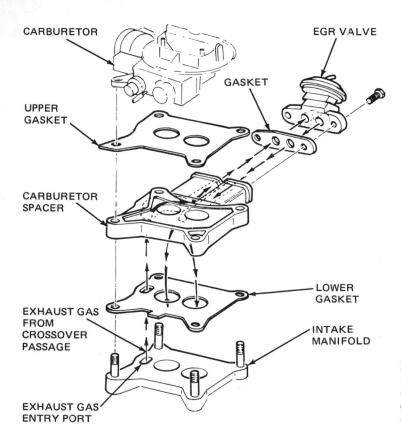

CARBURETOR

EGR VALVE

GASKET

UPPER
GASKET

CARBURETOR
SPACER

LOWER
GASKET

EXHAUST GAS
FROM
CROSSOVER
PASSAGE

INTAKE
MANIFOLD

EXHAUST GAS
ENTRY PORT

Fig. 15-30. EGR system using a spacer below the carburetor to recycle the exhaust gas. (*Ford Motor Company*)

brush, such as a valve-guide cleaning brush. Passages such as the exhaust-gas entry port (Fig. 15-30), when completely blocked by hard deposits, can be opened by holding a small drill between your fingers and turning it into the deposits to cut them out. When cleaning passages in the manifold, cover the bores with rags or masking tape. This will keep dirt from falling into the manifold.

For the EGR system to operate properly, the entire system must be free of vacuum leaks. Any cracked, brittle, or broken hoses may leak and must be replaced. Sometimes you will find hoses that are too short. These will not stay connected, and will often pull off the connector. Hoses that are too long may interfere with the throttle linkage. Also, long hoses may bend or kink, preventing the vacuum signal from passing through. Short hoses must be replaced. Long hoses must be cut to the correct length.

Figure 15-32 shows the engine vacuum-hose routing diagram for one car model. Vacuum diagrams, like schematic diagrams of electric circuits, are very important. For any vacuum-sensitive or vacuum-operated device to work, it must have the

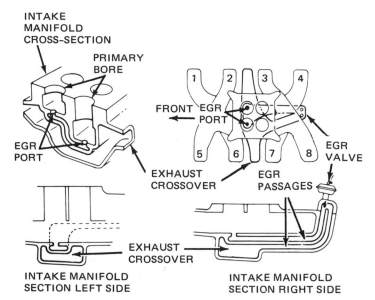

INTAKE
MANIFOLD
CROSS-SECTION

PRIMARY
BORE

FRONT EGR
PORT

EGR
PORT

EXHAUST
CROSSOVER

EGR PASSAGES

EGR
VALVE

EXHAUST
CROSSOVER

INTAKE MANIFOLD
SECTION LEFT SIDE

INTAKE MANIFOLD
SECTION RIGHT SIDE

Fig. 15-31. EGR system using ports in the intake-manifold floor to recycle the exhaust gas. (*Ford Motor Company*)

Servicing Exhaust Control Systems 231

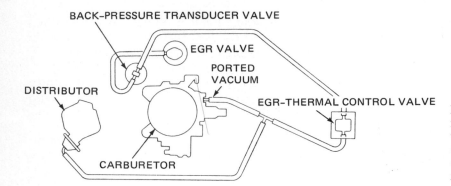

Fig. 15-32. Vacuum-hose routing for the EGR system on a late-model car. (*Oldsmobile Division of General Motors Corporation*)

proper vacuum line connected to it. Many complaints about engine operation and about the EGR system can be caused by a misrouted vacuum hose (⊘ 15-22). You know some of the basic connections, because you understand the operation of the attached devices. However, there are many vacuum hoses connecting various devices on and around the engine in a late-model car. Always check any questionable connection or hose routing. Refer to the engine vacuum-hose routing diagram for the engine you are servicing, in the manufacturer's shop manual.

⊘ 15-30 EGR Back-Pressure Transducer Valve Notice, in Fig. 15-32, that a back-pressure transducer valve (BPV) is connected into the vacuum line ahead of the EGR valve. The BPV valve is used in many late-model cars to help the EGR systems meet lower NO_x exhaust-emission standards. Its purpose is to modulate, or vary, the amount of exhaust-gas recirculation according to the load on the engine. This also improves driveability and fuel economy.

Briefly, here is how the BPV valve works. Vacuum to the EGR valve passes through an air bleed in the BPV valve. Under normal conditions of part throttle and light load, the spring above the diaphragm in the BPV valve forces the diaphragm down (left, in Fig. 15-33). This opens the air bleed and

allows a small amount of air to enter. This reduces the vacuum to the EGR valve, which in turn reduces the amount of exhaust-gas recirculation. But when the engine operates with a high load, exhaust back pressure increases in the manifold and in the exhaust-pressure tube. This pressure overcomes the spring in the BPV, raising the diaphragm and closing the air bleed (right, in Fig. 15-33). Now full vacuum is applied to the EGR valve, and the exhaust-gas recirculation system operates normally. As in the EGR system without a BPV valve, there is no exhaust-gas recirculation at idle or when the throttle is wide open.

The action of converting an exhaust-pressure signal into a vacuum signal is one type of transducer action used on the automobile. A transducer is any device which converts an input signal of one form into an output signal of a different form. A familiar example of a transducer is the car horn. It converts an electric signal into a noise, or audio, signal.

To test the back-pressure transducer valve, remove the air cleaner and plug the manifold-vacuum fitting. Set the fast-idle cam on the high step. Start the engine, and let it warm up. With a vacuum gauge, check the vacuum to the BPV valve. Next, use a T fitting to connect the vacuum gauge into the hose connecting the BPV valve to the EGR valve. Note the reading on the vacuum gauge. The vacuum should

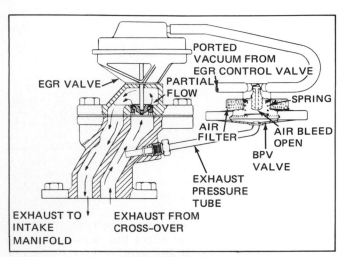
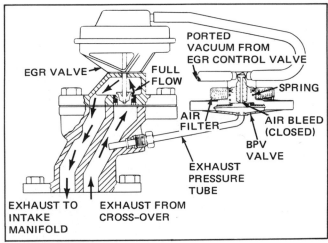

Fig. 15-33. Operation of the EGR-system back-pressure transducer valve (BPV). (*Oldsmobile Division of General Motors Corporation*)

be between 1.7 and 2.7 in Hg [43.2 and 68.6 mm Hg]. If the reading is not within specifications, replace the BPV valve. Remove the hose from the EGR valve, and plug the hose. Now read the vacuum gauge. The vacuum should be the same as the BPV-valve vacuum measured earlier. If the vacuum across the BPV valve varies by more than 2 in [50.8 mm] in this test, replace the BPV valve. If no vacuum is indicated, remove the BPV valve. Inspect the spacer port (used on some engines) and pressure tube for deposits and restrictions.

The BPV valve requires no regular service. However, in order for the BPV valve to work, the holes in the exhaust-manifold end of the pressure tube must be open and clear. Clean this area every time the EGR valve is cleaned.

⊘ **15-31 Catalytic Converters** Another method of treating the exhaust gas to remove excess amounts of unburned hydrocarbons (HC) and carbon monoxide (CO) is to use a catalytic converter. We discussed catalytic converters in ⊘ 9-2. Figure 9-4 shows the catalytic converter in the exhaust line of an engine. Some cars with V-type engines have two catalytic converters. However, installation and service is the same as for cars with a single converter. Figures 9-5 and 9-6 show a cutaway view of one type of catalytic converter and the flow of exhaust gas through it. Let's briefly review how this exhaust-emission control device works.

A catalyst is a substance that makes a chemical reaction take place faster. Although the catalyst may take part in the chemical reaction, at the end of the reaction the catalyst is unchanged. For example, without a catalyst, a temperature of $1,800°F$ [$982°C$] is required to change an amount of carbon monoxide (a harmful gas) to carbon dioxide (a harmless gas). That same amount can be converted at only $1,100°F$ [$593°C$] when a catalyst is used.

A catalytic converter is a small mufflerlike device mounted in the exhaust line, close to the exhaust manifold. The catalytic converters used on late-model cars are designed to convert unburned HC and CO to harmless water vapor and carbon dioxide. This chemical reaction takes place when the exhaust gases from the engine come in contact with the catalyst in the presence of heat.

⊘ **15-32 Catalytic-Converter Trouble-Diagnosis Chart** The chart that follows lists the various catalytic-converter complaints, their possible causes, and checks or corrections to be made. The information in the chart will shorten the time you need to correct a trouble. If you follow a logical procedure, you can locate the cause of the trouble quickly. On the other hand, haphazard guessing wastes time and effort.

NOTE: The troubles and possible causes are not listed according to how often they occur. That is, item 1 (or item a under "Possible Causes") does not necessarily occur more often than item 2 (or item b).

CATALYTIC-CONVERTER TROUBLE-DIAGNOSIS CHART

(See ⊘ 15-33 to 15-37 for detailed explanations of the causes and corrections listed below.)

COMPLAINT	POSSIBLE CAUSE	CHECK OR CORRECTION
1. Exhaust system noisy (⊘ 15-33)	a. Exhaust-pipe joints loose b. Catalytic converter ruptured c. Loose or missing catalyst-replacement plug	Tighten clamps Replace catalytic converter Tighten or replace plug; recharge catalyst
2. Poor car performance (⊘ 15-34)	Failed catalytic converter	Replace catalytic converter; check ignition and air-injection systems
3. BB-size particles coming out of tailpipe (⊘ 15-35)	Failed catalytic converter	Replace catalytic converter; check ignition and airfuel systems
4. Rotten-egg smell from exhaust (⊘ 15-36)	Improper carburetor adjustment	Adjust carburetor
5. High HC and CO levels (⊘ 15-37)	Failed catalytic converter	Replace catalytic converter; check ignition and air-injection systems; check for use of leaded gasoline

⊘ **15-33 Exhaust System Noisy** Any leak of exhaust gas from the exhaust system will cause noise. If no other exhaust-system leak can be located, check the catalytic-converter pipe joints for tightness. If the catalytic converter is bulged, distorted, or punctured, replace it. The converter used by General motors and American Motors Corporation has a catalyst-replacement plug in the bottom. If this plug works loose or falls out, excessive exhaust noise will be heard. To correct this problem, install the plug.

⊘ **15-34 Poor Car Performance** Normally, the catalytic converter does not affect the performance or operation of the car in any way. In fact, engineers like the catalytic converter because engines using it can be tuned for better fuel economy and driveability and still have low exhaust emissions. When a converter no longer provides catalytic action, it fails safe. That is, the only result of an inoperative catalytic converter is that the level of HC and CO in the exhaust gas goes up.

However, excessive engine oil consumption could partially plug the converter with carbon. This would restrict exhaust-gas flow, causing poor car performance. A leaking automatic-transmission vacuum modulator may allow so much automatic-transmission fluid to enter the combustion chambers that spark plugs foul. Should this occur, raw gasoline may pass through the engine into the catalytic converter and start burning inside it. Of course, combustion inside the converter destroys it. Operation of the engine with fouled spark plugs, ignition malfunction, or improper air-fuel mixture will raise the temperature in the catalytic converter. At a high temperature, the converter cover may bulge or distort. Inside the converter, the high temperature may melt the substrate, which is the material that the thin coating of platinum-and-palladium catalyst is applied to. Two different types of substrate construction are used. General Motors and American Motors Corporation use a pelletized substrate which is made of thousands of small, porous, alumina beads about the size of BB shot. Chrysler and Ford use a monolithic substrate which is a single-piece ceramic honeycomb.

If the substrate melts, even partially, normal exhaust-gas flow is blocked and catalytic action is lost. The converter must be replaced. Catalytic converters are installed like mufflers. No special tools are needed. However, when the catalytic converter fails, you must determine why before installing a new one. Damage due to heat is not the fault of the catalytic converter. Melted substrate is caused by temperatures inside the converter. The high temperatures, in turn, may be caused by any malfunction allowing an extremely rich air-fuel mixture to reach the converter, or by failure of the air-injection system. The catalytic converter requires a continuous supply of additional oxygen for catalytic action. For this reason, the air-injection system (⊘ 9-1 and 15-2 to 15-10) is used on engines equipped with catalytic converters.

⊘ 15-35 BB-Size Particles Coming Out of Tail Pipe
As discussed in ⊘ 15-34, General Motors and American Motors Corporation use a catalytic converter filled with thousands of small beads. Any time beads are found to be falling out of the tail pipe, the catalytic converter has failed. Inside the converter, the beads are held in place in a stainless-steel catalyst support. High temperatures may cause the catalyst support to distort, opening holes through which the exhaust gas may blow the beads. Although the pellet type of catalytic converter may be recharged with new beads, there is no way to open up a catalytic converter and repair a damaged catalyst support. If beads fall out of the tail pipe, replace the catalytic converter.

Before installing the new catalytic converter, find the cause of the high temperature in the converter. Locate and correct the problem in the ignition or air-injection system, to avoid the same damage to the new catalytic converter. Follow the trouble-diagnosis procedures outlined in this chapter and in Chap. 12, "Engine Trouble Diagnosis."

⊘ 15-36 Rotten-Egg Smell from Exhaust
Occasionally a catalytic converter may produce small amounts of hydrogen sulfide (H_2S) gas. As the catalyst ages, there is less tendency to produce this gas. Hydrogen sulfide gas smells like rotten eggs. It may be produced by a momentary rich air-fuel mixture entering a hot catalytic converter. The sulfur is in the gasoline. Since some gasolines contain more sulfur than others, the odor may be more noticeable with certain tankfulls of gasoline. When the rotten-egg smell is noticed, check the carburetor adjustments.

⊘ 15-37 High HC and CO Levels
A car equipped with a catalytic converter may fail to pass an inspection-station or other exhaust-emission test owing to contaminated catalyst or a damaged converter. However, high emission levels are generally the result of improper engine adjustments or malfunction of other exhaust-emission-system components. The catalytic converter may not be at fault when a car has high HC and CO levels in the exhaust gas. Check all other exhaust-emission systems and related equipment, including all engine tuneup specifications, before condemning the catalytic converter.

Prolonged use of leaded gasoline decreases the effectiveness of the catalyst. General Motors points out that, in an emergency, a small amount of leaded gasoline may be used.

NOTE: There are serious legal penalties for service stations that fuel catalyst-equipped cars with leaded gasoline.

The pellets recover most of their effectiveness when unleaded gasoline is again used. But each time leaded gasoline is used, the pellets lose some more of their effectiveness, until they are contaminated with lead beyond recovery. In such a case, the exhaust-emission levels of HC and CO rise. The pelletized-type catalytic converter can be recharged with new catalyst pellets. The monolithic-type catalytic converter cannot be recharged and must be replaced.

⊘ 15-38 Checking the Catalytic Converter
If an engine is maintained properly and unleaded gasoline is used, the catalytic converter should last the life of the vehicle. The converter itself does not require maintenance. It requires replacement only when abused (as when it is run on leaded gasoline) or when physically damaged in a collision.

An exhaust-gas analyzer (⊘ 13-8) can be used to

test the converter for proper operation. A quick check is to insert the probe of the analyzer in the tail pipe, with the engine idling and the transmission in neutral. Note the readings. If the readings are normal, that is, within the specifications for the engine you are testing, the catalyst is working. If one or both of the readings (HC and CO) are high, the catalyst may be damaged.

Some cars have a connection in the exhaust system, ahead of the catalytic converter, into which the exhaust-analyzer probe may be inserted. This enables you to compare readings taken before and after the exhaust gas passes through the converter. If the readings taken ahead of the converter and the readings at the tail pipe are the same, the catalyst is inoperative and possibly destroyed. Locate the cause of the catalyst failure. Then recharge or replace the converter as required. Possible causes of abnormal HC and CO readings are given in the chart in Fig. 15-34. Exhaust-emission specifications for the engine you are testing can be found in the manufacturer's service manual and in federal and state regulations.

Normal operation of the catalytic converter is indicated by high HC and CO readings ahead of the converter, and lower readings (within specifications) at the tail pipe. If the tail-pipe readings are not within specifications, check all other exhaust-emission systems and related equipment, including all engine tuneup specifications, before blaming the catalytic converter. Because of some engine, ignition, or carburetor malfunction, the engine exhaust gas may be too "dirty" for a properly operating catalytic converter to clean. Locate, in the chart in Fig. 15-34, the abnormal readings that you recorded. Then check out the causes listed until the problem is located.

On vehicles with an exhaust pipe welded to the catalytic converter, the analyzer probe cannot be inserted into the exhaust system ahead of the converter. Some tuneup experts suggest that approximate engine exhaust-emission levels can be obtained for comparison as follows: Remove the EGR valve without disconnecting its vacuum hose. Plug the EGR intake-manifold port (see Fig. 15-25). Insert the analyzer probe into the EGR exhaust-gas port (Fig. 15-25). Start the engine, and let it idle while quickly taking HC and CO readings. The EGR-port readings indicate the emission levels of the exhaust gas coming directly from the engine.

NOTE: HC and CO checks at the EGR port are only indicators of engine exhaust-emission levels. The probe does not always enter far enough to provide very accurate readings.

⊘ **15-39 Servicing Precautions for Catalyst-Equipped Cars** Manufacturers recommend that the following servicing and operating precautions be observed for vehicles equipped with catalytic converters:

1. Avoid prolonged idling, especially at fast idle after a cold start.
2. Do not attempt to start a car equipped with a catalytic converter by pushing or towing. Use another battery and jumper cables.

READING		SYMPTOMS	CAUSES
CO	HC		

Normal	High	Rough idle	1. Faulty Ignition:
			  a. Condenser defective (point–type ignition)
			  b. Poor point ground (point–type ignition)
			  c. Shortened or fouled spark plugs
			  d. Spark plug wires crossed.
			  e. Distributor cap cracked.
			  f. Timing advanced or retarded.

Low	High	Rough idle	2. Leaky valves. 3. Leaky cylinders.
Low	High	Rough idle	Vacuum leak.

High	High	Rough idle.
		Black smoke
		from tailpipe.
			1. Restricted air filter.
			2. PCV system restricted.
			3. Improper carburetion.
			  a. Idle air–fuel mixture too rich.
			  b. Leaking needle and seat.
			  c. Leaky power valve.
			  d. Wrong float setting.
			  e. Faulty choke action.

Fig. 15-34. Idle-speed exhaust-emissions trouble-diagnosis chart. (*Ford Motor Company*)

3. Avoid excessively prolonged cranking with an intermittently firing or flooded engine.

4. Avoid operating an engine under load if it is missing.

5. The use of liquid engine or carburetor cleaners, which are injected directly into the carburetor, is not recommended.

6. Do not turn off the ignition with the vehicle in motion.

7. Use only unleaded gasoline. Never use low-lead or leaded gasoline.

8. Avoid running out of gasoline while the engine is operating or while driving on the highway, especially at high speed. This may damage the converter.

9. Do not use engine or ignition replacement parts which are not certified, recommended, or approved as being equivalent to original equipment. The installation of non-original-equipment parts may be a violation of the antitampering provision of the Clean Air Act.

10. Do not pump the accelerator to start a hot engine that has stalled.

11. When raising or lowering the car on a hoist, be sure all hoist arms and other equipment are properly positioned to avoid damaging the converter and other under-car components. If the hoist makes contact with any part of the car other than the proper lift points, check all under-body components for physical damage and clearance before operating the vehicle.

12. A vehicle with a catalytic converter does not require extra time to cool down, but the converter does. With its heavier mass and insulation, the converter cools more slowly than the muffler.

13. When operating an engine equipped with a catalytic converter in a shop, use normal procedures to vent the engine exhaust gas to the outside with shop exhaust fans.

14. Cylinder balance tests and starting-motor tests can be performed in the same way as on cars without converters.

15. Do not run an engine more than 30 s with more than one spark-plug wire removed. The resulting overrich mixture may damage the converter. If possible, use an oscilloscope for ignition-system checks.

⊘ **15-40 Servicing the Catalytic Converter** Figure 15-35 is a schematic view of the exhaust system on a car equipped with a catalytic converter. The catalytic converter requires no service or maintenance in normal operation. By law, new-car manufacturers warranty catalytic converters to last for 5 years or 50,000 mi [80,467 km], whichever comes first, in normal usage. The converters used by American Motors Corporation and General Motors have a drain hole in the front bottom of the converter, for removing and replacing the pellets. The procedure is covered in ⊘ 15-42. Defective catalytic converters on Chrysler and Ford cars require installation of a new converter. A cutaway view of the round type of monolithic catalytic converter used by Ford is shown in Fig. 15-36. The catalyst in it cannot be replaced. Figure 15-37 shows an exploded view of the monolithic converter used by Chrysler. Like the Ford converter, the Chrysler converter must be replaced if it becomes defective or damaged.

No special tools are needed to replace a catalytic converter. Many converters can be removed by

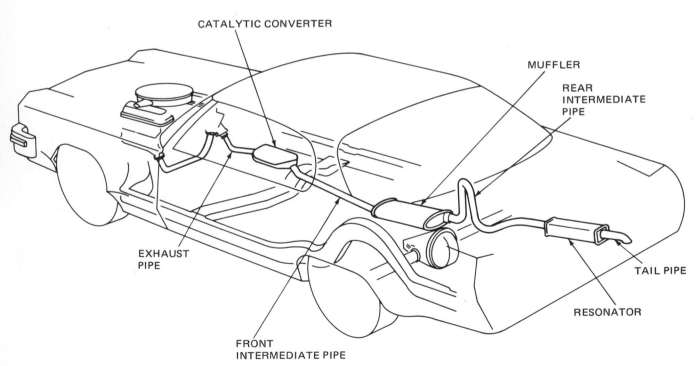

Fig. 15-35. Position of the catalytic converter in the exhaust system of a car. (*Oldsmobile Division of General Motors Corporation*)

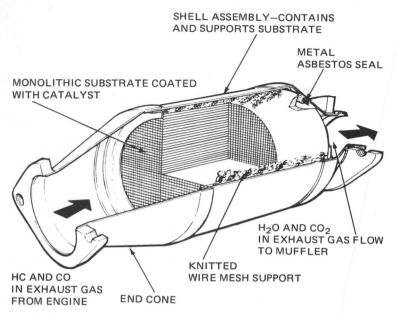

SHELL ASSEMBLY—CONTAINS AND SUPPORTS SUBSTRATE

METAL ASBESTOS SEAL

MONOLITHIC SUBSTRATE COATED WITH CATALYST

H_2O AND CO_2 IN EXHAUST GAS FLOW TO MUFFLER

HC AND CO IN EXHAUST GAS FROM ENGINE

END CONE

KNITTED WIRE MESH SUPPORT

Fig. 15-36. Construction of the round type of monolithic catalytic converter used by Ford. (*Ford Motor Company*)

raising the vehicle on a hoist and disconnecting the converter at the front and rear. Figure 15-38 shows how a converter mounts. When installing the new converter, use new nuts and bolts. Other converters have the exhaust pipe attached to the converter inlet. To replace the converter, cut the pipe.

If the bottom cover of a catalytic converter on a General Motors car is bulged, distorted, torn, or damaged, the cover can be replaced with the converter on the car. A repair kit is available from General Motors dealers. However, if the inner shell of the converter is damaged, the converter must be replaced. When heat damage to the converter is indicated (bulging and distortion), inspect the remainder of the exhaust system for damage also. Unless the catalytic converter has a hole in it, or the converter pipe clamps are loose, exhaust-system noise is not the fault of the catalytic converter. Cata-

lytic converters provide virtually no sound deadening. Cars equipped with catalytic converters use conventional mufflers to control exhaust noise.

The use of fuel additives is not recommended on cars equipped with catalytic converters. The additive may harm the catalyst. Before using any fuel additive, either in the fuel tank or in the carburetor, check that the additive is approved for use in cars with catalytic converters. Reasonable use of starting fluid will not harm the catalyst, according to General Motors.

⊘ **15-41 Servicing the Converter Heat Shields** Notice the upper and lower heat shields in Fig. 15-39. During the chemical reaction in the catalytic converter, when the exhaust gas passes over the catalyst, the exhaust-gas temperature may rise to 1,600°F [871°C]. Therefore, cars equipped with catalytic converters have heat shields and insulation pads to protect chassis components and the passenger-compartment floor from heat damage.

The heat shielding used by Chrysler on full-size cars is shown in Fig. 15-39. In this typical system, aluminized-steel heat shields are installed so that air passing rearward under the car (the road draft) carries away the heat. Interior insulating pads are placed under the carpet in the passenger compartment (Fig. 15-39). They prevent the floor from becoming uncomfortably hot and heating the passenger compartment. General Motors requires a minimum floor-pan–to–exhaust-system clearance of $\frac{5}{8}$ in [15.88 mm] at all points. Any floor covering and insulation pads that are removed during service *must* be reinstalled. If any components located in the vicinity of the exhaust system are moved during service, or as a result of a collision, they must be replaced in their original position. This is especially important with regard to wiring harnesses and fuel and brake lines.

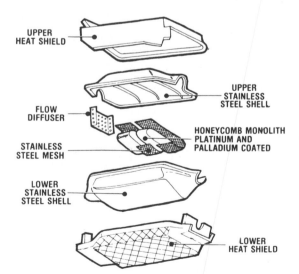

UPPER HEAT SHIELD

UPPER STAINLESS STEEL SHELL

FLOW DIFFUSER

HONEYCOMB MONOLITH PLATINUM AND PALLADIUM COATED

STAINLESS STEEL MESH

LOWER STAINLESS STEEL SHELL

LOWER HEAT SHIELD

Fig. 15-37. Exploded view of the heat shields and monolithic type of catalytic converter used by Chrysler. (*Chrysler Corporation*)

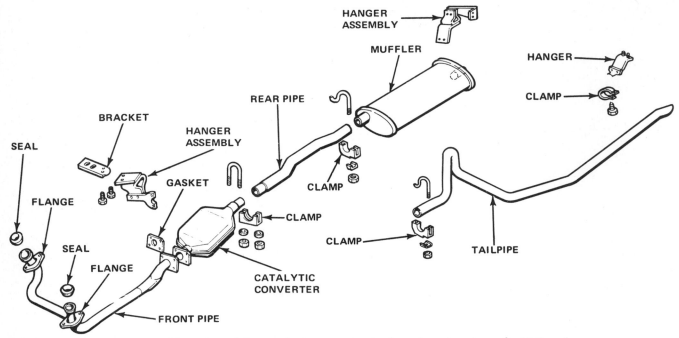

Fig. 15-38. Mounting of the catalytic converter in the exhaust system of a V-8 engine which uses only one converter. (*American Motors Corporation*)

CATALYTIC CONVERTER
HEAT SHIELD
LOWER SHIELD
HEAT SHIELD
FLOOR PAN
INTERIOR INSULATING PADS
HEAT SHIELD

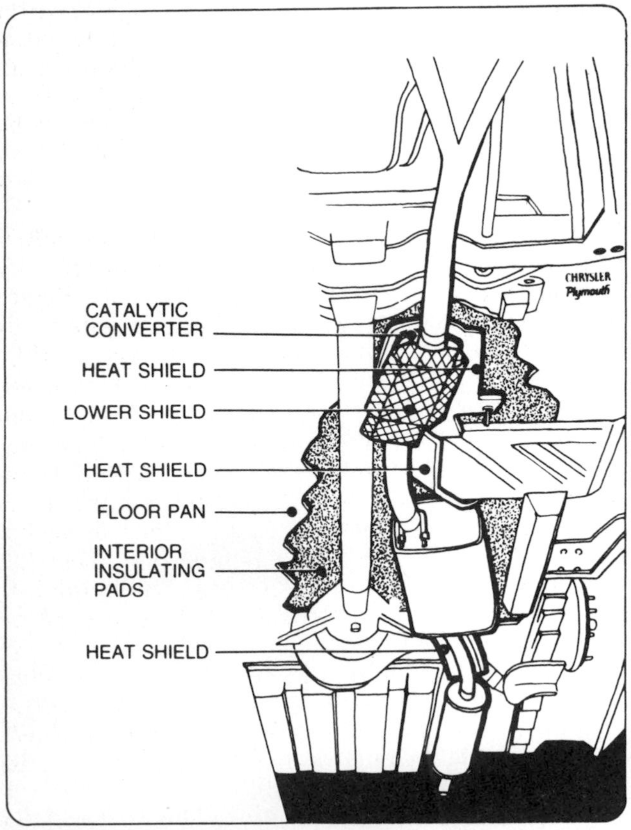

Fig. 15-39. Heat shields and insulating pads surrounding the catalytic converter. (*Chrysler Corporation*)

The lower heat shield (Fig. 15-39) provides added protection against road hazards and helps prevent such objects from puncturing the converter.

NOTE: Rustproofing and undercoating must be kept off the heat shields. These coatings reduce the efficiency of the shields in carrying away heat, and cause strong, objectionable odors.

While the catalytic converter requires no periodic maintenance, Ford recommends an inspection of the exhaust-system heat shields every 15 months or 15,000 mi [24,140 km], whichever comes first. The exhaust system should be checked for broken welds, damage, and deterioration. All debris should be removed. If a shield is missing, torn, or ripped, it must be replaced. Remove the damaged shield by carefully chiseling the shield loose at its welds. Whenever the vehicle has been operated on gravel roads, in off-road use, or under severe road-load conditions, Ford recommends a shield inspection at 5,000-mi [8,047-km] intervals.

⊘ **15-42 Replacing Catalyst Beads** The catalyst beads in the pellet-type catalytic converter can be changed. However, there is no scheduled maintenance for the converter. It is designed to last for the life of the car, in normal operation. If a car has high HC and CO levels, and the engine emission controls are operating to specifications, the catalyst beads may be spoiled and need replacement. The beads can be replaced with the converter in place on the car. For this, a special vibrator and vacuum pump (called an "aspirator" by General Motors) are used (Figs. 15-40 and 15-41).

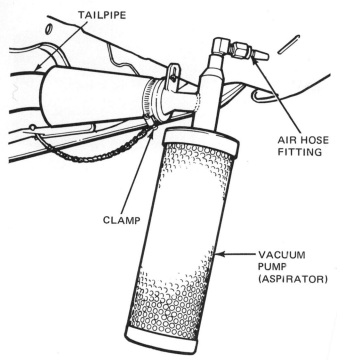

Fig. 15-40. Vacuum pump, or aspirator, mounted on the tail pipe of a car, in readiness to change the beads in a pellet-type catalytic converter. (*American Motors Corporation*)

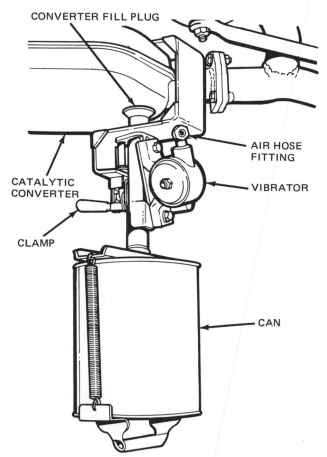

Fig. 15-41. Vibrator mounted on a catalytic converter. (*American Motors Corporation*)

To remove the catalyst beads, raise the car on a hoist. Separate hoses should be available to attach to the vacuum pump and vibrator. Minimum shop air pressure should be at least 80 psi [5.62 km/cm²]. Install the vacuum pump tightly to the tail pipe of the car. If the car has two tail pipes, attach the vacuum pump to one tail pipe (Fig. 15-40) and place a plug in the other tail pipe. Connect the shop air line to the vacuum pump. The vacuum pump creates a vacuum in the converter that holds the beads in place when the converter fill plug is removed. Use a ³/₄ in [19 mm] hex wrench to remove the fill plug.

Clamp the vibrator in place on the converter, with the upper tube inside the fill-plug opening (Fig. 15-41). Remove the fill-tube extension, and install the empty can on the vibrator. Disconnect the air supply to the vacuum pump. Connect the air supply to the vibrator. Now, as the vibrator shakes the converter, catalyst beads will drain from the converter into the can attached to the vibrator. It takes about 10 min for the converter to empty. Then discard the used catalyst beads.

To install new catalyst beads, first fill the can on the vibrator with new approved replacement beads. Install the fill-tube extension on the vibrator. Connect the shop air hoses to the vacuum pump and to the vibrator. Attach the can of catalyst to the vibrator. Beads will start flowing into the converter. After the beads stop flowing, disconnect the air hose to the vibrator. Remove the upper tube of the vibrator from the fill-plug opening, and check that the beads have filled the converter flush with the fill-plug hole. Add more catalyst, if required. Apply antiseize compound to the fill plug, and install it. Tighten the fill plug to a torque of 50 lb-ft (pound-feet) [6.91 kg-m (kilogram-meters)]. Disconnect the air supply to the aspirator, remove it, and lower the car.

⊘ **15-43 Servicing the Thermostatically Controlled Air Cleaner** The operation of the thermostatically controlled air cleaner is covered in ⊘ 7-34. Figure 7-50 shows the thermostatically controlled air cleaner in sectional view. To check the system (Fig. 7-50), first make sure the hoses and heat pipe are tightly connected. See that there are no leaks in the system. The system can be checked with a temperature gauge. Remember that failure of the thermostatic system usually results in the damper door staying open. This means that the driver will probably not notice anything wrong in warm weather. But, in cold weather, the driver will notice hesitation, surge, and stalling. A typical checking procedure follows.

Remove the air-cleaner cover. Install the temperature gauge as close to the sensor as possible. Allow the engine to cool below 85°F [29.4°C] if it is hot. Replace the air-cleaner cover without the wing nut.

Start and idle the engine. When the damper begins to open, remove the air-cleaner cover, and note the temperature reading. It should be between

85 and 115°F [29.4 and 46.1°C]. If it is difficult to see the damper, use a mirror.

If the damper does not open at the correct temperature, check the vacuum motor and sensor.

With the engine off, the control damper should be in the compartment or cold-air-delivery position (see Fig. 7-51). To determine if the vacuum motor is operating, apply at least 9 in Hg [228.6 mm Hg] of vacuum to the fitting on the vacuum motor (Fig. 15-42). The vacuum can be from the engine, from a distributor tester, or from a hand vacuum pump (Fig. 15-42). With vacuum applied, the damper should move to the hot-air-delivery position (Fig. 7-51).

If the vacuum motor does not work satisfactorily, it should be replaced (Fig. 15-43). This can be done by drilling out the spot welds and unhooking the linkage. The new motor can be installed with a retaining strap and sheet-metal screws. Other types of vacuum motors have locking tabs which disengage and engage when the vacuum motor is rotated (Fig. 15-43).

If the vacuum motor does work well, the sensor should be replaced (Fig. 15-44). This is done by prying up the tabs on the retaining clip. The new sensor is then installed, and the tabs are bent down again.

⬦ **15-44 Servicing the Early-Fuel-Evaporation (EFE) System** The need for early fuel evaporation and its use on late-model cars is explained in ⬦ 7-33. Basically, the EFE system is a vacuum-operated manifold heat-control valve, as shown in Fig. 7-46. By using vacuum control of the manifold heat valve, the EFE system provides heat quickly to warm the intake manifold when the car is driven cold. Rapid heating is needed for early fuel evaporation and even distribution of the air-fuel mixture. This improves cold-engine driveability.

Ford recommends lubricating and checking the heat-control valve every 30 months or 30,000 mi [48,280 km], whichever comes first. The exposed ends of the valve shaft are lubricated with graphite lube, or approved heat-valve lubricant (Fig. 15-45)—never with grease or oil. General Motors

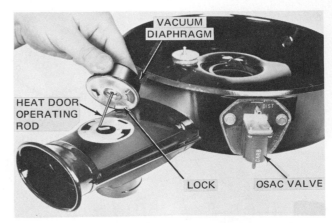

Fig. 15-43. Replacing the vacuum motor on a thermostatically controlled air cleaner. (*Chrysler Corporation*)

recommends checking the EFE valve 6 months or 7,500 mi [12,070 km] after sale of the car, and every 18 months or 22,500 mi [36,210 km] thereafter.

You can make a quick test of the EFE valve with the engine cold. Note the position of the actuator arm (Fig. 15-45). Have someone else start the engine while you watch the arm. The valve should close. The open and closed positions of the actuator arm are shown in Fig. 15-45. If the valve does not close, remove the hose from the EFE valve. Check it for vacuum by placing your finger over the open end. If vacuum is felt, check the EFE valve. Apply a vacuum of more than 8 in Hg [203.2 mm Hg], using a hand pump or other vacuum source (Fig. 15-45). The valve should close. If it does, the EFE valve is okay. If it does not close, be sure the valve shaft is free of deposits and lubricated. Then test the valve again. If the valve does not close now, replace it.

If you do not feel a vacuum when you place your finger over the end of the EFE-valve vacuum hose, be sure the engine is cold. Check the hoses and the vacuum switch to locate the cause of no vacuum to the EFE valve when the engine is cold.

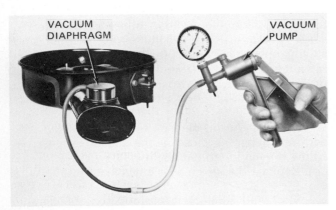

Fig. 15-42. Testing the vacuum motor on a thermostatically controlled air cleaner. (*Chrysler Corporation*)

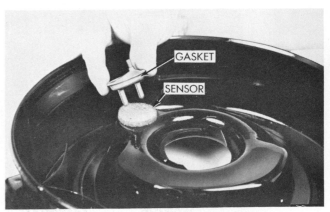

Fig. 15-44. Replacing the temperature sensor in a thermostatically controlled air cleaner. (*Chrysler Corporation*)

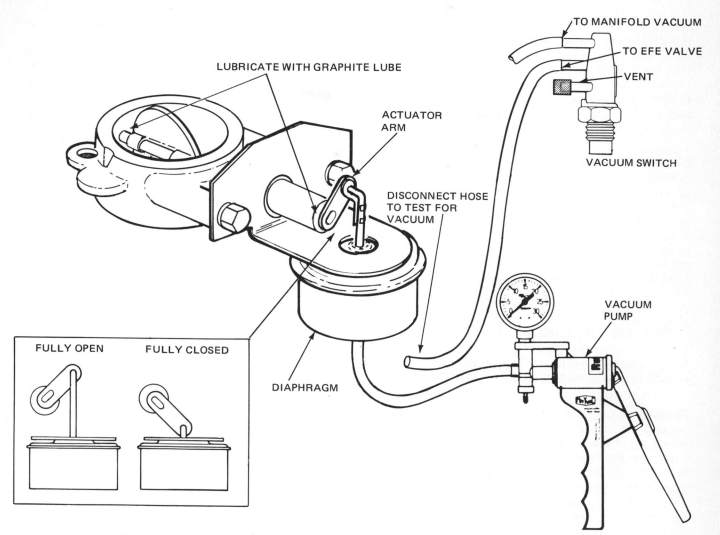

Fig. 15-45. Testing the vacuum-operated heat-control valve (EFE). (*Ford Motor Company*)

Check Your Progress

Progress Quiz 15-1 The chapter you have just completed is probably the most important in the book. To be an expert automotive emission control service technician, you must know about emission-control troubles, the causes of these troubles, and how to find the causes. As you have learned, an important part of the troubleshooting procedure is checking the engine and the ignition and fuel systems. The questions below will help you determine how well you have retained the information you studied in this chapter. If any question is hard to answer, re-read the pages in the book that give you the answer.

Correcting Lists The purpose of this exercise is to help you spot the unrelated item in a list. For example, "milk" does not belong in the list "shoes, pants, shirk, milk, tie, coat." It is the only item in the list that you could not put on and wear. In each of the following lists, there is one unrelated item. Write each list in your notebook, but do not write the item that does not belong. Check your lists with the answers at the back of the book.

1. Components of the air-injection system include an air pump, check valve, manifold heat-control valve, diverter valve, and injection tubes.
2. Components of the transmission-controlled spark system include a vacuum-advance solenoid, EGR valve, temperature switch, transmission switch, and time relay.
3. Components of the exhaust-gas recirculation system include an EGR valve, thermostatic switch, carburetor spacer, back-pressure transducer valve, and catalytic converter.
4. Components of the catalytic-converter system include heat shields, stainless-steel exhaust pipes, thermal reactor, air-injection system, and catalyst.
5. Components of the thermostatically controlled air cleaner include a vacuum motor, temperature sensor, muffler, hot-air pipe, and heat stove.

Questions As you know from studying this chapter, it contains much information that is important to the automotive technician. Here are some questions that deal with the servicing of exhaust control systems. In your notebook, write the answer to each question in your own words. If you do not know the answer, turn back through the pages of the chapter and re-study the material.

1. Name two exhaust-control systems that work by treating the exhaust gas.
2. How can you make a quick check to tell if the air pump is working?
3. What can cause a rotten-egg smell to come from a car?
4. What can cause an engine to backfire on deceleration?
5. List all the emission-control systems that are basically vacuum-advance controls.

CHAPTER 15 CHECKUP

NOTE: Since this is a chapter review test, you should review the chapter before taking the test.

Completing the Sentences The sentences below are incomplete. After each sentence there are several words or phrases, but only one of them correctly completes the sentence. Write each sentence in your notebook, ending it with the word or phrase that completes it correctly.

1. In the air-injection system, backfiring in the exhaust is prevented by the action of the: (*a*) check valve, (*b*) diverter valve, (*c*) ported vacuum switch, (*d*) thermal vacuum switch.
2. Air injection is basically a system to control exhaust emissions of: (*a*) HC and CO, (*b*) NO_x and CO, (*c*) HC and NO_x, (*d*) H_2O and CO_2.
3. The inlet air filter for the air-injection system is located in the: (*a*) crankcase, (*b*) valve cover, (*c*) oil filter, (*d*) air cleaner.
4. The temperature switch mounted in the door pillar is part of the: (*a*) TCS system, (*b*) TRS system, (*c*) PCV system, (*d*) evaporative control system.
5. On late-model cars, Chrysler mounts the OSAC valve in the: (*a*) firewall, (*b*) air cleaner, (*c*) carburetor, (*d*) intake manifold.
6. The Ford spark-delay valve delays vacuum advance during: (*a*) some acceleration conditions, (*b*) some deceleration conditions, (*c*) cold weather, (*d*) hot weather.
7. Engine stalling on deceleration may be caused by:

(*a*) a defective air pump, (*b*) an EGR valve stuck closed, (*c*) an EGR valve sticking open, (*d*) a spark-delay valve stuck open.
8. Detonation, or pinging, at part throttle may be caused by: (*a*) excessive exhaust-gas recirculation, (*b*) a plugged PCV valve, (*c*) a defective air pump, (*d*) insufficient exhaust-gas recirculation.
9. A ported vacuum switch is the same as a: (*a*) thermal vacuum switch, (*b*) spark-delay valve, (*c*) vacuum-advance solenoid, (*d*) check valve.
10. The back-pressure transducer valve is part of the: (*a*) EGR system, (*b*) air-injection system, (*c*) PCV system, (*d*) TCS system.

Definitions In the following, you are asked for the definitions of several words and phrases. Write them in your notebook. The act of writing the definitions does two things: it tests your knowledge, and it helps fix the information more firmly in your mind. Turn back into the chapter if you are not sure of an answer, or look up the definition in the glossary at the back of the book.

1. Define "air injection."
2. What is a diverter valve?
3. Define "air-bypass valve."
4. What is a backfire?
5. What is a centrifugal filter fan?
6. Define "TCS."
7. Define "TRS."
8. What is OSAC?
9. Define "thermal ignition control (TIC) valve."
10. What is a delayed-vacuum-bypass (DVB) system?

SUGGESTIONS FOR FURTHER STUDY

After studying this chapter and understanding it thoroughly, you will want to start checking out exhaust-emission control systems. One way to help yourself remember the procedures is to write each procedure on a 3- by 5-in [76.2- by 127.0-mm] card. Carry these cards around with you. Whenever you get a chance, as, for instance, when you are listening to music on the radio, eating your lunch, or getting ready for bed, take out one of the cards and study it. Soon you will know the procedures thoroughly.

Be sure to get as much shop experience as you can, by checking emission systems on various cars and trucks. Discuss the problems that you find with your instructor and with any automotive service technicians that you know. In your notebook, write the conditions that you find on each job, and the cause and correction of each complaint.

chapter 16

RETROFIT SMOG DEVICES FOR USED CARS

Many kits and devices, now available, enable you to reduce the emissions from older cars. These devices are called retrofit devices, or used-car smog devices. California requires the installation of certain of these devices to control crankcase emissions, and other devices to control exhaust emissions. Under California law, any 1955 or later model car must have a PCV system. Also, any 1955 through 1965 model must have a device to control exhaust emissions of HC and CO. In addition, California requires every 1966 through 1970 model car to have a device that controls NO_x exhaust emissions.

⊘ **16-1 Crankcase Devices for Used Cars** The road-draft tube was generally used to ventilate the crankcases of passenger-car engines built through 1960. In 1961, automobile manufacturers installed the open PCV system on cars made for sale in California; beginning in 1963, all cars used this system. In 1964, California required the closed PCV system. This system became standard on 1968 and all later cars produced in the United States.

To install a PCV system on a car with a road-draft tube, purchase, at your local auto-parts store, a PCV kit that fits the year, make, and model of engine in the car. Each kit contains the proper gaskets, hose, hardware, and PCV valve, along with detailed installation instructions for that particular engine. Most PCV kits simply bolt in.

To install the kit shown in Fig. 16-1, remove the road-draft tube from the engine. In its place, bolt in

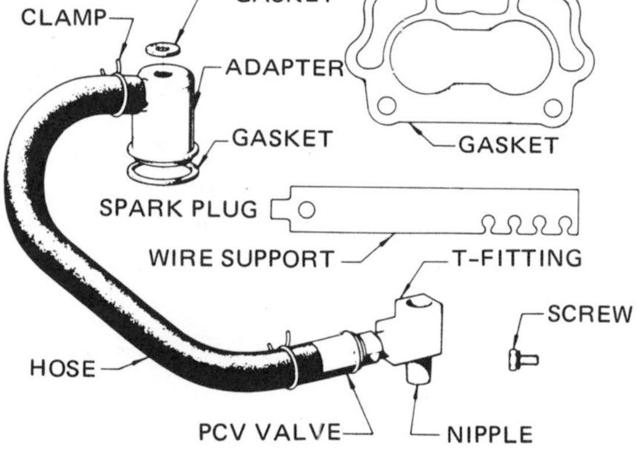

Fig. 16-1. Kit for installing a positive crankcase ventilation system on an engine. (*AC-Delco Division of General Motors Corporation*)

the adapter shown in the upper left of Fig. 16-1. Use the bolt and washer from the road-draft tube. On some engines, you must reroute the spark-plug wires. In this case, install the new spark-plug-wire support from the kit, and discard the old one from the engine. Remove the carburetor from the engine, and discard the gasket. Clean the gasket surfaces on the carburetor and intake manifold.

At the rear of the carburetor throttle body, there is a vacuum fitting. Remove it. Install the new nipple in the new T fitting from the kit (Fig. 16-1). Screw the nipple into the carburetor throttle body. Now install the old vacuum fitting (which was removed from the throttle body) into the opening in the T fitting. Assemble the PCV valve from the kit into the side opening of the T (Fig. 16-1), and tighten the valve.

Place the new gasket on the intake manifold. Install the carburetor and all lines and linkages that were removed. Then connect and clamp the hose from the adapter to the PCV valve. Operation of this system may be checked with the PCV-system testers discussed in Chaps. 6 and 14.

PCV installation kits are not all exactly alike. On engines without an accessible source of intake-manifold vacuum, a hole must be drilled into the manifold and a fitting installed. Other kits use a spacer with a vacuum port that you install between the carburetor and the manifold to obtain a vacuum source.

An open PCV system can be made into a closed system by installing a closed breather cap, and adding a tube from the cap to the air cleaner. If you have to add a tube to the air cleaner, purchase, at your local auto-parts store, a closed-crankcase ventilation kit, or an air-cleaner kit, for the year, make, and model of engine in the car. The kit will contain a new closed breather cap that is not vented to the

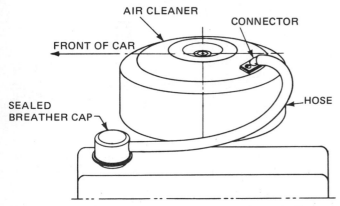

Fig. 16-2. Hose routing and connections after installing a tube-to-air-cleaner kit. (*AC-Delco Division of General Motors Corporation*)

outside air. The cap has a nipple on it, which allows the crankcase vapors to pass through. By connecting a hose from the nipple on the new cap to a suitable connector on the air cleaner, you close the PCV system. Figure 16-2 shows a typical air-cleaner kit installed on an engine.

Also in the kit are the connector for installation on the air cleaner, and a paper template to show you where to drill the holes. Some connectors mount on the clean-air side, or inside, of the air filter. Others mount on the outside, or dirty-air side, of the filter. Follow the instructions in the kit. You must remove any supplementary or external rocker-arm oil system from the engine. This is necessary to prevent excess oil consumption once the kit is installed.

When installing the kit, be careful not to obstruct the airflow through the hose with sharp bends. Make sure that the hose does not interfere with the carburetor linkage. To install the air-cleaner kit, replace the old breather cap with the new cap. Locate the connector on the air cleaner, and mark the best position to avoid interference with any other linkage or hose on the engine. Then remove the air cleaner, and drill the holes for the connector. Install the connector, using the gasket and screws from the kit. Service the air cleaner as recommended by the car manufacturer, and then reinstall it on the engine.

Install the hose from the kit between the nipple on the new breather cap and the connector you installed on the air cleaner. If the hose is too long, shorten it to keep water from collecting in low spots.

⊘ **16-2 Exhaust-Emission Control Devices for 1955 to 1965 Vehicles** New cars built during the years 1955 through 1965 had no exhaust-emission controls. In 1972, Los Angeles and other municipalities in California began to require installation of exhaust-emission control devices on these cars. Recall, from Chap. 3, that hydrocarbons and nitrogen oxides combine in the presence of sunlight to form photochemical smog. Reducing the amount of HC and NO_x emitted by 1955 to 1965 model cars reduces smog and improves air quality. We shall discuss two different types of devices used to control exhaust emissions on 1955 to 1965 cars. They are the General Motors device and the device manufactured by Air Quality Products.

Installation of the General Motors device requires leaning out of the idle mixture, as already described, and elimination of the distributor vacuum advance under normal operating conditions. Figure 16-3 shows the features of this device. Figure 16-4 shows the parts in the kit. Figure 16-5 is the instruction sheet that accompanies the kit. Note that it calls for increased idle speed, a leaner idle mixture, and setting of the ignition timing. The thermo-vacuum switch is connected into the hose at the top of the radiator tank. It has one purpose—to permit vacuum advance in case the engine begins to overheat. During normal operation, the thermo-vacuum switch blocks off the vacuum line between the intake manifold and the ignition distributor. However, as the engine approaches an overheating condition, a wax pellet inside the switch begins to expand. As it does, it moves a plunger to open the line between the intake manifold and the ignition distributor. Now, vacuum advance increases engine speed so engine temperature falls. This, in turn, shrinks the wax pellet and moves the plunger to close the line to the distributor. Now, vacuum advance is eliminated.

The General Motors exhaust-emission control device is designed to reduce exhaust emissions from

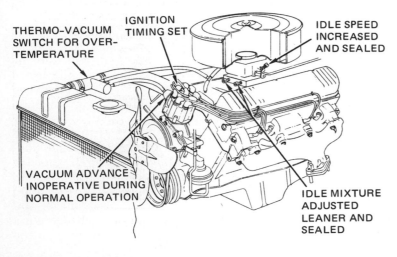

Fig. 16-3. General Motors exhaust-emission control kit which can be installed on 1955 to 1965 model used cars. (*General Motors Corporation*)

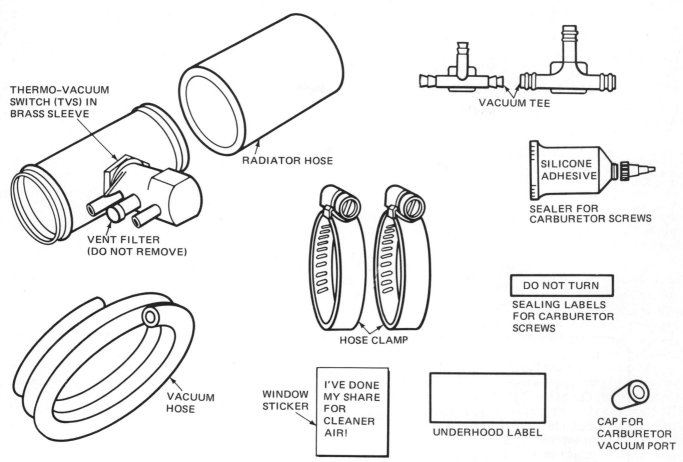

Fig. 16-4. Parts in the General Motors exhaust-emission control kit for used cars. (*General Motors Corporation*)

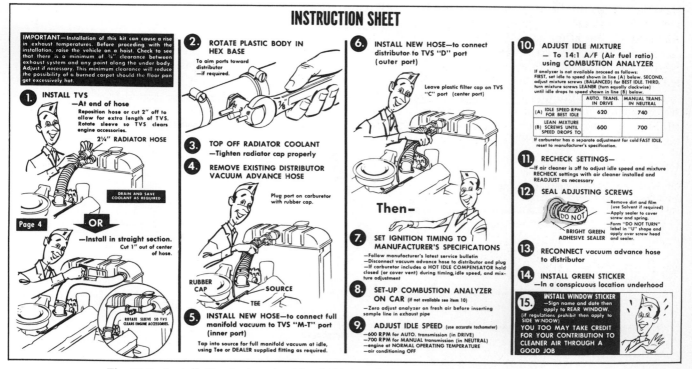

Fig. 16-5. Installation instructions for the General Motors exhaust-emission control kit. (*General Motors Corporation*)

Fig. 16-6. Pure Power exhaust-emission control device for 1955 to 1965 model cars. The device includes a capacitive-discharge ignition system. (*Air Quality Products, Inc.*)

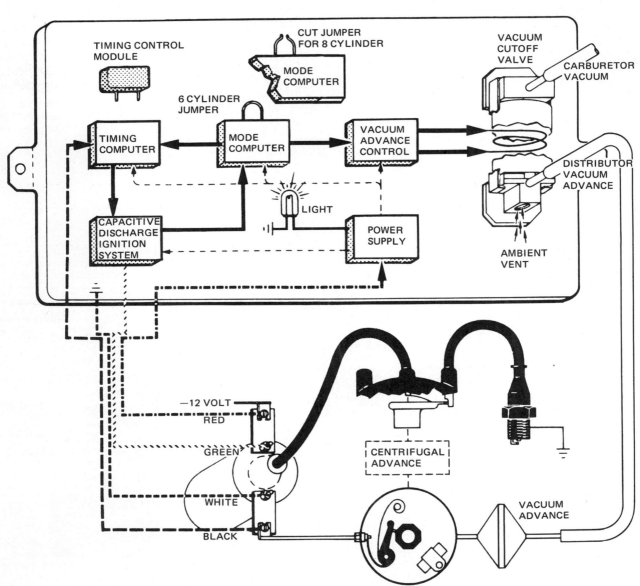

Fig. 16-7. Block diagram showing the operation of the Pure Power device. (*Air Quality Products, Inc.*)

an engine under normal operating conditions. The device does not improve engine performance or economy. Do not install the kit on an engine with major problems, such as dead cylinders or misfiring spark plugs, unless the owner is willing to have the engine problems corrected. The General Motors kit can be used on vehicles with gross vehicle weight (GVW) of 6,001 lb [2,722 kg] or less, and engines with over 140 in^3 (cubic inches) [2,294 cc] of displacement. General Motors does not recommend installing this kit on 1966 and 1967 California model cars, or on any 1968 or later models with factory-installed exhaust-emission control systems. The kit is not to be installed on engines that use a distributor without a centrifugal-advance mechanism.

Air Quality Products, Inc., manufactures an exhaust-emission control device for 1955 to 1965 cars equipped with six-cylinder or eight-cylinder engines (Fig. 16-6). This device combines a capacitive-discharge electronic ignition system with a cutoff of the distributor vacuum advance between about 900 rpm and 1,800 rpm. Figure 16-7 is a block diagram of the device. Normal vacuum spark advance is restored at higher speeds, and there is some additional retarding of the spark timing at low speeds. In addition, a lean idle mixture and a fast idle-speed adjustment are used with the device (Fig. 16-8).

Installation is simple. The device mounts under the hood, usually on the fender well near the distributor. The engine is first set to specifications.

Then the two vacuum hoses are connected as shown in Fig. 16-8. All wires are removed from the battery terminal of the coil and attached to the small red tab of the device. All wires are removed from the distributor terminal of the coil and attached to the black tab of the device. Then the red tab is installed on the coil battery terminal, and the black tab on the coil distributor terminal. This completes the installation.

⊘ 16-3 NO$_x$ Exhaust-Emission Control Devices

The exhaust-emission control devices that were factory-installed on most 1966–1970 model cars controlled HC and CO. However, these early devices caused an increase of NO$_x$ from the engine. In 1973, to roll back the NO$_x$ emissions to the level of 1965 and earlier cars, California began to require installation of an NO$_x$ exhaust-emission control device on 1966 to 1970 model cars. Several different types of devices are available. Some reduce NO$_x$ emissions by disconnecting the distributor vacuum advance. Other devices provide for exhaust-gas recirculation to control NO$_x$ formation. The Air Quality Products device discussed in ⊘ 16-2 can also be used on 1966 to 1970 cars. We shall discuss a few of the devices available for controlling NO$_x$ emissions from used cars.

An example of a device which disconnects the distributor vacuum advance is the Carter emission-

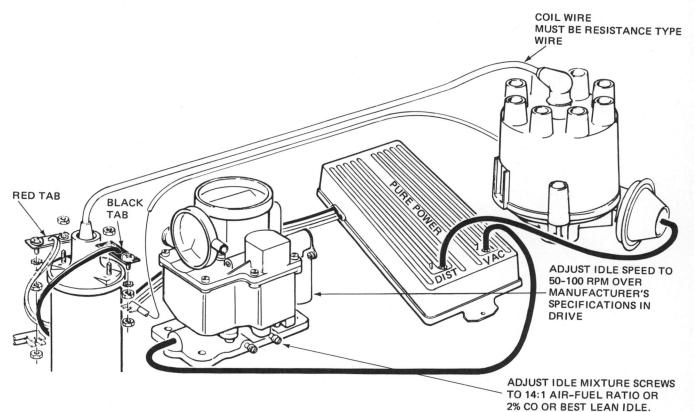

Fig. 16-8. Installation of the Pure Power device on the engine. (*Air Quality Products, Inc.*)

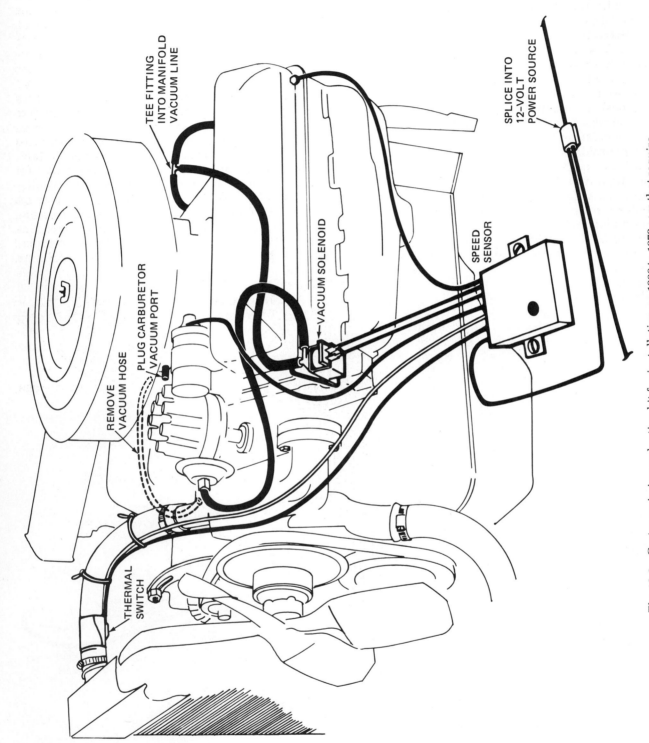

Fig. 16-9. Carter emission-reduction kit for installation on 1966 to 1970 cars that require additional control of NO_x exhaust emissions. (*Carter Carburetor Division of ACF Industries*)

TEE FITTING INTO MANIFOLD VACUUM LINE

SPLICE INTO 12-VOLT POWER SOURCE

REMOVE VACUUM HOSE

PLUG CARBURETOR VACUUM PORT

VACUUM SOLENOID

SPEED SENSOR

THERMAL SWITCH

reduction kit (Fig. 16-9). This device is operated by an electronic speed-sensing unit. This speed sensor controls a vacuum solenoid which, in turn, connects or disconnects the distributor vacuum advance. Like a tachometer, the electronic speed sensor monitors engine rpm through a wire connected to the negative terminal of the coil. As long as the vehicle is operating at speeds under 65 mph [104.6 km/h], the vacuum advance is disconnected. When the engine rpm is equivalent to 65 mph [104.6 km/h] in high gear, normal vacuum advance is restored. A thermal switch, or thermostat, taped to the outside of the upper radiator hose automatically provides vacuum advance when the engine starts to overheat.

Another device which can be installed to control NO_x emissions from 1966 to 1970 cars is the STP pollution-control device (Fig. 16-10). This device does not disconnect the distributor vacuum advance, although it is slightly modified by installation of a distributor air bleed. The STP device uses exhaust-gas recirculation (EGR) to prevent NO_x formation. Installation of the device requires drilling a $7/16$-in [11.11-mm] hole in the heat-riser chamber of the intake manifold, and then threading the hole. The EGR valve mounts on a standpipe which screws into the hole (Fig. 16-10). Tubing connects the outlet of the EGR valve into the PCV line, through a special Y-shaped connector (called a *velocity nozzle*) which comes with the kit. A hose from the EGR-valve inlet is connected to a fitting which must be installed on the clean-air side of the air-cleaner element (⊘ 16-1).

Echlin manufactures an NO_x control system which they claim works by sonic means. The word sonic refers to sound. A sonic wave is a sound wave. The sonic carburetor uses sound waves to help break up the fuel droplets. The sound waves help to atomize the fuel droplets so that they vaporize better and produce a more uniform air-fuel mixture. A number of experimental sonic carburetors have been designed, but none is being built today for original installation on vehicles.

The Echlin system is shown in Fig. 16-11. It is a retrofit device designed to improve combustion and thus to reduce pollutants in the exhaust gas. The principle is simple. A carburetor plate is installed between the carburetor and the intake manifold. An

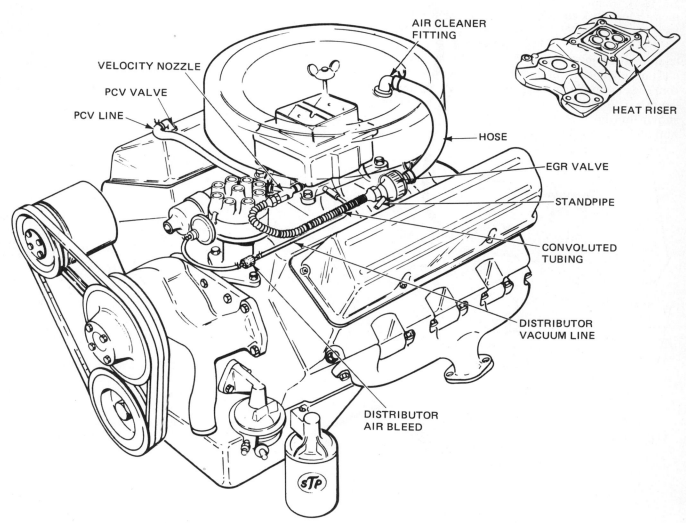

Fig. 16-10. NO_x emission-control kit manufactured by STP for used cars. The device is an add-on type of exhaust-gas recirculation system. (*STP Corporation*)

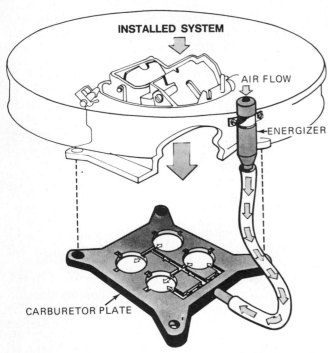

Fig. 16-11. Sonic device which, along with disconnecting the vacuum spark advance, acts to reduce NO$_x$ emissions from used cars. (*Echlin Manufacturing Company*)

energizer is connected to the special passages in the carburetor plate through a tube. When the engine is running, a small amount of air flows through the energizer to the passages in the carburetor plate, as shown by the arrows. The important point here is not that the air is flowing, but that it is carrying high-frequency sound waves with it. These sound waves are far above any frequency that the human ear can hear. Their purpose is to enter the ingoing air-fuel mixture, as shown by the arrows. As they enter, the sound waves meet particles, or droplets, of fuel that have not yet vaporized. In effect, the sound waves shake these droplets and break them up into still smaller droplets. This speeds vaporization. At the same time, the sound waves help to mix the gasoline vapor and air, so that a more even mixture results. Recall, from our discussion of fuel distribution in the intake manifold, how liquid droplets tend to go to the ends of the intake manifold and enrich the end-cylinder mixtures. If no droplets enter the intake manifold, this cannot happen. The sonic device reduces the chances of any droplet being left to enter the intake manifold. When the Echlin device is installed on an engine, the vacuum advance is disconnected. Ignition timing is set at 2° before top dead center (BTDC).

⊘ **16-4 Evaporative Controls for Auxiliary Fuel Tanks** The owners of light trucks—trucks with a gross vehicle weight (GVW) of 6,001 lb [2,722 kg] or less—often have auxiliary fuel tanks installed. In past years, these auxiliary fuel tanks were vented to the atmosphere. However, beginning in 1974, California required that only approved auxiliary fuel tanks with evaporative control systems be installed on vehicles having factory-installed evaporative control systems as original equipment.

Two different types of auxiliary fuel-tank installations are possible. One type connects the auxil-

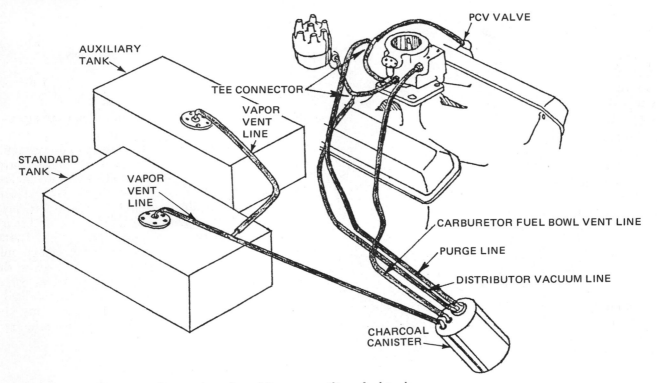

Fig. 16-12. Connections for adding an auxiliary fuel tank to the vehicle evaporative control system.

iary fuel tank to the charcoal canister for the evaporative control system on the vehicle (Fig. 16-12). This system can be used when the combined capacity of the standard fuel tank and the auxiliary fuel tank does not exceed 50 gal [189 liters]. The other system requires installation of a second charcoal canister to store vapors from the auxiliary fuel tank. The second canister should be used when the total capacity of both tanks exceeds 50 gal [189 liters], but does not exceed 100 gal [378 liters]. For each additional 50 gal [189 liters] of fuel-tank capacity, the fuel vapors must be vented to a 500- or 625-g-capacity activated-charcoal canister.

CHAPTER 16 CHECKUP

NOTE: Since the following is a chapter review test, you should review the chapter before taking the test.

You have completed the service part of the book. This part is designed to give you practical guidance in working on automotive emission controls. Many servicing procedures on automotive emission control devices have been discussed. You should, of course, remember the essentials of the various procedures. Then, when you are in the shop, you should have a good idea of what to do and why you should do it. The checkup below will give you a chance to test yourself on how well you remember these procedures.

Service Procedures Write down, in your notebook, the procedures asked for below. Do not copy from the book, but try to write each procedure in your own words, just as you would explain it to another person. Give a step-by-step description. This will help you remember the procedures later, when you go into the shop and have service jobs assigned to you. In addition, you will be filling your notebook with valuable information, to which you can easily refer.

1. Explain how to install a PCV valve on an engine equipped with a road-draft tube.
2. Explain how to install a tube to the air cleaner to make an open PCV system into a closed PCV system.
3. Explain how to install the General Motors exhaust-emission control device.
4. Explain how to install the Air Quality Products exhaust-emission control device.
5. Explain how to install the Carter emission-reduction kit.

Completing the Sentences The sentences below are incomplete. After each sentence there are several words or phrases, but only one of them correctly completes the sentence. Write each sentence in your notebook, ending it with the word or phrase that completes it correctly.

1. A retrofit smog device is: (a) factory-installed on new cars, (b) a device that is not available now, (c) installed by an automotive technician on a used car, (d) for garden tractors.
2. You can make an open PCV system on an engine into a closed PCV system by: (a) adding a tube from the crankcase to the air cleaner, (b) adding a second charcoal canister, (c) adding an exhaust-gas recirculation device, (d) disconnecting the vacuum spark advance.
3. Vacuum advance is restored by the General Motors exhaust-emission control device when the: (a) car speed exceeds 65 mph [105 km/h], (b) throttle is closed, (c) throttle is open, (d) engine overheats.
4. The device that incorporates a capacitive-discharge ignition system is manufactured by: (a) General Motors, (b) Air Quality Products, Inc., (c) Echlin, (d) STP.
5. The STP device controls NO_x by use of: (a) vacuum spark-advance disconnect, (b) sonic waves, (c) exhaust-gas recirculation, (d) a tube to the air cleaner.

Manufacturers Here is a list of five manufacturers. In your notebook, write the type of device that each manufacturer produces. The act of writing does two things: it tests your knowledge, and it helps fix the information more firmly in your mind. Turn back into the chapter if you are not sure of an answer.

1. General Motors
2. Air Quality Products, Inc.
3. Carter
4. STP
5. Echlin

SUGGESTIONS FOR FURTHER STUDY

When you are in a shop that does automotive emission control work, keep your eyes and ears open so that you can learn more about how various devices are installed and serviced. Study the installation instructions for each smog device. By studying these instructions, along with the device, you will learn when to install the device, and better understand any special features it may have. Keep a notebook, and jot down every important fact you learn in the shop or when you are reading about retrofit smog devices for used cars. You will find that this helps you to remember the facts. At the same time, the notebook will become an increasingly valuable reference for you.

chapter 17

AUTOMOTIVE EMISSIONS: A SUMMARY[1]

⊘ **17-1 Introduction**   In order to understand the significance of vehicle emission problems, we should have a basic knowledge of the important emissions and their relation to the overall air pollution problem. The three main pollutants emitted from automobiles are carbon monoxide (CO), unburned hydrocarbons (HC), and oxides of nitrogen (NO_x). There are also small quantities of sulfur oxides (SO_x) and particulates.

Carbon monoxide is a colorless, odorless gas which as most people know, can be fatal in high concentrations for a long period of time. It can also have other physical effects such as headaches, or sickness, or loss of mental alertness in less than fatal dosages. Its effects have been shown to be reversible, that is, one can recover from non-fatal exposures with little or no permanent harm. Fatal levels of CO are in the vicinity of 700 parts per million (ppm) for continuous eight hour exposure. Much higher levels can be tolerated on a short term basis, as cigarette smoke, for example, contains 40,000 ppm of CO. Levels of 5–20 ppm in urban areas would be typical, although one could expect to find higher levels in areas of high traffic density.

Unburned hydrocarbons are a wide variety of compounds that are the result of incomplete burning of all the fuel. These compounds are essentially non-toxic and do not comprise a health hazard in themselves at levels emitted from vehicles. They do, however, in the presence of oxides of nitrogen and sunlight tend to form a highly undesirable substance known as photochemical smog.

The oxides of nitrogen commonly found in vehicle exhaust are nitric oxide (NO) and small amounts of nitrogen dioxide (NO_2). Nitric oxide is thought to be less toxic than nitrogen dioxide, but it is not found alone in the atmosphere since it reacts with the oxygen in the air to form nitrogen dioxide. Nitrogen dioxide is quite toxic by itself with harmful effects starting at levels as low as 1–10 ppm. Levels usually encountered in the atmosphere are below one part per million. The main harmful effects of the nitrogen oxides come about through their participa-

tion in the photochemical smog mechanism. Under certain atmospheric conditions, namely a lack of air movement that would disperse pollutants away from the source area, an abundance of sunlight and the presence of reactive hydrocarbons and oxides of nitrogen, a complex chemical reaction can occur which results in the formation of photochemical smog. This is the well know Los Angeles smog which is responsible for a brown haze which reduces visibility and causes irritation of the eyes, nose, and throat. Some effects of smog which are not as well known are its detrimental effects on plants, rubber and fabrics.

We know that there is an air quality problem, and we should then ask what is the magnitude of the problem and what is the relative contribution of motor vehicles to this problem. Shown in Fig. 17-1 are statistics from the United States Environmental Protection Agency (EPA) for the estimated total amount of pollutants emitted in the United States by various sources in 1970. From these numbers, one can see that all forms of transportation vehicles contributed 75% of the carbon monoxide, 51% of the oxides of nitrogen and 56% of hydrocarbons. Emissions of particulates and oxides of sulfur are about 3% of the total, a relatively insignificant fraction. Figure 17-2 lists the 1971 Federal Ambient Air Quality Standards for the various pollutants.

In particular, it should be noted that the ambient air standard for carbon monoxide is considera-

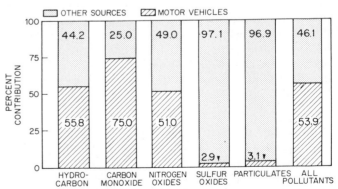

Fig. 17-1. Percentage of air pollution caused by motor vehicles and by other sources. (*Society of Automotive Engineers, Inc.*)

[1] © 1975, VEHICLE EMISSIONS, Public Affairs Report #3, Reprinted with the permission of the Society of Automotive Engineers, Inc., Warrendale, Pennsylvania.

Substance	Standard
Carbon Monoxide	40 milligrams/cubic meter [35 ppm] for 1-hour average
Hydrocarbons	0.16 milligrams/cubic meter [0.24 ppm] for 3-hour average
Oxides of Nitrogen	0.1 milligrams/cubic meter [0.05 ppm] for annual average
Sulfur Dioxide	0.08 milligrams/cubic meter [0.03 ppm] for annual average
Particulates	0.075 milligrams/cubic meter for annual average

Fig. 17-2. Ambient air quality standards for each pollutant. (*Society of Automotive Engineers, Inc.*)

bly higher than those of the other pollutants, that is, carbon monoxide is less toxic than the other pollutants. This would tend to lower the health related impact of vehicle emissions since the major emission of vehicles by weight is carbon monoxide and, per pound, it is less toxic than the other emissions. It does not alter the fact that vehicles comprise a major source of hydrocarbons and oxides of nitrogen.

These numbers provide us some interesting insight into the air pollution problem, but in order to get a more complete understanding of the problem we should look a bit further. One question of interest is how does man compare with nature as far as the amounts of these potentially harmful substances injected into the atmosphere.

In the case of carbon monoxide, it appears that man-made sources are the smallest, as they contribute only about 270 million tons per year world-wide, whereas natural sources are estimated to be responsible for about 3.5 billion tons per year. Man-made (pollution) sources of oxides of nitrogen are estimated to be about 53 million tons per year while natural sources are responsible for about 1100 million tons of oxides of nitrogen. Hydrocarbons from man-made sources are estimated at 90 million tons per year, a third of which are photochemically reactive in smog formation. Natural sources contribute about 2,000 million tons of hydrocarbon, the bulk of which are methane and do not participate in the photochemical smog process. It has been estimated that forests produce about 200 million tons per year of hydrocarbons that can form hazes. Many of these natural sources are not well understood. As air quality problems are studied further, new sources and methods of eliminating the pollutants may be discovered which could alter the above estimates.

From the preceding discussion, we can see that in most cases, natural sources produce much more "pollutants" than man-made sources. If this is the case with some pollutants, why don't we have a world-wide pollution problem? The reason is that the pollutants which are emitted do not stay in the atmosphere indefinitely. Nature, in addition to contributing pollutants, has provided methods of eliminating the pollutants. It has been shown, for exam-

ple, that micro-organisms in the soil consume large amounts of carbon monoxide. Oxides of nitrogen participate in the nitrogen cycle which maintains a balance of nitrogen compounds between the atmosphere, the soil and the marine environment. It is of interest to point out that the world-wide concentrations of pollutants in the atmosphere have not changed over the past several decades. The world-wide average concentration of carbon dioxide, which is not generally considered a pollutant, has been steadily increasing throughout the 20th century.

The major pollution problems arise during the period between the formation of the pollutants and the time at which they are dispersed and removed from the atmosphere. Most of the man-made sources are highly concentrated in urban areas. The high density of mobile, industrial and residential pollutant sources in our cities causes pollutant levels to become much higher on a local basis than if the pollutants were evenly distributed throughout the atmosphere.

Pollution problems then tend to be localized in urban centers, and different cities will have different types of problems depending on the make-up of the sources (industrial, mobile, residential), climate, geography and other factors. In cities where there are few heavy industries, the pollution problems are due mostly to transportation and residential sources and would be expected to be of a photochemical smog and carbon monoxide nature. In the heavy industrial centers, there is the additional problem of sulfur oxides and particulates which are products of coal and fuel oil burning and many industrial processes.

⊘ **17-2 History of Automobile Emission Control** In 1952, a theory was proposed that Los Angeles-type smog is formed by the action of sunlight on the air contaminants, hydrocarbons and nitrogen oxides. This theory has been confirmed by actually preparing smog in the laboratory. The automobile was immediately suspect as a major source of the necessary ingredients for the smog synthesis. The American Petroleum Institute and the Society of Automotive Engineeers acting jointly under the auspices of the Coordinating Research Council sent a group of engineers to the Los Angeles area in 1955 to conduct a preliminary field test on California cars to assess the magnitude of the emissions problem. A more exhaustive test program was carried out in 1956 on randomly selected parking lot automobiles to evaluate the extent of the emission of hydrocarbons, carbon monoxide and nitrogen oxide pollutants. The massive quantity of analytical data obtained from 293 cars, operating under controlled driving schedules, confirmed that the automobile was, indeed, a prime contributor to atmospheric pollution.

Any history of the development of emission controls would be incomplete without a review of government regulations and standards. California has been the leader in this respect. Basic legislation

Hydrocarbons	275 parts per million by volume (as hexane)
Carbon Monoxide	1.5% by volume

Fig. 17-3. 1966 California standards for motor vehicle exhaust emissions. (*Society of Automotive Engineers, Inc.*)

was passed in 1947 which established the machinery for air pollution control. The 1959 legislature passed a bill requiring the establishment of standards relating to vehicular exhaust emissions by February 1, 1960. After several revisions, standards were issued that were applicable to 1966 automobiles. These standards are listed in Fig. 17-3.

These standards, on the basis of the then available data, were expected to result in an 80% reduction in hydrocarbons and a 60% reduction in carbon monoxide. Nitrogen oxides were not included in the standards since the basic air quality standards did not call for their reduction as a toxic substance, among other reasons.

While the state of California was developing exhaust standards, a significant source of automotive hydrocarbon emissions was identified as those caused by engine blow-by issuing from the oil fill-cap crankcase ventilation tube. It is estimated that crankcase hydrocarbons amount to as much as 25% of the total vehicle hydrocarbon emissions.

The preceding work led to the first device for control of automotive hydrocarbon emissions, namely the Positive Crankcase Ventilation (PCV) System. All cars sold in California in 1961 were equipped with PCV systems, and most cars on a national basis were so equipped beginning with the 1963 model year. The function of the early "open system" was to circulate piston blow-by from the crankcase back into the induction system. There were several variants of the PCV system. However, they all suffered from the same limitation, that is, in the case of worn engines, the extent of blow-by into the crankcase may exceed the capacity of any given "open system," hence hydrocarbons are emitted through the vented oil-fill cap. The closed PCV system was introduced in California with the 1964 model year. In the closed system there is no vent to the outside. All cars in the United States have been fitted with closed PCV systems since the 1968 model year.

Another source of hydrocarbon emissions from cars is fuel evaporation from carburetors and fuel tanks. There are two systems for eliminating these emissions; a vapor recovery system, and an absorption-regeneration system. The former stores the fuel, which evaporates from the fuel tank and the carburetor float bowl in the crankcase for later recycle to the engine. The latter stores the vapor in charcoal with provisions for desorption and recycle of fuel to the engine. The charcoal system is now most widely used. Devices of this type were first installed in 1970 cars sold in California to meet that state's regulations of evaporative emission. These same regulations were applied nationwide to 1971 model cars.

Returning now to the development of government emissions standards, the California legislature passed the Pure Air Act of 1968 which established the California emission limits through the 1974 model year. These are given in Fig. 17-4 in terms of grams per mile rather than parts per million as in Fig. 17-3. This takes into consideration the fact that smaller cars emit less total exhaust.

The automobile industry introduced engine modifications to meet California exhaust emission standards for the 1966 model year. According to the California Motor Vehicle Pollution Control Board, some 800,000 new cars and light trucks in California met the standards, based on actual emission tests on 404 public vehicles. This meant that these 1966 cars were emitting substantially less hydrocarbons and carbon monoxide than automobiles without emission controls. Most American manufacturers accomplished the reduction in emissions with air injection systems designed to oxidize hydrocarbons and carbon monoxide in the exhaust gas. Major components of the system were: air pump, air injection into each exhaust port, and carburetor and distributor modifications. Minor components include: an anti-backfire valve, check valves, and a high-speed pressure relief valve. One manufacturer met the 1966 California requirements with an engine modification system involving optimum fuel-air mixture and ignition timing for minimum emissions at the operating conditions used in the test.

As a result of the Clean Air Act of 1965, the United States Department of Health, Education and Welfare (HEW) published regulations applicable to 1968 model year vehicles nationwide. These standards were similar to the California 1966 model year regulations. Most American-made cars sold in 1968 and 1969 used the approach of optimizing fuel-air mixture and ignition timing to meet these standards.

In June, 1968, the HEW adopted the California standards for nationwide application in the 1970 and later model year vehicles. The reductions of hydrocarbons and carbon monoxide emissions were accomplished by changes related to the operation of engines; namely, retarded ignition timing, decreased

Component	Before Control	California Requirements				
		1966	1970	1971	1972	1974
Hydrocarbons, g/mi	15	6.3	4.1	4.1	2.9	2.9
Carbon Monoxide, g/mi	87	51.0	34.0	34.0	28.0	28.0
NOx, g/mi	**	**	**	6.2	4.6	2.1

Fig. 17-4. 1966 to 1974 California standards for passenger car exhaust emissions, based on the 1975 federal test procedure. There were no official NO$_x$ standards until 1971, although NO$_x$ was estimated at 4.6 grams per mile. The level of NO$_x$ emitted from uncontrolled automobiles has been the subject of extensive debate. (*Society of Automotive Engineers, Inc.*)

compression ratio, changes in fuel-air ratio, and a new system for control of spark advance. Further changes in spark timing, fuel-air ratio and compression ratio allowed for modest control of oxides of nitrogen to meet the 1971 model year requirement in California. The oxides of nitrogen emissions had increased somewhat due to hydrocarbon and carbon monoxide control measures.

In November, 1970, the HEW adopted a completely new test procedure using a different driving schedule and analytical methods. This procedure was introduced in an effort to accurately measure total pollutants and takes into account actual exhaust flow, cold startup emissions, and a more valid driving operation. The driving cycle in this procedure includes stop and start driving at speeds which might be encountered in urban or suburban driving. This procedure was applicable to 1972 through 1974 model year vehicles with hydrocarbon and carbon monoxide standards about 20% stricter than the 1970 model year standards. Further, this procedure was used when oxides of nitrogen standards became effective nationwide on 1973 model year cars. 1973 standards reduced oxides of nitrogen emissions by about 25% from the 1971 model cars. 1973 model cars were the first to be equipped with a control system designed specifically for this purpose. These cars are equipped with exhaust gas recirculation (EGR) systems which return exhaust gas to the intake manifold to reduce the peak combustion temperature, thereby reducing the quantity of NO_x formed.

The formation of the Environmental Protection Agency (air pollution regulation was previously vested in HEW) in late 1970 and the passage by Congress of the 1970 Clean Air Amendments established the Federal government in a dominant position with respect to the vehicle emissions picture. Whereas, the state of California estimated a 53% reduction of hydrocarbon and a 61% reduction in carbon monoxide emission in 1970, EPA is now required by law to reduce these same emissions by an additional 90% beginning with 1975 cars. Thus, the overall reduction in hydrocarbons and carbon monoxide emissions from uncontrolled cars (pre-1961) amounts to approximately 97%. Furthermore, the law requires that in the 1976 model year, oxides of nitrogen be reduced 90% below measured values for 1971 automobiles.

The standard values listed in Fig. 17-5 are based on a slightly modified test procedure which also took

into account hot startup emissions. It will be noted that the standards listed in Fig. 17-5 are much more restrictive than the California standards listed in Fig. 17-4. The 1970 Clean Air Act Amendments provided for the postponement of these standards by one year if the Administrator of EPA determines that certain conditions listed in the Act are met. In such an event, he must prescribe interim standards which reflect the greatest degree of control which is achievable with available technology. The standards were postponed and interim standards were set. In addition, the Congress has recently acted to extend the interim standards and delay implementation of the lowest standards an additional year. The Federal Emissions Standards as of this printing are listed in Fig. 17-6.

To meet these standards in 1975 model cars, most manufacturers have decided that oxidation catalyst devices would be required on their cars built for sale in California. Many cars built for sale in other states will also be equipped with oxidizing catalysts. In some instances, the use of an oxidation catalyst allows for changing spark timing and fuel-air ratios for the purpose of obtaining improved fuel economy.

It is expected that the 1977 standards will be met by improvements in the catalyst device approach used to meet the 1975–76 interim standards. To meet the 1978 standards it is expected that the use of a dual catalytic converter will be required. In the first converter, a reducing catalyst changes the oxides of nitrogen to nitrogen and water. After addition of air to the exhaust stream, the second converter oxidizes the carbon monoxide and hydrocarbons to carbon dioxide and water. Catalytic systems can be very effective in emission reduction, but maintaining the durability of the catalyst over an extended period of time has been a major problem.

⊘ **17-3 Effect of Emission Controls on the Energy Supply** An area of increasing concern regarding emissions controls is that of their effect on the consumption of energy, or more specifically, the use of petroleum. At the present time, about 44% of the total energy requirement in the United States is filled by petroleum, the balance being supplied mainly by natural gas (33%) and coal (20%). The consumption of

Component	1975	1976
Hydrocarbons, g/mi	0.41	0.41
Carbon Monoxide, g/mi	3.4	3.4
Oxides of Nitrogen, g/mi	3.1	0.4

Fig. 17-5. Federal emissions standards required by the Clean Air Amendments of 1970. The standards are based on the 1975 federal test procedure. (*Society of Automotive Engineers, Inc.*)

	California	Nationwide		
	1975-76	1975-76	1977	1978
Hydrocarbon/mi	0.9	1.5	0.41	0.41
Carbon Monoxide/mi	9	15	3.4	3.4
Oxides of Nitrogen/mi	2.0	3.1	2.0	0.4

Fig. 17-6. Comparison of California and federal emissions standards. The standards are based on the 1975 federal test procedure. (*Society of Automotive Engineers, Inc.*)

Automotive Emissions: A Summary 255

petroleum by automobiles amounts to approximately 12–13% of the total national energy consumption, or slightly more than half of the total energy consumed by our total transportation system. In terms of absolute quantities, this amounts to about 5 million barrels of gasoline per day (a barrel is 42 gallons) out of a total petroleum consumption of about 17 million barrels per day as of 1970. It was estimated before the "energy crisis" that the total United States demand for petroleum would increase by about 1 million barrels per day every year over the next ten years. It appears at the present time that conservation measures may have lowered this demand somewhat.

From these figures, it can be seen that changing the fuel economy of automobiles can have a significant effect on the future United States petroleum needs. We then need to look at what effect emissions controls have had in the past and to estimate some possible effects in the future.

As was pointed out earlier, most manufacturers have met the lower emissions standards through the combined use of engine modifications such as retarded ignition timing, lower compression ratios, carburetor modifications and exhaust gas recirculation. The combined effect of these modifications has been to lower the efficiency of the engines, resulting in a decrease in the miles per gallon obtained on the road. While the exact loss of fuel economy due to emission controls will vary for different makes and models of cars, estimates of the average loss in fuel economy due to emission controls alone for 1973 model cars are in the vicinity of 15%. In addition to a fuel economy penalty, the emission controls used have also had the effect of lowering driveability performance.

While the emissions controls which the automobile manufacturers have adopted to meet the government emissions standards have affected gasoline mileage, they are not the only factors. Vehicle weight, which is the most significant variable affecting mileage, has been increasing steadily the past several years. Weights of comparable models of cars have increased from 5–10% since 1968, resulting in either decreased mileage and/or decreased performance. Some of this added weight is due to modifications made by manufacturers to meet government safety standards. Increased use of accessories has also contributed to mileage losses. The use of power steering and air conditioning, for example, has been shown to decrease mileage in some cars 1½ miles per gallon.

The impact of future emission controls on the United States petroleum demand will be strongly affected by three important factors: the level of emissions which governmental regulations permit, the techniques used by the automobile manufacturers to meet these emission levels, and the automobile size and weight distribution and use of accessories, as determined by the public in its purchasing behavior. For example, the percentage of compact and subcompact cars on the road has increased from 21%

in 1969 to 38% in early 1974. This has helped to ease the impact of increased fuel consumption since the smaller cars do give better fuel consumption than the larger cars.

The 1975–76 standards are more stringent than the 1974 standards. To meet the 1975–76 standards it is anticipated that there will be widespread use of oxidizing catalytic converters. This control device allows adjustment of the engine to give better fuel economy than 1974 levels. The situation beyond 1976 is not clear. Some control systems which have been proposed to meet the 1977–78 standards result in substantial fuel economy penalties over 1974 levels. On the other hand, development of alternative engine types such as stratified charge engines holds potential for meeting future emission standards with reasonable fuel consumption. It is also expected that the 1977 and later standards will be reviewed by the government. Fuel economy and new developments in emission control technology will be important considerations.

As a result of the emission controls, we can expect cleaner air throughout the country. This is shown in Fig. 17-7, which is a plot of the estimated future rate of automobile emissions for vehicles meeting federal emissions standards. It can be seen that total automotive emissions will decrease in spite of the projected increase in the number of vehicles on the road. This benefit of cleaner air is not without its cost since we have seen the adverse effects on fuel economy and performance in addition to the cost of added equipment associated with emission controls.

Throughout this report, attention has been focused on the problem of vehicle emissions and the steps government and industry have taken in order to achieve the goals of cleaner air. In closing, another important area should be pointed out; the role of the public in emission control. As we have seen, new automobiles must meet exhaust emissions standards and receive certification by the govern-

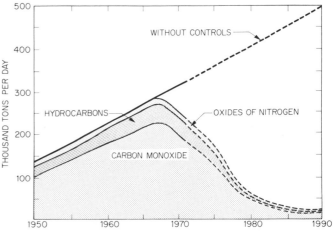

Fig. 17-7. Nationwide automotive emissions of hydrocarbons, carbon monoxide, and nitrogen oxides, 1950 to 1990. (*Society of Automotive Engineers, Inc.*)

ment that they do so. The maintenance of automobiles after sale, however, is determined by action of the consumer. Emission controls on automobiles, like any mechanical equipment, require periodic maintenance for optimum performance. The general public, therefore, can play an important role in securing clean air by making sure that automobiles are regularly serviced and inspected. The use of car pools and the elimination of unnecessary trips can also help, not only in the area of lower emissions but in decreased fuel use.

The path to clean air is not an easy one. Hopefully, with everyone doing his or her share we can reach this goal swiftly and in a realistic manner.

GLOSSARY

This glossary of automotive terms used in the book provides a ready reference for the student. The definitions may differ somewhat from those given in a standard dictionary. They are not intended to be all-inclusive but to refresh the memory on automotive terms. More complete definitions and explanations of the terms are found in the text.

ABDC Abbreviation for *after bottom dead center;* any position of the piston between bottom dead center and top dead center, on the upward stroke.

Acceleration An increase in velocity or speed.

Accelerator A foot-operated pedal, linked to the throttle valve in the carburetor; used to control the flow of gasoline to the engine.

Accelerator Pump In the carburetor, a pump (linked to the accelerator) which momentarily enriches the air-fuel mixture when the accelerator is depressed at low speed.

A.C.I.D. Abbreviation for a four-mode driving-test cycle used to test exhaust emissions or vehicle driveability; the modes are accelerate, cruise, idle, and decelerate.

Additive A substance added to gasoline or oil to improve some property of the gasoline or oil.

Adjust To bring the parts of a component or system to a specified relationship, dimension, or pressure.

Adjustments Necessary or desired changes in clearances, fit, or settings.

Adsorb To collect in a very thin layer on the surface of another material.

Advance The moving ahead of the ignition spark in relation to piston position; produced by centrifugal or vacuum devices in accordance with engine speed and intake-manifold vacuum.

Afterboil Boiling of fuel in the carburetor or coolant in the engine immediately after the engine is stopped.

Afterburner On an automobile engine, a type of exhaust manifold that burns any HC and CO remaining in the exhaust gas.

Afterrunning The situation in which an engine continues to run after the ignition is turned off. Sometimes referred to as *dieseling.*

Air Bleed An opening into a gasoline passage through which air can pass, or bleed, into the gasoline as it moves through the passage.

Air Cleaner A device, mounted on or connected to the carburetor, for filtering dirt and dust out of air being drawn into the engine.

Air-Cooled Engine An engine that is cooled by the passage of air around the cylinders, and not by the passage of a liquid through water jackets.

Air Filter A filter that removes dirt and dust particles from air passing through it.

Air-Fuel Mixture The air and fuel traveling to the combustion chamber after being mixed by the carburetor.

Air-Fuel Ratio The proportions of air and fuel (by weight) supplied for combustion.

Air Guard Name used by American Motors Corporation for the air-injection system of exhaust-emission control.

Air Horn In the carburetor, a tubular passage on the atmospheric side of the venturi through which the incoming air must pass, and which contains the choke valve.

Air-Injection System An exhaust-emission control system; injects air at low pressure into the exhaust manifold or thermal reac-tor to complete the combustion of unburned hydrocarbons and carbon monoxide in the exhaust gas.

Air Nozzle In an air-injection system, the tube through which air is delivered to the exhaust gas.

Air Pollution Contamination of the air by natural and people-made pollutants.

Air Pressure Atmospheric pressure, equal to 14.7 psi (pounds per square inch) [1.03 kg/cm² (kilograms per square centimeter)] at sea level; also the pressure produced by an air pump or by compression of air in a cylinder.

Air Pump Any device for compressing air. In the air-injection system of exhaust-emission control, an engine-driven (belt-driven) pump incorporating a rotor and vanes.

Antibackfire Valve A valve used, in the air-injection system, to prevent backfiring in the exhaust system during deceleration.

Antifreeze A chemical, usually ethylene glycol, that is added to the engine coolant to raise the coolant boiling point and lower its freezing point.

Anti-Icing System A carburetor system designed to prevent the formation of ice on a surface or in a passage.

Antiknock Compound An additive put into gasoline to suppress spark knock or detonation—usually a lead compound (which becomes an air pollutant from the engine exhaust, according to some authorities).

Antipercolator A vent in the carburetor that opens to release fuel vapors when the throttle is closed; prevents fuel from being pushed out through the fuel nozzle by pressure buildup.

Antisiphon System A small passage designed into a carburetor to prevent fuel from siphoning from the float bowl into the engine.

Arcing Name given to the spark that jumps the air gap between two electrical conductors; for example, the arcing of the distributor contact points.

Aspirator Vacuum pump. Any device that uses a vacuum to draw up gases or small grainy materials; also, the vacuum pump used in catalytic-converter bead replacement.

ATDC Abbreviation for *after top dead center;* any position of the piston between top dead center and bottom dead center, on the downward stroke.

Atmosphere The mass of air that surrounds the earth.

Atmospheric Pollution See *air pollution.*

Atomization The spraying of a liquid through a nozzle so that the liquid is broken into a very fine mist.

Attrition Wearing down by rubbing or by friction; abrasion.

Automatic Choke A choke that positions the choke valve automatically in accordance with engine temperature.

Automotive Air Pollution Evaporated and unburned fuel and other undesirable by-products of combustion which escape from a motor vehicle into the atmosphere; mainly carbon monoxide (CO), hydrocarbons (HC), nitrogen oxides (NO_x), sulfur oxides (SO_x), and particulates.

Automotive Emissions See *automotive air pollution.*

Backfire-Suppressor Valve An antibackfire valve used in the air-injection system of exhaust-emission control.

Backfiring Preexplosion of the air-fuel mixture so that the explosion passes back around the opened intake valve and through the intake manifold and carburetor. Also applied to the loud explosion of overly rich exhaust gas in the exhaust manifold, which exits through the muffler and tail pipe with a loud popping or banging noise.

Back Pressure Pressure in the exhaust manifold of a running engine; affects volumetric efficiency.

Balanced Carburetor Carburetor in which the float bowl is vented into the air horn to compensate for the possible effects of a clogged air filter.

Ballast Resistor See *ignition resistor.*

Barrel Term sometimes applied to the cylinders in an engine; used in referring to the number of throttle bores in a carburetor.

BDC Abbreviation for *bottom dead center.*

Bellows A device, usually metal, that can lengthen or shorten much like an accordian. Some cooling-system thermostats are of the bellows type.

Belt Tension The tightness of a drive belt.

Bimetal A thermostatic element made up of two metals with different heat expansion rates. Temperature changes produce a bending or distortion of the element.

Block See *cylinder block.*

Blow-By Leakage of compressed air-fuel mixture and burned gases (from combustion) past the piston rings into the crankcase.

Bore An engine cylinder, or any cylindrical hole. Also used to describe the process of enlarging or accurately refinishing a hole, as "to bore an engine cylinder." The bore size is the diameter of the hole.

Bottom Dead Center (BDC) The piston position at the lower limit of its travel in the cylinder, such that the cylinder volume is at its maximum.

Breaker Cam See *distributor cam.*

Breakerless System An electronic ignition system which does not use mechanical breaker contacts for timing or triggering purposes, but retains the distributor for distribution of the secondary voltage.

Breaker Points See *contact points.*

Breather On engines without emission-control devices, the opening that allows air to circulate through the crankcase and thus produces crankcase ventilation.

BTDC Abbreviation for *before top dead center;* any position of the piston between bottom dead center and top dead center, on the upward stroke.

Butane A type of liquefied petroleum gas that is liquid below 32°F [0°C] at atmospheric pressure.

Butterfly A type of valve used for the choke and throttle valve in a carburetor; a movable flat plate that governs the flow of air into the carburetor.

Bypass A separate passage which permits a liquid, gas, or electric current to take a path other than that normally used.

Calibrate To check or correct the initial setting of a test instrument.

Cam A rotating lobe or eccentric which can be used with a cam follower to change rotary motion to reciprocating motion.

Cam Angle See *dwell.*

Cam Follower See *valve lifter.*

Camshaft The shaft in the engine which has a series of cams for operating the valve mechanisms. It is driven by gears, or sprockets and toothed belt or chain, from the crankshaft.

Canister A cylindrical container, in an evaporative control system, that contains charcoal to trap vapors from the fuel system.

Capacitor See *condenser.*

Capacity The ability to perform or to hold.

Carbon (C) A black deposit left on engine parts such as pistons, rings, and valves by the combustion of fuel, and which inhibits their action.

Carbon Dioxide (CO_2) A colorless, odorless gas which results from complete combustion; usually considered harmless. The gas absorbed from air by plants in photosynthesis; also used to carbonate beverages.

Carbon Monoxide (CO) A colorless, odorless, tasteless, poisonous gas which results from incomplete combustion. A pollutant contained in engine exhaust gas.

Carburetion The actions that take place in the carburetor: converting liquid fuel to vapor and mixing it with air to form a combustible mixture.

Carburetor The device in an engine fuel system which mixes fuel with air and supplies the combustible mixture to the intake manifold.

Carburetor Heated Air A system in which heated air, radiated from the exhaust manifold, is routed to the carburetor for more complete combustion and better engine performance with a leaner air-fuel mixture.

Carburetor Insulator A spacer, or insulator, used to prevent excess engine heat from reaching the carburetor.

Carburetor Kickdown Moderate depressing of the accelerator pedal to change the engagement of the choke–fast–idle–speed screw from the high step to a lower step of the cam.

Carcinogen or Carcinogenic A substance or agent that produces or incites cancer.

Catalyst A substance that can speed or slow a chemical reaction between substances, without itself being consumed by the reaction. In the catalytic converter, platinum and palladium are the active catalysts.

Catalytic Converter A mufflerlike device for use in an exhaust system; it converts harmful exhaust gases into harmless gases by promoting a chemical reaction between a catalyst and the pollutants.

CC Abbreviation for *cubic centimeter,* a unit of volume in the metric system.

CCS Abbreviation for *controlled-combustion system.*

CEC Abbreviation for *combination emission control system.*

CEC Solenoid A two-position electrically operated control used in some TCS systems; either allows or denies distributor vacuum advance, depending on transmission-gear selection. The control-solenoid plunger, when extended, maintains a predetermined throttle opening.

Centrifugal Advance A rotating-weight mechanism in the distributor; advances and retards ignition timing through the centrifugal force resulting from changes in the engine distributor rotational speed.

Centrifugal Filter Fan A filter fan mounted on the air-pump drive shaft; used to clean the air entering the air pump.

Ceramic A type of material made from various minerals by baking or firing at high temperatures; can be used as an electrical insulator or as a catalyst substrate in a catalytic converter.

Cetane Number An indicator of the ignition quality of diesel fuel. A high-cetane fuel ignites more easily (at lower temperature) than a low-cetane fuel.

Charcoal Canister A container filled with activated charcoal, used to trap gasoline vapor from the fuel tank and carburetor while the engine is off.

Check To verify that a component, system, or measurement complies with specifications.

Check Valve A valve that opens to permit the passage of air or fluid in one direction only, or operates to prevent (check) some undesirable action.

Chemical Reaction The formation of one or more new substances when two or more substances are brought together.

Choke In the carburetor, a device used when starting a cold engine; it "chokes off" the airflow through the air horn, producing a partial vacuum in the air horn for greater fuel delivery and a richer mixture. Operates automatically on many newer cars.

Choke Plate In the carburetor, a valve that "chokes off" the air flow through the air horn, producing a partial vacuum in the carburetor for greater fuel delivery and a richer mixture.

Closed Crankcase Ventilation System A system in which the crankcase vapors (blow-by gases) are discharged into the engine intake system and pass through the engine cylinders, rather than being discharged into the air.

Coasting-Richer System A system, controlled by a carburetor electromechanical solenoid valve, which provides fuel enrichment while the vehicle is coasting; prevents popping in the exhaust manifold due to the operation of the air-injection system. Used on Chevrolet LUV light trucks.

Coil In an automobile ignition system, a transformer used to step up the battery voltage (by induction) to the high voltage required to fire the spark plugs.

Combination Emission Control System An exhaust-emission control system used on some General Motors cars; combines a transmission-controlled spark system and a deceleration throttle-positioning device.

Combustion Burning; fire produced by the proper combination of fuel, heat, and oxygen. In the engine, the rapid burning of the air-fuel mixture in the combustion chamber.

Combustion Chamber The space between the top of the piston and the cylinder head, in which the air-fuel mixture is burned.

Compound Vortex-Controlled Combustion Engine A type of stratified-charge engine built by Honda. See *Honda system.*

Compression Reducing the volume of a gas by squeezing it into a smaller space. Increasing the pressure reduces the volume and increases the density and temperature of the gas.

Compression Ignition Ignition of fuel solely by the heat produced when air is compressed in the cylinder; the method of ignition in a diesel engine.

Compression Pressure The pressure in the combustion chamber at the end of the compression stroke.

Compression Ratio The volume of the cylinder when the piston is at BDC, divided by the volume of the cylinder when the piston is at TDC.

Compression Ring The upper ring or rings on a piston, designed to hold the compression in the combustion chamber and prevent blow-by.

Compression Stroke The piston movement from BDC to TDC immediately following the intake stroke, during which both the intake and exhaust valves are closed while the air-fuel mixture in the cylinder is compressed.

Compression Tester An instrument for testing the amount of pressure, or compression, developed in an engine cylinder during cranking.

Condensation A change of state during which a gas turns to liquid, usually because of temperature or pressure changes. Also, moisture from the air, deposited on a cool surface.

Condenser In the ignition system, a device that is also called a *capacitor;* connected across the contact points to reduce arcing by providing a storage place for electricity (electrons) as the contact points open. In an air-conditioning system, the radiatorlike heat exchanger in which refrigerant vapor loses heat and returns to the liquid state.

Contact Points In the conventional ignition system, the stationary and the movable point in the distributor which open and close the ignition primary circuit.

Controlled-Combustion System An exhaust-emission control system used by General Motors; regulates engine combustion efficiency through special settings of the carburetor, distributor, and vacuum advance, by heating the carburetor intake air, and with a higher engine operating temperature. Also known as the *engine modification system,* and used by other manufacturers under other names.

Coolant The liquid mixture of about 50 percent antifreeze and 50 percent water used to carry heat out of the engine.

Cooling System The system that removes heat from the engine by the forced circulation of coolant, and thereby prevents engine overheating. It includes the water jackets, water pump, radiator, and thermostat.

Crankcase The lower part of the engine in which the crankshaft rotates; includes the lower section of the cylinder block and the oil pan.

Crankcase Breather The opening or tube that allows air to enter and leave the crankcase and thus permit crankcase ventilation.

Crankcase Dilution Dilution of the lubricating oil in the oil pan; caused by liquid gasoline condensing from the blow-by in a cold engine and seeping down the cylinder walls.

Crankcase Emissions Pollutants emitted into the atmosphere from any portion of the engine-crankcase ventilation or lubrication system.

Crankcase Ventilation The circulation of air through the crankcase of a running engine to remove water, blow-by, and other vapors; prevents oil dilution, contamination, sludge formation, and pressure buildup.

Cross-Firing Jumping of a high-voltage surge in the ignition secondary circuit to the wrong high-voltage lead, so that the wrong spark plug fires. Usually caused by improper routing of the spark-plug wires, faulty insulation, or a defective distributor cap or rotor.

CRS Abbreviation for *coasting-richer system.*

Cubic Inch Displacement The cylinder volume swept out by the pistons of an engine as they move from BDC to TDC, measured in cubic inches.

Cut Out In a running engine, to miss momentarily but not stall.

CVCC Abbreviation for *compound vortex-controlled combustion;* see also *Honda system.*

Cycle Any series of events which repeat continuously. In the engine, the four (or two) piston strokes that together produce the power.

Cylinder A circular tubelike opening in an engine cylinder block or casting in which a piston moves up and down.

Cylinder Block The basic framework of the engine, in and on which the other engine parts are attached. It includes the engine cylinders and the upper part of the crankcase.

Cylinder Compression Tester See *compression tester.*

Cylinder Head The part of the engine that covers and encloses the cylinders. It contains cooling fins or water jackets and, on I-head engines, the valves.

Cylinder Leakage Tester A testing device that forces compressed air into the cylinder through the spark-plug hole, when the valves are closed and the piston is at TDC on the compression stroke. The percentage of compressed air

that leaks out is measured, and the source of the leak accurately pinpoints the defective part.

Dashpot A device on the carburetor that prevents the throttle valve from closing too suddenly.

Deceleration A decrease in velocity or speed. Also, allowing the car or engine to coast to idle speed from a higher speed with the accelerator at or near the idle position.

Deceleration Valve A device used in conjunction with the dual-diaphragm vacuum-advance unit to advance the timing under deceleration conditions.

Detonation Commonly referred to as *spark knock* or *ping.* In the combustion chamber, an uncontrolled second explosion (after the spark occurs at the spark plug) with spontaneous combustion of the remaining compressed air-fuel mixture, resulting in a pinging noise.

Device A mechanism, tool, or other piece of equipment designed to serve a special purpose or perform a special function.

Diagnosis A procedure followed in locating the cause of a malfunction.

Diaphragm A thin dividing sheet or partition which separates an area into compartments; used in fuel pumps, modulator valves, vacuum-advance units, and other control devices.

Die Out To stall or stop running, as an engine.

Diesel Cycle An engine operating cycle in which air is compressed, and fuel oil is injected into the compressed air at the end of the compression stroke. The heat produced by the compression ignites the fuel oil, eliminating the need for spark plugs or a separate ignition system.

Dieseling A condition in which an automobile engine continues to run after the ignition is off. Caused by carbon deposits or hot spots in the combustion chamber glowing sufficiently to furnish heat for combustion.

Dipstick The engine oil-level indicator.

Disassemble To take apart.

Displacement The total volume of

air-fuel mixture an engine is theoretically capable of drawing into all cylinders during one operating cycle. Also, the volume swept out by the piston in moving from one end of a stroke to the other.

Distributor Any device that distributes. In the ignition system, the rotary switch that directs high-voltage surges to the engine cylinders in the proper sequence. See *ignition distributor.*

Distributor Advance See *centrifugal advance, ignition advance,* and *vacuum advance.*

Distributor Cam The cam on the top end of the distributor shaft which rotates to open and close the contact points.

Distributor Plate The plate in the ignition distributor that is fastened to the distributor housing and does not move.

Distributor Timing See *ignition timing.*

Distributor Vacuum-Advance Control Valve See *deceleration valve.*

Diverter Valve In the air-injection system of exhaust-emission control, a valve that diverts air-pump output into the air cleaner or the atmosphere during deceleration; prevents backfiring and popping in the exhaust system.

Double-Overhead-Camshaft Engine An engine with two camshafts in each cylinder head to actuate the valves; one camshaft operates the intake valves, and the other operates the exhaust valves.

Downdraft Carburetor A carburetor in which the air horn is so arranged that the air passes down through it on its way to the intake manifold.

Driveability The general operation of an automobile, usually rated from good to poor; based on characteristics of concern to the average driver, such as smoothness of idle, even acceleration, ease of starting, quick warmup, and tendency to overheat at idle.

Dual-Area Diaphragm An automatic-transmission shift-control diaphragm which has sources of vacuum from the intake manifold and EGR port.

Dual Carburetors Two carburetors mounted on one engine.

Dual-Diaphragm Advance A vacuum-advance mechanism with two diaphragms; attaches to the engine distributor to control spark timing. One diaphragm provides normal ignition timing advance for starting and acceleration; the other diaphragm retards the spark during idling and part-throttle operation.

Dual-Point System A system that controls spark timing by electromechanical selection of separate advance and retard distributor points; used on Chevrolet LUV light trucks. Sometimes used to refer to any ignition system which has two sets of contact points in the distributor.

Dual Quad Performance term for a carburetion setup that uses two four-barrel carburetors.

Duct A tube or channel used to convey air or liquid from one point to another. In emission systems, a tube on an air cleaner, with a vacuum motor mounted on it, to help regulate the temperature of the carburetor intake air.

Durability The quality of being useful for a long period of time and service. Used to indicate the useful life of a catalyst or emission-control system.

Dwell The number of degrees the distributor shaft or cam rotates while the distributor points are closed.

Dwell Meter A precision electrical instrument used to measure the dwell, or number of degrees during which the distributor points are closed while the engine is running.

Dynamometer A device for measuring the power output, or brake horsepower, of an engine. An *engine* dynamometer measures the power output at the flywheel; a *chassis* dynamometer measures the power output at the drive wheels.

Efficiency The ratio between the power of an effect and the power expended to produce the effect; the ratio between an actual result and the theoretically possible result.

EGR System Abbreviation for *exhaust-gas recirculation system.*

Electric-Assist Choke A choke in which a small electric heating element warms the choke spring, causing it to release more quickly. This reduces exhaust emissions during the startup of a cold engine.

Electrode In a spark plug, either of the two metal conductors between which the spark is made to jump. The wire passing through the insulator is the center electrode. The small piece of metal welded to the spark-plug shell (and to which the spark jumps) is the side, or ground, electrode.

Electronic Fuel-Injection System A system that injects gasoline into a spark-ignition engine, and that includes an electronic control to time and meter the fuel flow.

Electronic Ignition System A transistorized ignition system which does not have mechanical contact points in the distributor, but which uses the distributor for distributing the secondary voltage to the spark plugs.

Electronic Spark Control A system that controls the vacuum to the distributor, preventing vacuum advance below a selected vehicle speed; generally used by Ford on cars with automatic transmission.

Emission Control Any device or modification added onto or designed into a motor vehicle for the purpose of reducing air-polluting emissions.

Emission Standards Allowable automobile emission levels, set by local, state, and federal legislation.

Emitter An engine with considerable exhaust emissions; sometimes preceded by the word "high" or "low" to indicate the degree of emission.

Engine A machine that converts heat energy into mechanical energy. A device that burns fuel to produce mechanical power; sometimes referred to as a *power plant.*

Engine Tune-Up The procedure of checking and adjusting engine components so that engine is restored to top operating condition.

Engine Vacuum Gauge See *vacuum gauge.*

Environmental Protection Agency The independent agency of the United States government that sets standards and coordinates activities related to automotive emissions and the environment.

EPA Abbreviation for *Environmental Protection Agency*.

ESC Abbreviation for *electronic spark control*.

Ethyl See *tetraethyl lead*.

Evaporation The transforming of a liquid to the gaseous state.

Evaporation Control System A system which prevents the escape of gasoline vapors from the fuel tank or carburetor to the atmosphere while the engine is off. The vapors are stored in a charcoal canister or in the engine crankcase until the engine is started.

Exhaust Emissions Pollutants emitted into the atmosphere through any opening downstream of the exhaust ports of an engine.

Exhaust Gas The burned and unburned gases that remain (from the air-fuel mixture) after combustion.

Exhaust-Gas Analyzer A device for sensing the amounts of air pollutants in the exhaust gas of a motor vehicle. The analyzers used in automotive shops check HC and CO; those used in testing laboratories can also check NO_x.

Exhaust-Gas Recirculation System An NO_x control system that recycles a small part of the inert exhaust gas back through the intake manifold at all throttle positions except idle and wide open, to lower the combustion temperature.

Exhaust Manifold A device with several passages through which exhaust gases leave the engine combustion chambers and enter the exhaust piping system.

Exhaust Pipe The pipe connecting the exhaust manifold with the muffler.

Exhaust Stroke The piston stroke (from BDC to TDC) immediately following the power stroke, during which the exhaust valve opens so that the exhaust gases can escape from the cylinder to the exhaust manifold.

Exhaust System The system through which exhaust gases leave the vehicle. Consists of the exhaust manifold, exhaust pipe, muffler, tail pipe, and resonator (if used).

Exhaust Valve The valve that opens during the exhaust stroke to allow burned gases to flow from the cylinder to the exhaust manifold.

Expansion Tank A tank at the top of an automobile radiator; provides room for heated coolant to expand and to give off any air that may be trapped in the coolant. Also, a similar device used in some fuel tanks to prevent fuel from spilling out of the tank through expansion.

Fan The bladed device on the front of the engine that rotates to draw cooling air through the radiator, or around the engine cylinders.

Fast-Idle Cam A mechanism on the carburetor, connected to the automatic choke, that holds the throttle valve slightly open when the engine is cold; causes the engine to idle at a higher rpm as long as the choke is applied.

Filter A device through which air, gases, or liquids are passed to remove impurities.

Firing Line The high-voltage vertical spike, or line, that appears on the oscilloscope pattern of the ignition-system secondary circuit. The firing line shows when the spark plug begins to fire, and the voltage required to fire it.

Firing Order The order in which the engine cylinders fire, or deliver their power strokes, beginning with No. 1 cylinder.

Flat Spot Lack of normal acceleration or response to throttle opening; implies no loss of power but also no increase in power.

Float Bowl In a carburetor, the reservoir from which gasoline is metered into the passing air.

Float Level The float position at which the needle valve closes the fuel inlet to the carburetor, to prevent further delivery of fuel.

Float System In the carburetor, the system that controls the entry of fuel and the fuel level in the float bowl.

Flooded Term used to indicate that the engine cylinders received "raw" or liquid gasoline, or an air-fuel mixture too rich to burn.

Fluid Any liquid or gas.

Four-Barrel Carburetor A carburetor with four throttle valves. In effect, two two-barrel carburetors in a single assembly.

Four-Cycle See *four-stroke cycle*.

Four-Stroke Cycle The four piston strokes—intake, compression, power, and exhaust—that make up the complete cycle of events in the four-stroke-cycle engine. Also called *four-cycle* and *four-stroke*.

Fuel Any combustible substance. In an automobile engine, the fuel (gasoline) is burned, and the heat of combustion expands the resulting gases, which force the piston downward and rotate the crankshaft.

Fuel Decel Valve A device which supplies additional air-fuel mixture to the intake manifold during deceleration to control exhaust-gas hydrocarbon emissions.

Fuel Filter A device located in the fuel line, ahead of the float bowl; removes dirt and other contaminants from fuel passing through.

Fuel Gauge A gauge that indicates the amount of fuel in the fuel tank.

Fuel-Injection System A system which delivers fuel under pressure into the combustion chamber, or into the airflow just as it enters each individual cylinder. Replaces the conventional carburetor.

Fuel Line The pipe or tubes through which fuel flows from the fuel tank to the carburetor.

Fuel Nozzle The tube in the carburetor through which gasoline feeds from the float bowl into the passing air. In a fuel-injection system, the tube that delivers the fuel into the compressed air or the passing airstream.

Fuel Pump The electrical or mechanical device in the fuel system which forces fuel from the fuel tank to the carburetor.

Fuel System In an automobile, the system that delivers the combustible mixture of vaporized fuel and air to the engine cylinders. Consists of the fuel tank and lines, gauge, fuel pump, carburetor, and intake manifold.

Fuel Tank The storage tank for fuel on the vehicle.

Fuel-Vapor Recovery System See *vapor-recovery system*.

Full Throttle Wide-open throttle position, with the accelerator pressed all the way down to the floorboard.

Gap The air space between two electrodes, as the spark-plug gap or the contact-point gap.

Gas A state of matter in which the matter has neither a definite shape nor a definite volume; air is a mixture of several gases. In an automobile, the discharge from the tailpipe is called the *exhaust gas*. Also, gas is a slang expression for the liquid fuel gasoline.

Gasket A layer of material, usually made of cork or metal or both, that is placed between two machined surfaces to provide a tight seal between them.

Gasoline A liquid blend of hydrocarbons, obtained from crude oil; used as the fuel in most automobile engines.

Gas-Turbine Engine A type of internal-combustion engine in which the shaft is spun by the pressure of combustion gases flowing against curved turbine blades located around the shaft.

Gauge Pressure A pressure read on a scale which ignores atmospheric pressure. Thus, the atmospheric pressure of 14.7 psi absolute is equivalent to 0 psi gauge.

Grams Per Mile Unit of measurement for the amount (weight) of pollutants emitted into the atmosphere with the vehicle exhaust gases. Antipollution laws set maximum limits for each exhaust pollutant in grams per mile.

Grommet A device, usually made of hard rubber or a like material, used to encircle or support a component. In emission systems, a grommet is located in the valve-cover assembly to support and help seal the PCV valve.

Gulp Valve In the air-injection system, a type of antibackfire valve which allows a sudden intake of fresh air through the intake manifold during deceleration; prevents backfiring and popping in the exhaust system.

HC Abbreviation for *hydrocarbon*.
Head See *cylinder head*.
Header Performance term for a special exhaust manifold or exhaust tubes.
Head-Land Ring A compression ring with an L-shaped cross-section; used as the top compression ring.
Heat A form of energy; released by the burning of fuel. In an engine, heat energy is converted to mechanical energy.

Heat-Control Valve In the engine, a thermostatically operated valve in the exhaust manifold; diverts heat to the intake manifold to warm it before the engine reaches normal operating temperature.

Heated-Air System A system in which a thermostatically controlled air cleaner supplies hot air from a stove around the exhaust manifold to the carburetor during warm-up; improves cold-engine operation.

Heat of Compression An increase in temperature brought about by the compression of air or air-fuel mixture.

Hemispherical Combustion Chamber A combustion chamber resembling a hemisphere, or half a round ball.

Hesitation Momentary pause in the rate of acceleration; momentary lack of throttle response at some car speed other than acceleration from a standing start.

High-Compression Term used to refer to the increased compression ratios of modern automotive engines, as compared to engines built in the past.

High-Energy Ignition (HEI) System A General Motors electronic ignition system without contact points, and with all ignition-system components contained in the distributor. Capable of producing 35,000 V.

High-Speed System In the carburetor, the system that supplies fuel to the engine at speeds above about 25 mph [40 km/h]. Also called the *main metering system*.

Honda System A type of controlled-combustion system for spark-ignition engines. Has a small chamber that surrounds the spark-plug electrodes with a rich mixture; once the rich mixture ignites, it enters the main chamber, igniting the leaner air-fuel mixture in that chamber.

Horsepower A measure of mechanical power, or the rate at which work is done. One horsepower equals 33,000 ft · lb of work per minute; it is the power necessary to raise 33,000 lb a distance of 1 ft in 1 min.

Hot-Idle Compensator A thermostatically controlled carburetor valve that opens whenever inlet air temperatures are high. Allows additional air to discharge below the throttle plates at engine idle, to improve idle stability and prevent overly rich air-fuel mixtures.

Hot Soak A condition that may arise when an engine is stopped for a prolonged period after a hard, hot run. Heat transferred from the engine evaporates fuel out of the carburetor, so that the carburetor needs priming before the engine will start and run smoothly. Requires a longer cranking period.

H₂O Chemical symbol for water.

Hydrocarbon An organic compound containing only carbon and hydrogen, usually derived from fossil fuels such as petroleum, natural gas, and coal; an agent in the formation of photochemical smog. Gasoline is a blend of liquid hydrocarbons refined from crude oil.

Hydrocarbon Reactivity A measure of the smog-forming potential of a hydrocarbon.

Hydrogen A colorless, odorless, highly flammable gas whose combustion produces water; the simplest and lightest element.

IC See *internal-combustion engine*.
Idle Engine speed when the accelerator is fully released, and there is no load on the engine.

Idle Limiter A device that controls the maximum richness of the idle air-fuel mixture in the carburetor; also aids in preventing overly rich idle adjustments. Limiters are of two types: external plastic caps installed on the heads of the idle-mixture adjustment screws, and internal needles located in the idle passages of the carburetor.

Idle-Limiter Cap A plastic cap placed over the head of the idle-mixture adjustment screw, to limit its travel and prevent the idle mixture from being set too rich.

Idle Mixture The air-fuel mixture supplied to the engine during idling.

Idle-Mixture Adjustment Screw The adjustment screw (on some carburetors) that can be turned in or out to lean out or enrich the idle mixture.

Idle Port The opening into the throttle body through which the idle system in the carburetor discharges fuel.

Idle Speed The speed, or rpm, at which the engine runs without load when the accelerator is released.

Idle-Stop Solenoid An electrically operated two-position plunger used to provide a predetermined throttle setting at idle.

Idle System In the carburetor, the passages through which fuel is fed when the engine is idling.

Idle Vent An opening from an enclosed chamber through which air can pass under idle conditions.

Ignition The action of the spark in starting the burning of the compressed air-fuel mixture in the combustion chamber.

Ignition Advance The moving forward, in time, of the ignition spark relative to the piston position. TDC or 1° ATDC is considered advanced as compared to 2° ATDC.

Ignition Coil The ignition-system component that acts as a transformer to step up (increase) the battery voltage to many thousands of volts; the high-voltage surge from the coil is transmitted to the spark plug to ignite the compressed air-fuel mixture.

Ignition Distributor The ignition-system component that closes and opens the primary circuit to the ignition coil at the proper times and distributes the resulting high-voltage surges from the ignition coil to the proper spark plugs.

Ignition Reserve Difference between the minimum available and maximum required voltages. An adequate ignition reserve is important if an engine is to be reasonably free from troubles caused by moisture or dirt losses, leaky secondary leads, and fouled spark plugs.

Ignition Resistor A resistance connected into the ignition primary circuit to reduce the battery voltage to the coil during engine operation.

Ignition Retard The moving back, in time, of the ignition spark relative to the piston position. TDC or 1° BTDC is considered retarded as compared to 2° BTDC.

Ignition Switch The switch in the ignition system (usually operated with a key) that opens and closes the ignition-coil primary circuit. May also be used to open and close other vehicle electric circuits.

Ignition System In the automobile, the system that furnishes high-voltage sparks to the engine cylinders to fire the compressed air-fuel mixture. Consists of the battery, ignition coil, ignition distributor, ignition switch, wiring, and spark plugs.

Ignition Timing The delivery of the spark from the coil to the spark plug at the proper time for the power stroke, relative to the piston position.

I-Head Engine An overhead-valve (OHV) engine: an engine with the valves in the cylinder head.

IMCO Abbreviation for *improved combustion system*, an exhaust-emission control system used by Ford and comprised mainly of carburetor and distributor modifications. See also *controlled-combustion system*.

Indicator A device used to make some condition known by use of a light or a dial and pointer; for example, the temperature indicator or oil-pressure indicator.

Infrared Analyzer A nondispersive infrared test instrument used to measure very small quantities of pollutants in exhaust gas. See *exhaust-gas analyzer*.

In-Line Engine An engine in which all the cylinders are located in a single row or line.

Inspect To examine a component or system for surface, condition, or function.

Install To set up for use on a vehicle any part, accessory, option, or kit.

Insulation Material that stops the travel of electricity (electrical insulation) or heat (heat insulation).

Insulator A poor conductor of electricity or of heat.

Intake Manifold A device with several passages through which the air-fuel mixture flows from the carburetor to the combustion chambers.

Intake Stroke The piston stroke (from TDC to BDC) immediately following the exhaust stroke, during which the intake valve opens and the cylinder fills with air-fuel mixture from the intake manifold.

Intake Valve The valve that opens during the intake stroke to allow the air-fuel mixture to enter the cylinder from the intake manifold.

Integral Built into, as part of the whole.

Internal-Combustion Engine An engine in which the fuel is burned inside the engine itself, rather than in a separate device (as is the case for a steam engine).

Jet A calibrated passage, in the carburetor, through which fuel flows.

Kilogram In the metric system, a unit of weight and mass; approximately equal to 2.2 lb.

Kilometer In the metric system, a unit of linear measure; equal to 0.621 mi.

Kilowatt A unit of power, equal to about 1.34 hp.

Knock A heavy metallic engine sound which varies with engine speed; usually caused by a loose or worn bearing. Name also used for detonation, pinging, and spark knock. See *detonation*.

Leaded Gasoline Gasoline to which small amounts of tetraethyl lead are added to improve engine performance and reduce detonation.

Lean Mixture An air-fuel mixture that has a relatively high proportion of air and a relatively low proportion of fuel. An air-fuel ratio of 16:1 indicates a lean mixture, compared to an air-fuel ratio of 13:1.

L-Head Engine An engine with its valves located in the cylinder block.

Light-Duty Vehicle A motor vehicle manufactured primarily for transporting persons or property and having a gross vehicle weight of 6,000 lb [2,727.6 kg] or less.

Linkage An assembly of rods, or links, used to transmit motion.

Liquefied Petroleum Gas A hydrocarbon suitable for use as an engine fuel, obtained from petroleum and natural gas; a vapor at atmospheric pressure but becomes a liquid under sufficient pressure. Butane and propane are the liquefied gases most frequently used in automotive engines.

Liquid-Cooled Engine An engine that is cooled by the circulation of liquid coolant around the cylinders.

Liter In the metric system, a measure of volume; approximately equal to 0.26 gal (U.S.) or about 61 in³. Used as a metric measure of engine-cylinder displacement.

Loading An enrichment of the air-fuel mixture to the point of rough engine idle; sometimes causes missing and is usually accompanied by the emission of black smoke from the tail pipe.

Lobe A projecting part; for example, the rotor lobe or the cam lobe.

Low-Lead Fuel Gasoline which is low in tetraethyl lead, containing not more than 0.5 g/gal.

Low-Speed System The system in the carburetor that supplies fuel to the air passing through during low-speed, part-throttle operation.

LPG Abbreviation for *liquefied petroleum gas*.

Lugging Low-speed, full-throttle engine operation in which the engine is heavily loaded and overworked; usually caused by failure of the driver to shift to a lower gear when necessary.

Main Jet The fuel nozzle, or jet, in the carburetor that supplies fuel when the throttle is partially to fully open.

Make A distinctive name applied to a group of vehicles produced by one manufacturer; may be further subdivided into carlines, body types, etc.

Malfunction Improper or incorrect operation.

Manifold A device with several inlet or outlet passageways through which a gas or liquid is gathered or distributed. See *exhaust manifold* and *intake manifold*.

Manifold Heat Control See *heat-control valve*.

Manifold Vacuum The vacuum in the intake manifold that develops as a result of the vacuum in the cylinders on their intake strokes.

Manufacturer Any person, firm, or corporation engaged in the production or assembly of motor vehicles or other products.

Metering Rod and Jet A device consisting of a small, movable, cone-shaped rod and a jet; increases or decreases fuel flow according to engine throttle opening, engine load, or a combination of both.

Misfire In the engine, a failure to ignite the air-fuel mixture in one or more cylinders. This condition may be intermittent or continuous in one or more cylinders.

Missing See *misfire*.

Mode Term used to designate a particular set of operating characteristics.

Model Year The production period for new motor vehicles or new engines, designated by the calendar year in which the period ends.

Modification An alteration; a change from the original.

Molecule The smallest particle into which a substance can be divided and still retain the properties of the substance.

MON Abbreviation for *motor octane number*.

Monolithic Made as a single unit. In catalytic-converter construction, a substrate or supporting structure for the catalyst, made as a single unit (usually in the shape of a honeycomb), is monolithic; however, the coated-bead or pellet-type catalytic converter is not.

Monolithic Timing Making accurate spark-timing adjustments with an electronic timing device which can be used while the engine is running.

Motor Octane Number (MON) Laboratory octane rating of a fuel, established on single-cylinder variable-compression-ratio engines.

Motor Vehicle A vehicle propelled by a means other than muscle power, usually mounted on rubber tires, which does not run on rails or tracks.

MPH Abbreviation for *miles per hour*, a unit of speed.

Muffler In the engine exhaust system, a device through which the exhaust gases must pass and which reduces the exhaust noise.

Needle Valve A small, tapered, needle-pointed valve which can move into or out of a valve seat to close or open the passage through the seat. Used to control the carburetor float-bowl fuel level.

Neoprene A synthetic rubber that is not affected by the various chemicals that are harmful to natural rubber.

Nitrogen A colorless, tasteless, odorless gas that constitutes 78 percent of the atmosphere by volume and is a part of all living tissues.

Nitrogen Oxides Any chemical compound of nitrogen and oxygen. Nitrogen oxides result from high temperature and pressure in the combustion chambers of automobile engines and other power plants during the combustion process. When combined with hydrocarbons in the presence of sunlight, nitrogen oxides form smog. A basic air pollutant; automotive exhaust-emission levels of nitrogen oxides are controlled by law.

Noble Metals Metals (such as gold, silver, platinum, and palladium) which do not readily oxidize or enter into other chemical reactions, but do promote reactions between other substances. Platinum and palladium are used as the catalysts in catalytic converters.

Nonleaded Gasoline See *unleaded gasoline*.

NO$_x$ Abbreviation for *nitrogen oxides*.

NO$_x$ Control System A device or system used to reduce the amount of NO$_x$ produced by an engine.

Nozzle The opening, or jet, through which fuel passes when it is discharged into the carburetor venturi.

Octane Number The number used to indicate the octane rating of a gasoline.

Octane Rating A measure of the antiknock properties of a gasoline. The higher the octane rating, the more resistant the gasoline is to knocking, or detonation.

Octane Requirement The minimum-octane-number fuel required to enable a vehicle to operate without knocking.

OEM Abbreviation for *original-equipment manufacturer*.

OHC See *overhead-camshaft engine*.

OHV See *overhead-valve engine*.

Oil A liquid lubricant; made from crude oil and used to provide lubrication between moving parts. In a diesel engine, oil is used for fuel.

Oil Pan The detachable lower part of the engine, made of sheet metal, which encloses the crankcase and acts as an oil reservoir.

Oil Seal and Shield Two devices used to control oil leakage past the valve stem and guide, and into the ports or the combustion chamber of an engine.

Oil Separator A device for separating oil from air or from another liquid. Used with some engine-crankcase emission-control systems.

Open System A crankcase emission control system which draws air through the oil-filler cap, and does not include a tube from the crankcase to the air cleaner.

Orifice A small opening, or hole, into a cavity.

Orifice Spark-Advance Control (OSAC) A system used on some engines to aid in the control of NO_x. Consists of a valve which delays the change in vacuum to the distributor vacuum-advance unit between idle and part throttle.

O Ring A type of sealing ring, made of a special rubberlike material; in use, the O ring is compressed into a groove to provide the sealing action.

OSAC Abbreviation for *orifice spark-advance control*.

Oscilloscope A high-speed voltmeter which visually displays voltage variations on a television-type picture tube. Widely used to check engine ignition systems; can also be used to check charging systems and electronic fuel-injection systems.

Otto Cycle The cycle of events in a four-stroke-cycle engine. Named for the inventor, Dr. Nikolaus Otto.

Overflow Spilling of the excess of a substance; also, to run or spill over the sides of a container, usually because of overfilling.

Overflow Tank See *expansion tank*.

Overhaul To completely disassemble a unit, clean and inspect all parts, reassemble it with the original or new parts, and make all adjustments necessary for proper operation.

Overhead-Camshaft (OHC) Engine An engine in which the camshaft is mounted over the cylinder head instead of inside the cylinder block.

Overhead-Valve (OHV) Engine An engine in which the valves are mounted in the cylinder head above the combustion chamber, instead of in the cylinder block; in this type of engine, the camshaft is usually mounted in the cylinder block, and the valves are actuated by pushrods.

Overheat To heat excessively; also to become excessively hot.

Oversquare Term applied to an automotive engine in which the bore is larger than the stroke.

Oxidation Burning or combusting; the combining of a material with oxygen. Rusting is slow oxidation, and combustion is rapid oxidation.

Oxidation Catalyst In a catalytic converter, a substance that promotes the combustion of exhaust-gas hydrocarbons and carbon monoxide at a lower temperature.

Oxides of Nitrogen See *nitrogen oxides*.

Oxygen A colorless, tasteless, odorless, gaseous element which makes up about 21 percent of air. Capable of combining rapidly with all elements except the inert gases in the oxidation process called burning. Combines very slowly with many metals in the oxidizing process called rusting.

Parade Pattern An oscilloscope pattern showing the ignition voltages on one line, from left to right across the scope screen in engine firing order.

Particle A very small piece of metal, dirt, or other impurity which may be contained in the air, fuel, or lubricating oil used in an engine.

Particulates Small particles of lead occurring as solid matter in the exhaust gas.

Passage A small hole or gallery in an assembly or casting, through which air, coolant, fuel, or oil flows.

Passenger Car Any four-wheeled motor vehicle manufactured primarily for use on streets and highways and carrying 10 passengers or fewer.

PCV Abbreviation for *positive crankcase ventilation*.

PCV Valve The valve that controls the flow of crankcase vapors in accordance with ventilation requirements for different engine speeds and loads.

Percolation The condition in which a bowl vent fails to open when the engine is turned off, and pressure in the fuel bowl forces raw fuel through the main jets into the manifold.

Petroleum The crude oil from which gasoline, lubricating oil, and other such products are refined.

Photochemical Smog Smog caused by hydrocarbons and nitrogen oxides reacting photochemically in the atmosphere. The reactions take place under low wind velocity, bright sunlight, and an inversion layer in which the air mass is trapped (as between the ocean and mountains in Los Angeles). Can cause eye and lung irritation.

Piston A movable part, fitted to a cylinder, which can receive or transmit motion as a result of pressure changes in a fluid. In the engine, the cylindrical part that moves up and down within a cylinder as the crankshaft rotates.

Piston Displacement The cylinder volume displaced by the piston as it moves from the bottom to the top of the cylinder during one complete stroke.

Piston Rings Rings fitted into grooves in the piston. There are two types: compression rings for sealing the compression in the combustion chamber, and oil rings to scrape excess oil off the cylinder wall. See *compression ring*.

Pollutant Any substance that adds to the pollution of the atmosphere. In a vehicle, any such substance in the exhaust gas from the engine, or evaporating from the fuel tank or carburetor.

Pollution Any gas or substance, in the air, which makes it less fit to breathe. Also, noise pollution is the name applied to excessive noise from machinery or vehicles.

Polyurethane A synthetic substance used in filtration materials; normally associated with the filtering of carburetor inlet air.

Pop-Back Condition in which the air-fuel mixture is ignited in the intake manifold. Because combustion takes place outside the combustion chamber, the combustion may "pop back" through the carburetor.

Port In the engine, the opening in which the valve operates and through which air-fuel mixture or burned gases pass; the valve port.

Ported Vacuum Switch A water-temperature-sensing vacuum control valve used in distributor and EGR vacuum circuits. Sometimes called the vacuum control valve or coolant override valve.

Positive Crankcase Ventilation A crankcase ventilation system; uses intake-manifold vacuum to return the crankcase vapors and blow-by gases from the crankcase to the intake manifold to be burned, thereby preventing their escape into the atmosphere.

Power Piston In some carburetors, a vacuum-operated piston that allows additional fuel to flow at wide-open throttle; permits delivery of a richer air-fuel mixture to the engine.

Power Plant The engine or power source of a vehicle.

PPM Abbreviation for *parts per million;* the unit used in measuring the level of hydrocarbons in exhaust gas with an exhaust-gas analyzer.

Precombustion Chamber In some diesel engines, a separate small combustion chamber into which the fuel is injected and where combustion begins.

Preignition Ignition of the air-fuel mixture in the combustion chamber by any means, before the ignition spark occurs at the spark plug.

Premium Gasoline The best or highest-octane gas available to the motorist.

Pressure Force per unit area, or force divided by area. Usually measured in pounds per square inch (psi) and kilograms per square centimeter (kg/cm²).

Pressurize To apply more than atmospheric pressure to a gas or liquid.

Preventive Maintenance The systematic inspection of a vehicle to detect and correct failures, either before they occur or before they develop into major defects. A procedure for economically maintaining vehicles in a satisfactory and dependable operating condition.

Primary The low-voltage circuit of the ignition system.

Primary Winding The outer winding, of relatively heavy wire, in an ignition coil.

PROCO Short for *programmed combustion;* a research type of stratified-charge engine developed by Ford.

Programmed Combustion See *PROCO.*

Programmed Protection System In a catalytic converter, a system employing bypass valves to protect the catalysts and their containers from destructive overtemperature conditions that might result from certain modes of operation, or from engine malfunctions.

Progressive Linkage A carburetor linkage used with multiple-carburetor installations to progressively open the secondary carburetors.

Propane A type of LPG that is liquid below −44°F [−42°C] at atmospheric pressure.

PSI Abbreviation for *pounds per square inch,* a unit of pressure.

Pulley A metal wheel with a V-shaped groove around the rim; drives, or is driven by, a belt.

Pump A device that develops pressure or transfers gas or liquid from one place to another.

PVS Abbreviation for *ported vacuum switch.*

Quad Carburetor A four-barrel carburetor.

Quench The removal of heat during combustion from the end gas or outside layers of air-fuel mixture by the cooler metallic surfaces of the combustion chamber, thus reducing the tendency for detonation to occur.

Quench Area The area of the combustion chamber near the cylinder walls which tends to cool (quench) combustion through the effect of the nearby cool water jackets.

Radiator In the cooling system, the device that removes heat from coolant passing through it; takes hot coolant from the engine and returns the coolant to the engine at a lower temperature.

Radiator Pressure Cap A type of cap placed on the radiator filler tube; pressurizes the cooling system for more efficient operation.

Ram-Air Cleaner An air cleaner for high-performance cars that opens an air scoop on the hood, to provide a ram effect, when the throttle is wide open.

Raster Pattern An oscilloscope pattern showing the ignition voltages one above the other, from the bottom to the top of the screen in the engine firing order.

Ratio Proportion; the relative amounts of two or more substances in a mixture. Usually expressed as a numerical relationship, as in 2:1.

RC Engine Abbreviation for *rotary-combustion engine.* See *Wankel engine.*

Relief Valve A valve that opens when a preset pressure is reached. This relieves or prevents excessive pressures.

Reluctor In an electronic ignition system, the metal rotor (with a series of tips) which replaces the conventional distributor cam.

Remove and Reinstall (R and R) To perform a series of servicing procedures on an original part or assembly; includes removal, inspection, lubrication, all necessary adjustments, and reinstallation.

Replace To remove a used part or assembly and install a new part or assembly in its place; includes cleaning, lubricating, and adjusting as required.

Required Voltage The voltage required to fire a spark plug.

Research Octane Number A number used to describe the octane rating of a marketed gasoline. See also *motor octane number.*

Resonator A device in the exhaust system that reduces the exhaust noise.

Retard Usually associated with the spark-timing mechanisms of the engine: the opposite of spark advance. Also, to delay the introduction of the spark into the combustion chamber.

Rich Mixture An air-fuel mixture that has a relatively high proportion of fuel and a relatively low proportion of air. An air-fuel ratio of 13:1 indicates a rich mixture, compared to an air-fuel ratio of 16:1.

Ring Gap The gap between the ends of a piston ring when the ring is in place in the cylinder.

Ring Ridge The ridge left at the top of a cylinder as the cylinder wall below is worn away by piston-ring movement.

Road-Draft Tube A method of scavenging the engine crankcase of fumes and pressure, used prior to the introduction of crankcase emission control systems. The tube, which was connected into the crankcase and suspended a few inches from the ground, depended on venturi action to create a partial vacuum as the vehicle moved. The method was ineffective below about 20 mph [32 km/h].

Road Load A constant vehicle speed on a level road.

RON Abbreviation for *research octane number.*

Room Temperature 68 to 72°F [20 to 22°C].

Rotary Term describing the motion of a part that continually turns.

Rotary-Combustion Engine See *Wankel engine.*

Rotor A revolving part of a machine, such as an alternator rotor, disk-brake rotor, distributor rotor, or Wankel-engine rotor.

RPM Abbreviation for *revolutions per minute,* a measure of rotational speed.

Run-On See *dieseling.*

SA Designation for lubricating oil that is acceptable for use in engines operated under the mildest conditions.

SAE Abbreviation for *Society of Automotive Engineers.* Used to designate a grade or weight of oil measured according to Society of Automotive Engineers standards.

SAG A momentary decrease in acceleration rate; does not occur immediately after throttle application (as in a hesitation), but after the vehicle has acquired some speed.

SB Designation for lubricating oil that is acceptable for minimum-duty engines operated under mild conditions.

SC Designation for lubricating oil that meets requirements for use in the gasoline engines in 1964 to 1967 passenger cars and trucks.

Scavenging The displacement of exhaust gas from the combustion chamber by fresh air.

SD Designation for lubricating oil that meets requirements for use in the gasoline engines in 1968 to 1971 passenger cars and some trucks.

SDV Abbreviation for *spark delay valve;* a calibrated restrictor in the vacuum-advance hose which delays the vacuum spark advance.

SE Designation for lubricating oil that meets requirements for use in the gasoline engines in 1972 and later cars, and in certain 1971 passenger cars and trucks.

Seal A part or material that is used to close off the area of contact between two machine parts, usually to prevent oil leakage.

Seat The surface upon which another part rests, as a valve seat; Also, to wear into a good fit; for example, new piston rings seat after a few miles of driving.

Secondary Air Air that is pumped to thermal reactors, catalytic converters, exhaust manifolds, or the cylinder-head exhaust ports, to promote the chemical reactions that reduce exhaust-gas pollutants.

Secondary Available Voltage Voltage that is available for firing the spark plug.

Secondary Circuit The high-voltage circuit of the ignition system; consists of the coil, rotor, distributor cap, spark-plug cables, and spark plugs.

Service Manual A book published annually by each vehicle manufacturer, listing the specifications and service procedures for each make and model of vehicle. Also called a shop manual.

Service Rating A designation that indicates the type of service for which an engine lubricating oil is best suited. See *SA, SB, SC, SD,* and *SE.*

Short Circuit A defect in an electric circuit which permits current to take a short path, or circuit, instead of following the desired path.

Shroud A hood placed around an engine fan to improve fan action.

Single-Chamber Capacity In a Wankel engine, a measurement of the displacement, or maximum volume, of the rotor chamber.

Single-Overhead-Camshaft (SOHC) Engine An engine in which a single camshaft is mounted over each cylinder head, instead of inside the cylinder block.

Sludge An accumulation of water, dirt, and oil in the oil pan; sludge is very viscous and tends to reduce lubrication.

Smog A term coined from the words smoke and fog. First applied to the foglike layer that hangs in the air under certain atmospheric conditions; now generally used to describe any condition of dirty air and/or fumes or smoke. Smog is compounded from smoke, moisture, and numerous chemicals which are produced by combustion.

Smoke Small gasborne or airborne particles, exclusive of water vapor, that result from combustion; such particles emitted by an engine into the atmosphere in sufficient quantity to be observable.

Smoke In Exhaust A visible blue or black substance often present in the automotive exhaust. A blue color indicates excessive oil in the combustion chamber; black indicates excessive fuel in the air-fuel mixture.

SOHC See *single-overhead-camshaft engine.*

Solenoid An electromechanical device which, when connected to an electrical source such as a battery, produces a mechanical movement. This movement can be used to control a valve or to produce other movements.

Solenoid Switch A switch that is opened and closed electromagnetically, by the movement of a solenoid core. Usually the core also causes a mechanical action, such as the movement of a drive pinion into mesh with flywheel teeth for cranking.

Solid-State Regulator An alternator regulator encapsulated in a plastic material and mounted in the alternator.

Spark Decel Valve A vacuum-actuated valve, located between the carburetor and distributor, which advances the spark during deceleration to reduce emissions. (Should not be confused with the spark-delay valve.)

Spark Duration The length of time a spark is established across a spark gap, or the length of time current flows in a spark gap.

Spark Knock See *detonation*.

Spark Line Part of the oscilloscope pattern of the ignition secondary circuit; the spark line shows the voltage required to sustain the spark at the spark plug, and the number of distributor degrees through which the spark exists.

Spark Plug A device that screws into the cylinder head of an engine; provides a spark to ignite the compressed air-fuel mixture in the combustion chamber.

Spark-Plug Heat Range The distance heat must travel from the center electrode to reach the outer shell of the spark plug and enter the cylinder head.

Spark Test A quick check of the ignition system; made by holding the metal spark-plug end of a spark-plug cable about $3/16$ in [4.76 mm] from the cylinder head, or block; cranking the engine; and checking for the existence and intensity of a spark.

Specifications Information, provided by the manufacturer, that describes each automotive system and its components, operation, and clearances. Also, the service procedures that must be followed for a system to operate properly.

SPECS Short for *specifications*.

Speed The rate of motion; for vehicles, measured in miles per hour or kilometers per hour.

Squish The action in some combustion chambers in which the last part of the compressed air-fuel mixture is pushed, or squirted, out of a decreasing space between the piston and cylinder head.

Stacked Pattern See *raster pattern*.

Standpipe Assembly See *vapor-liquid separator*.

Steam Engine An external-combustion engine operated by steam generated in a boiler.

Stirling Engine A type of internal-combustion engine in which the piston is moved by changes in the pressure of a working gas that is alternately heated and cooled.

Stratified Charge In a gasoline-fueled spark-ignition engine, an air-fuel charge with a small layer of very rich air-fuel mixture; the rich layer is ignited first, after which ignition spreads to the leaner mixture filling the rest of the combustion chamber. The diesel engine is a stratified-charge engine.

Stroke In an engine cylinder, the distance that the piston moves in traveling from BDC to TDC or from TDC to BDC.

Stumble A condition related to vehicle driveability; the tendency of an engine to falter, and then catch, resulting in a noticeable hesitation felt by the driver. A momentary abrupt deceleration during an acceleration.

Substrate In a catalytic converter, the supporting structure to which the catalyst is applied; usually made of ceramic. Two types of substrate used in catalytic converters are the monolithic or one-piece substrate and the bead or pellet-type substrate.

Sulfur Oxides Acids that can form in small amounts as the result of a reaction between hot exhaust gas and the catalyst in a catalytic converter.

Supercharger In the intake system of the engine, a device that pressurizes the ingoing air-fuel mixture. This increases the amount of mixture delivered to the cylinders and thus increases the engine output. If the supercharger is driven by the engine exhaust gas, it is called a turbocharger.

Superimposed Pattern On an oscilloscope, a pattern showing the ignition voltages one on top of the other, so that only a single trace, and variations from it, can be seen.

Surface Ignition Ignition of the air-fuel mixture, in the combustion chamber, by hot metal surfaces or heated particles of carbon.

Surge Condition in which the engine speed increases and decreases slightly but perceptibly, in spite of the fact that the driver has not changed the throttle position.

S/V Ratio The ratio of the surface area S of the combustion chamber to its volume V, with the piston at TDC. Often used as a comparative indicator of hydrocarbon emission levels from an engine.

Switch A device that opens and closes an electric circuit.

Tachometer A device for measuring engine speed, or revolutions per minute.

TCS See *transmission-controlled spark system*.

TDC Abbreviation for *top dead center*.

TEL Abbreviation for *tetraethyl lead*.

Temperature Gauge A gauge that indicates, to the driver, the temperature of the coolant in the engine cooling system.

Temperature Indicator See *temperature gauge*.

Tetraethyl Lead A chemical which, when added to engine fuel, increases its octane rating, or reduces its knocking tendency. Also called ethyl.

Thermactor See *air-injection system*.

Thermal Of or pertaining to heat.

Thermal-Conductivity Gas Analyzer The conventional exhaust-gas analyzer, used in service shops for many years to check and adjust the carburetor air-fuel mixtures.

Thermal Efficiency Ratio of the energy output of an engine to the energy in the fuel required to produce that output.

Thermal Reactor A large exhaust manifold in which unburned exhaust-gas hydrocarbons and carbon monoxide react with oxygen so that the pollutants burn up almost completely. It is simple and durable, but must operate at very high temperatures. Used on the Mazda car with the Wankel engine.

Thermostat A device for the automatic regulation of temperature; usually contains a temperature-sensitive element that expands or contracts to open or close off the flow of air, a gas, or a liquid.

Thermostatic Vacuum Switch A temperature-sensing device screwed into the coolant system; connects full manifold vacuum to the distributor when its critical temperature is reached. The resultant spark advance causes an increase in engine rpm, which cools the engine.

Thermostatically Controlled Air Cleaner An air cleaner in which a thermostat controls the preheating of intake air.

Three-Mode Cycle A quick test procedure used over the past several years to study the causes of high emissions and to compare different types of testers; consists of taking readings at idle speed and at 2,000 rpm, and maximum readings on deceleration. The test can be performed on a dynamometer under load, or in a service area without load.

Throat Performance term for a carburetor venturi.

Throttle A disk valve in the carburetor base that pivots in response to accelerator-pedal position; allows the driver to regulate the volume of air-fuel mixture entering the intake manifold, thereby controlling the engine speed. Also called the *throttle plate* or *throttle valve*.

Throttle-Return Check Same as *dashpot*.

Throttle Solenoid Positioner An electric solenoid which holds the throttle plate open (hot-idle position) but also permits the throttle plate to close completely when the ignition is turned off, to prevent "dieseling."

Throttle Valve A round disk valve in the throttle body of the carburetor; can be turned to admit more or less air, thereby controlling engine speed.

Timing In an engine, delivery of the ignition spark or operation of the valves (in relation to the piston position) for the power stroke.

See *ignition timing* and *valve timing*.

Timing Light A light that can be connected to the ignition system to flash each time the No. 1 spark plug fires; used for adjusting the timing of the ignition spark.

Top Dead Center The piston position when the piston has reached the upper limit of its travel in the cylinder, and the center line of the connecting rod is parallel to the cylinder walls.

Torque Turning or twisting effort; usually measured in pound-feet or kilogram-meters. Also, a turning force such as that required to tighten a connection.

Torque Wrench A wrench that indicates the amount of torque being applied with the wrench.

Transducer Any device which converts an input signal of one form into an output signal of a different form. For example, the automobile horn converts an electric signal to sound.

Transistor An electronic device that can be used as an electric switch; used to replace the contact points in electronic ignition systems.

Transmission-Controlled Spark (TCS) System A General Motors NO_x exhaust-emission control system; makes use of the transmission-gear position to allow distributor vacuum advance in high gear only.

Transmission-Regulated Spark (TRS) System A Ford exhaust-emission control system, similar to the General Motors transmission-controlled spark system; allows distributor vacuum advance in high gear only.

Trouble Diagnosis The detective work necessary to find the cause of a trouble.

TRS See *transmission-regulated spark system*.

Tuneup A procedure for inspecting, testing, and adjusting an engine, and replacing any worn parts, to restore the engine to its best performance.

Turbocharger A supercharger driven by the engine exhaust gas.

Turbulence The state of being violently disturbed. In the engine, the rapid swirling motion imparted to the air-fuel mixture entering a cylinder.

TVS Abbreviation for *thermostatic vacuum switch*.

Two-Barrel Carburetor A carburetor with two throttle valves.

Two-Cycle Short for *two-stroke cycle*.

Two-Stroke Cycle The two piston strokes during which fuel intake, compression, combustion, and exhaust take place in a two-stroke-cycle engine.

Unit Distributor A General Motors ignition distributor that uses a magnetic pickup coil and timer core instead of points and a condenser. The ignition coil is assembled into the distributor as a unit.

Unleaded Gasoline Gasoline to which no lead compounds have been intentionally added. Gasoline that contains 0.05 g or less of lead per gallon; required by law to be used in 1975 and later vehicles equipped with catalytic converters.

Unloader A device linked to the throttle valve; opens the choke valve when the throttle is moved to the wide-open position.

Vacuum Negative gauge pressure, or a pressure less than atmospheric pressure. Vacuum can be measured in psi, but is usually measured in inches or millimeters of mercury (Hg); a reading of 30 in Hg [762 mm Hg] would indicate a perfect vacuum.

Vacuum Advance The advancing (or retarding) of ignition timing by changes in intake-manifold vacuum, which reflect throttle opening and engine load. Also, a mechanism on the ignition distributor that uses intake-manifold vacuum to advance the timing of the spark to the spark plugs.

Vacuum-Advance Control Any type of NO_x emission control system designed to allow vacuum advance only during certain modes of engine and vehicle operation.

Vacuum-Advance Solenoid An electrically operated two-position valve which allows or denies intake-manifold vacuum to the distributor vacuum-advance unit.

Vacuum-Control Temperature-Sensing Valve A valve that connects manifold vacuum to the distributor advance mechanism under hot-idle conditions.

Vacuum Gauge In automotive-engine service, a device that measures intake-manifold vacuum and thereby indicates actions of engine components.

Vacuum Motor A small motor, powered by intake-manifold vacuum; used for jobs such as raising and lowering headlight doors.

Vacuum Switch A switch that closes or opens its contacts in response to changing vacuum conditions.

Valve A device that can be opened or closed to allow or stop the flow of a liquid or gas.

Valve Overlap The number of degrees of crankshaft rotation during which the intake and exhaust valves are open together.

Valve Seat The surface against which a valve comes to rest to provide a seal against leakage.

Valve-Seat Recession The tendency for valves, in some engines run on unleaded gasoline, to contact the seat in such a way that the seat wears away, or recesses, into the cylinder head. Also known as lash loss.

Valve Timing The timing of the opening and closing of the valves in relation to the piston position.

Vane Flat, extended surface that is moved around an axis by or in a fluid. Part of the internal revolving portion of an air-supply pump.

Vapor A gas; any substance in the gaseous state, as distinguished from the liquid or solid state.

Vaporization A change of state from liquid to vapor or by evaporation or boiling; a general term including both evaporation and boiling.

Vapor-Liquid Separator A device in the evaporative emission control system; prevents liquid gasoline from traveling to the engine through the charcoal-canister vapor line.

Vapor Lock A condition in the fuel system in which gasoline vaporizes in the fuel line or fuel pump; bubbles of gasoline vapor restrict or prevent fuel delivery to the carburetor.

Vapor-Recovery System An evaporative emission control system that recovers gasoline vapor escaping from the fuel tank and carburetor float bowl. See *evaporation control system*.

Vapor-Return Line A line from the fuel pump to the fuel tank; allows vapor that has formed in the fuel pump to return to the fuel tank.

Vapor-Saver System Same as *vapor-recovery system*.

VDV Abbreviation for *vacuum-delay valve*.

Vehicle Vapor Recovery See *vapor-recovery system*.

Vent An opening through which air can leave an enclosed chamber.

Ventilation The circulating of fresh air through any space to replace impure air. The basis of crankcase ventilation systems.

Venturi In the carburetor, a narrowed passageway or restriction which increases the velocity of air moving through it; produces the vacuum responsible for the discharge of gasoline from the fuel nozzle.

Volatile Evaporating readily. For example, Refrigerant-12 is volatile (evaporates quickly) at room temperature.

Volatility A measure of the ease with which a liquid vaporizes; has a direct relationship to the flammability of a fuel.

Voltage The force which causes electrons to flow in a conductor. The difference in electrical pressure (or potential) between two points in a circuit.

Volumetric Efficiency The ratio of the amount of air-fuel mixture that actually enters an engine cylinder to the theoretical amount that could enter under ideal conditions.

VVR Abbreviation for *vehicle-vapor recovery*. See *vapor-recovery system*.

Wankel Engine A rotary engine in which a three-lobe rotor turns eccentrically in an oval chamber to produce power.

Wedge Combustion Chamber A combustion chamber resembling a wedge in shape.

WOT Abbreviation for *wide-open throttle*.

D

Dashpot, 109
Detonation, 125–126
Diesel engine, 46–49, 128–129
  emissions from, 48–49
  fuel injection, 128–129
  lubrication of, 168
  precombustion chamber in, 48–49
  smoke from, 49
Distributor, ignition, 19–24, 160–162,
  168–169
  servicing of, 169
  testers for, 160–162
Dynamometer, chassis, 189–190

E

**Early fuel-evaporation system
  (EFE),** 116–117, 240
  servicing of, 240
ECS (evaporation control system),
  83–91
  (see also Vapor-recovery system)
EEC (evaporation emission control),
  83–91
  (see also Vapor-recovery system)
EFE (early fuel evaporation) system,
  116–117, 240
  servicing of, 240
**EGR (exhaust-gas recirculation)
  system,** 32–33, 132–133, 226–
  233
  servicing of, 226–233
  testing of, 229
  trouble-diagnosis of, 227–229
Electric-assist choke, 114
Electric cars, 60–61
Electric-generating-plant emissions,
  61–62
Electronic fuel injection, 127–129
Electronic ignition systems, 21–24
  testers for, 162
Emissions, 32–44, 61–62, 252–257
  automotive controls for, 32–44,
  252–257
  from electric-generating-plant,
  61–62
Engine, 10–30, 46–65
  alternative types of, 46–65
  computer diagnosis of, 196–198
  cylinder in, 10
  diesel, 46–49, 128–129
  future of, 65
  gas turbine, 52–54
  noises, 179–181
  operation of, 10–30
  rotary, 49–54
  steam, 54–57
  Stirling, 58–60
  testing instruments, 183–190
  testing procedures, 183
  trouble-diagnosis of, 171–181
  tuneup of, 183–198
  Wankel, 49–52
Engine cooling system, 27–30

Engine fuel system, 24–25
Engine lubricating system, 24–27
Evaporative control system, 42–44,
  83–91, 208–212
  for auxiliary fuel tanks, 250–251
  charcoal canister in, 85–87
  crankcase vapor storage, 91
  need for, 83
  purge valve in, 85–87
  servicing of, 209–212
  trouble-diagnosis of, 208–209
Exhaust-emission controls, 42, 214–
  241, 244–247
  requirements for, 42
  retrofit types of, 244–247
  servicing of, 214–241
  for used cars, 244–247
Exhaust gas, 5–7
  air-injection system for, 138, 214–
  218
  analyzer for, 186–189
  catalytic converters for, 138–142
  emission controls required, 42
  pollutants in, 5–7
  recirculation system for, 132–133,
  226–233
  retrofit emission control devices
  for, 244–247
  thermal reactor for, 138
  treating, 138–143
  used car devices for, 244–247
Exhaust-gas analyzer, 186–189
**Exhaust-gas recirculation (EGR)
  system,** 32–33, 132–133, 226–
  233
  (see also EGR system)
Exhaust stroke, 16
Expansion tank, cooling system,
  27–28
  fuel system, 91

F

Fast idle, 121–122
Float-bowl vents, 101–103
Float system, 101
Flywheel propulsion, 63–65
Four-stroke cycle, 16
Fuel gauges, 150
Fuel injection, 127–129
  diesel-engine, 128–129
  electronic, 127–129
  gasoline engine, 129
Fuel-mileage tester, 178–179
Fuel pump, 24–25, 150–152
  servicing of, 150–152
  troubles, 150–151
Fuel-return line, 85
Fuel system, 24–25, 147–156
  safety cautions, 148
  servicing of, 147–156
  troubles, 147–148
Fuel tank, 89–90, 141–142, 150, 210–
  211
  auxiliary, 210–211
  cap for, 141–142
  filler neck for, 141–142

Fuel tank (*Cont.*):
  sealed, 89–90
  servicing of, 150
Fuel-vapor recovery, 42–44
  (see also Evaporative control
  system)

G

Gasoline, lead in, 141–143
Gas turbine engine, 52–54
  emissions from, 54
**General Motors High-Energy
  Ignition (HEI) system,** 23–24

H

HAS system, 118–120
HC (hydrocarbon), 5–6, 138–141,
  252–255
  (see also Gasoline)
Heated-air system, 118–120
High-energy ignition system, 23–24
Honda stratified charge system, 127
Hot-idle compensator valve, 103
Hybrid cars, 67
Hydrocarbon (HC), 5–6, 32–44, 138–
  141, 252–255
  (see also Gasoline)
  air-fuel ratio vs. HC emissions, 39
  exhaust-gas emissions vs. coolant
  temperature, 38
  sources from automobile, 32–44
  testing for, 186–189

I

Idle-enrichment system, 103–104
Idle system, 103–104
Ignition system, 19–24, 157–170
  centrifugal-advance mechanism,
  21
  coil in, 20
  condenser in, 20
  contact points in, 20
  distributor in, 19–20
  electronic, 21–24
  failure causes in, 166–167
  function of, 21–24
  high-energy (HEI), 23–24
  primary resistor in, 20–21
  quick checks of, 167–168
  servicing of, 157–170
  spark advance mechanism, 21
  spark plugs in, 19–20
  timing of, 163–164, 189
  troubles in, 168
  unit distributor in, 23
  vacuum-advance mechanism, 21
Ignition timing, 163–164, 189, 236–237
  monolithic, 236–237
  using timing light, 189
IMCO (see Controlled-combustion
  system)

ANSWERS TO QUESTIONS

The answers to questions in the progress quizzes and chapter checkups are given below. In some questions, you are asked to list parts, describe the purpose and operation of components, define terms, and so on. The answers to such questions cannot be given here, since that would mean repeating most of the book. Therefore, you are asked to refer to the book and to the glossary to check those answers.

If you want to figure your grade on any quiz, divide the number of questions in the quiz into 100. This gives you the value of each question. For instance, suppose there are 8 questions. Since 100 divided by 8 is 12.5, each correct answer is worth 12.5 points. If you got 6 correct out of the 8, then your grade is 75 (that is, 6 × 12.5).

If you are not satisfied with the grade you make on a quiz or checkup, restudy the chapter or section and then take the quiz again. This review will help you remember the important facts.

Remember this: When you are taking a course in a school, you can pass and graduate even though you make a grade of less than 100. But in servicing automotive air conditioners, you must be 100 percent right all the time. If you make one error out of a hundred service jobs, for example, your average is 99. In school, that is a fine average. But in the automotive shop, that one error could cause such serious trouble (a ruined compressor, inoperative valve) that it would outweigh all the good jobs you performed. Therefore, always proceed carefully in performing any service job. Make sure you know exactly what you are supposed to do, and how you are to do it.

CHAPTER 1

Progress Quiz 1-1
Completing the Sentences 1. (b) 2. (d) 3. (c) 4. (a) 5. (a) 6. (c) 7. (d) 8. (b) 9. (b) 10. (a)

Chapter 1 Checkup
Matching

1. Smog	smoke and fog
2. Inversion	smog producer
3. Combustion	source of people-made smog
4. Exhaust system	source of automobile pollution
5. Perfect combustion	carbon dioxide and water
6. Incomplete combustion	carbon monoxide
7. Gasoline	hydrocarbon
8. Carbon monoxide	dangerously poisonous gas
9. Air	80 percent nitrogen, 20 percent oxygen
10. Tetraethyl lead	improves gasoline octane ratings

CHAPTER 2

Progress Quiz 2-1
Correcting Lists 1. camshaft 2. O ring 3. slower engine speed 4. valve-cover gasket 5. overlap

Completing the Sentences 1. (b) 2. (d) 3. (a) 4. (c) 5. (a) 6. (b) 7. (c) 8. (a) 9. (d) 10. (d)

Chapter 2 Checkup
Completing the Sentences 1. (b) 2. (c) 3. (d) 4. (a) 5. (b) 6. (b) 7. (d) 8. (d) 9. (c) 10. (a)

CHAPTER 3

Progress Quiz 3-1
Correcting Lists 1. fuel pump 2. ignition distributor 3. positive crankcase ventilation 4. carbon monoxide 5. healthful

Completing the Sentences 1. (d) 2. (a) 3. (a) 4. (b) 5. (c) 6. (c) 7. (d) 8. (b) 9. (b) 10. (b)

Chapter 3 Checkup
Completing the Sentences 1. (d) 2. (a) 3. (d) 4. (a) 5. (c) 6. (b) 7. (c) 8. (d) 9. (c) 10. (a)

CHAPTER 4

Progress Quiz 4-1
Completing the Sentences 1. (d) 2. (b) 3. (a) 4. (b) 5. (a) 6. (d) 7. (b) 8. (a) 9. (b) 10. (d)

Chapter 4 Checkup
Completing the Sentences 1. (c) 2. (c) 3. (a) 4. (c) 5. (d) 6. (d) 7. (c) 8. (a) 9. (d) 10. (b)

CHAPTER 5

Progress Quiz 5-1
Completing the Sentences 1. (d) 2. (b) 3. (a) 4. (a) 5. (c) 6. (b) 7. (b) 8. (d) 9. (b) 10. (c)

Chapter 5 Checkup
Completing the Sentences 1. (a) 2. (c) 3. (d) 4. (c) 5. (a) 6. (d) 7. (d) 8. (a) 9. (d) 10. (b)

CHAPTER 6

Chapter 6 Checkup
Completing the Sentences 1. (b) 2. (c) 3. (a) 4. (d) 5. (b) 6. (d) 7. (d) 8. (a) 9. (d) 10. (a)

CHAPTER 7

Progress Quiz 7-1
Completing the Sentences 1. (c) 2. (b) 3. (a) 4. (b) 5. (d) 6. (d) 7. (d) 8. (a) 9. (b) 10. (a)

Chapter 7 Checkup
Completing the Sentences 1. (b) 2. (b) 3. (d) 4. (c) 5. (a) 6. (a) 7. (c) 8. (d) 9. (b) 10. (d)

Correcting Lists 1. ignition system 2. air cleaner 3. manifold heat-control valve 4. factory-adjustable part throttle

CHAPTER 8

Chapter 8 Checkup
Completing the Sentences 1. (a) 2. (c) 3. (a) 4. (b) 5. (d) 6. (b) 7. (d) 8. (b) 9. (c) 10. (a)

Correcting Lists 1. treating the exhaust gas 2. throttle-return check 3. ignition of lean mixture first 4. turbo-charger 5. high combustion temperature

CHAPTER 9

Chapter 9 Checkup
Completing the Sentences 1. (c) 2. (b) 3. (a) 4. (d) 5. (a) 6. (c) 7. (d) 8. (a)

CHAPTER 10

Chapter 10 Checkup
Completing the Sentences 1. (d) 2. (a) 3. (c) 4. (a) 5. (b) 6. (b) 7. (d) 8. (c) 9. (c) 10. (a)

CHAPTER 11

Chapter 11 Checkup
Completing the Sentences 1. (a) 2. (c) 3. (c) 4. (a) 5. (b) 6. (a) 7. (c) 8. (a) 9. (c) 10. (b)

CHAPTER 12

Chapter 12 Checkup
Completing the Sentences 1. (b) 2. (c) 3. (d) 4. (d) 5. (b) 6. (a) 7. (c) 8. (b) 9. (b) 10. (b)

CHAPTER 13

Chapter 13 Checkup
Completing the Sentences 1. (b) 2. (a) 3. (a) 4. (c) 5. (c) 6. (a) 7. (b) 8. (b) 9. (d) 10. (b)

Grouping Ignition Troubles Loss of energy in primary circuit: points improperly set, discharged battery or defective alternator, excessive resistance in primary circuit, condenser shorted, coil primary grounded.

Loss of energy in secondary circuit: defective high-voltage wiring, leakage across distributor cap or rotor, plugs fouled or broken.

Out of time: timing incorrectly set, centrifugal advance defective, vacuum advance defective, distributor bearing or shaft worn.

CHAPTER 14

Chapter 14 Checkup
Completing the Sentences 1. (d) 2. (c) 3. (b) 4. (a) 5. (d) 6. (d) 7. (a) 8. (b) 9. (c) 10. (a)

CHAPTER 15

Progress Quiz 15-1
Correcting Lists 1. manifold heat-control valve 2. EGR valve 3. catalytic converter 4. thermal reactor 5. muffler

Chapter 15 Checkup
Completing the Sentences 1. (b) 2. (a) 3. (d) 4. (b) 5. (b) 6. (a) 7. (c) 8. (d) 9. (a) 10. (a)

CHAPTER 16

Chapter 16 Checkup
Completing the Sentences 1. (c) 2. (a) 3. (d) 4. (b) 5. (c)